BUILD

UNIVERS

GW00676386

David Arumainayagam

Letters to a Friend

europe books

© 2023 **Europe Books**| London
www.europebooks.co.uk | info@europebooks.co.uk

ISBN 9791220133067
First edition: May 2023

Letters to a Friend

For Chloe & Holly

Thank you for being such delightful daughters,
and for your unconditional love.
You have been, and always will be,
a magically bright light in my life.

***

For C

True love is so very rare and a gift to be cherished.
Listen always to your heart for it speaks of such
boundless and beautiful love.
Seek not the beauty that lies without and impair that
which lies within.
OUR ring... OUR love.

Love so needs to love that it will endure almost anything,
even abuse, just to flicker for a moment.
But the sky's mouth is kind, it's song will never hurt you,
for I sing those words."

Rumi

"There is one difference between a long life and a great dinner; in the dinner the sweetest things come last."
Audrey Hepburn

Prologue

After my wife and I separated, I never thought I could really love again. After twenty odd years of marriage and all the pain of separation, counselling, and so on, I felt emotionally exhausted and was not sure I could, nor would want to, generate emotion for any great love again. I thought that my life would, from that point on, be a series of meaningless sexual encounters. Probably not a bad thing one would have thought, given my lack of success when compared to some men who seem to leap successfully from divorce directly into the arms of another willing lady participant.

But I knew that even opportunities for meaningless sex were not likely to present themselves that often. Not in Harare! This is the bleakest of dating environments. A wonderful environment for raising young children but, sadly one with a dearth of single women seeking relationships that would suit me. I resigned myself to accepting my fate, even if I was not sure that such a thing as fate existed. I did speculate, from time to time, if a predetermined life path truly existed for us, but am yet to reach a satisfactory conclusion on this matter. I do feel occasionally, during such cogitations, especially with all that has happened to me recently, that had I been told much earlier that my life was going to pan out as it did; I would have preferred to have been gently drowned at birth.

Meeting H gave me renewed hope. I have fallen madly in love with her. I never meant to. She was supposedly someone to meet and have a casual affair with. It is a relationship that has very little prospect of success, no matter how romantic one's perspective.

I had assumed, having reached this conclusion rather objectively, that I would be able to continue to find other possible companions on my journey through life. Despite all attempts at sensibility and even a course of therapy, I have been unable to dislodge thoughts of H from either the forefront or recesses of my mind.

I am probably not currently the best prospect for any lady anyway, unless she sought only emotional investment, which I am capable of providing by the truckload, for I find myself at a financial low point, attempting to keep a business afloat in a challenging economic environment, coupled to a mountain of personal debt arising from an illness and a broken marriage. The only redeeming aspect in all of this is the fact that I have two lovely daughters. I feel so sorry for them. They deserve so much more than what I can currently and effectively offer them as a parent. Given all of this, why do I continue to feel so much love for a woman like H? Unlike me, she is not burdened with any obligation of any kind emotionally or otherwise, which makes my wish to be with her for the rest of my life so much more inexplicable. This is no 'Love in the Time of Cholera', it is more a story of 'Demented Love in the Time of Cancer'.

Regardless of the current circumstances, I do wake up many mornings feeling reasonably optimistic about my future. Could I, in reality, resuscitate my career and create success? Will I ever finish writing this book, even if it is only to be circulated amongst a few friends to whom I have divulged my secret fantasies about H? I really have no idea. I merely have this wish to bare my soul about this undeniable love for someone, which holds no rationality whatsoever. Audrey Hepburn was once quoted as saying "I was born with an enormous need for affection, and a terrible need to give it." It appears to apply so absolutely perfectly to me also.

I came to the erudite conclusion recently that the best approach to release, and attempt to rationalise, my emotions was to capture them in writing. The hope was that as soon as I applied quill to parchment and read the regurgitated words in the cold light of day, they may reveal greater coherence, and suggest the existence of nothing more than a passing infatuation.

The problem with this theory, is that it takes little or no account of the vivid dreams I have had about H. I have been in love before and even had dreams about the recipient of my affections, but none have provided me with such amazing visions of a possible future.

I have tried to, in my musings here, relate as accurately as possible my recollections of these visualisations. I have no explanation for these dreams, nor for my continued wish to believe that they may come true. Neither have I any comprehension of continued thoughts of her, which I have now recorded in writing. In fact, there is a great likelihood that anyone reading this will come to the swift conclusion that I have truly and finally reached the point of irrectifiable and comprehensive insanity.

I only wish that, in the event of my premature demise, someone will convey to H my apparent undying love for her. If a prediction I was once advised of, turns out to be correct, I may have to opportunity to meet her again in my next life. Even if that were the case, and we were to return in the next life as amoebas, my soul would be inextricably linked to H's in some form of single cell existence.

Given that my thoughts about H do not follow any rational or chronological route, it was best for me to convey my thoughts and feelings in a series of letters to a very good friend of mine, Geoff.

It also allowed me the opportunity to provide accounts of my previous loves, my thoughts on various subjects and the aspirations that prevailed at various points in my life which had influenced, and in some cases continue to.

I am, even after completion of this narrative, not at all sure that the story of my existence would be of particular interest to anyone else, unless they were strapped firmly to a chair, or otherwise rendered incapable of escape from the torture of listening to me recount my tale of woe. But there may the odd character or two, especially within my circle of friends who could possibly relate to some of the events or episodes that had a bearing on mine.

Not all of the tale is, nor was, bad though. Many of my youthful escapades still bring a smile to my face, as I hope it will to whoever chooses to read this. How ironic is it therefore, that we spend much of our teen years wishing to be older, when on reflection now, they appear to be the happiest of all our years.

Those carefree days, when, certainly in my case, all there was to worry about was how to entrap a girl in one's web of charm and guile; what delightful meal awaited one; when one would lose one's virginity; when facial hair would take firm root; how to sneak out of school without getting caught; discovering how much alcohol one could consume without falling over; how to save enough to buy a particular item of clothing that caught one's eye; how to pass exams with minimal effort; how much chocolate one could safely consume without causing one's teeth to rot; and how to hoist the housemaster's underpants up the school flagpole without being discovered.

All those thoughts roughly in that order of deemed importance. Now we, or some of us anyway, have emotional arrangements of great complexity, question marks over our intellectual capacity and agility to thrive in modern society, and financial obligations of enormous magnitude. I shall continue to count my blessings however, fewer though they may seem with each passing year!

By creating an understanding of the person that I am and providing some rationale for my behaviour in various circumstances, I hoped to develop a road map of sorts from my point of origin to this state, and stage of my life. Even it was merely for my own sake, I felt that there needed to be some definition of context to my perceived lunacy on matters of love.

Why had I chosen Geoff, and not any one of my other wonderful friends? It is very simple. He is someone I have known for many years, and the only one of my friends who has actually met H. He has been at the receiving end of many a painful (for him at least), conversation about her.

In terms of acknowledgements for this attempt at literary endeavour, I would like to obviously thank Geoff for his enduring patience in listening to my recounts of love for H. Also, for the many laughs we enjoyed together in the dining areas of the Landsdowne Club and elsewhere. Should I ever marry again, which I might add currently has a very slim chance of occurrence, I would dearly love him to be my best man.

In terms of my endless ramblings about H, I have to express my gratitude to Margaret also. Her patience in this and other matters on which I sought her counsel is worthy of several medals and awards. I truly appreciate the kindness and comfort she provided, and hope that some of her unbounded optimism may have rubbed off on me. Unfortunately, the only aspect so far, that I have adopted from the liaison, is a penchant for green tea.

I must thank H too, for it was my love for her that inspired me to write this book in the first place. I have never really understood my love for her, nor it appears, that I ever will. I have no regrets, however. And there are no better words to describe my view than Tennyson's poetic declaration that *"'tis better to have loved and lost than never to have loved at all"*!

My darling daughters, of course. I could not have wished for two more wonderful children. I may have failed in many things, as I have indicated in the following story of my life but being part of their creation and upbringing is easily the most successful of my undertakings. I hope that they grow up to enjoy all of their dreams coming true. Their care and concern for me during my time in hospital were the only motivators to help me pull through those lost, dark and dismal days.

My family both immediate and wider naturally, especially my siblings. Having lost more than half the members of my immediate family, the remnants have become even more treasured. I have long since forgiven them for all the teasing I stoically endured when I was a child, and I truly appreciate all the kindness, generosity, care and support they have shown throughout my life, and even more when I was diagnosed with my illness.

Also, my many friends whose love and support I could never do without. I am so lucky to have accumulated so many lovely people in my life, from school, university (both UCL and Cranfield), and socially, who have helped me realise the meaning of happiness. It is just a pity that I appear to have lost some of them as a result of my divorce, but I shall continue to hold dear memories of many happy days with them. My gratitude to the many friends who provided wonderful feedback and support in developing this narrative.

To all the women who brought a considerable wealth of colourful emotions into my life, without which much of my life would have been drab and uninteresting. Thank you for allowing me to love and be in receipt of much in return.

To the late Audrey Hepburn, images of whom are indelibly imprinted in my mind's eye. She epitomises everything that I dreamt a woman could and should be, ever since I was knee high to a grasshopper, not quite literally, but more specifically from the moment I grew up to appreciate femininity in every sense of the word. There are insufficient adjectives to describe her poise and radiant beauty. She is probably one of the greatest humanitarians to grace this world, and her seemingly boundless love for children of all creed and colour could never be adequately replaced. Her grace, elegance and humility at every stage of her life are qualities, that make her beauty even more admirable and timeless. If our souls were to meet, and my spirit managed to secure a single floating waltz with hers, it will be the happiest one orbiting this earth.

Finally, a big thanks to my parents, who are sadly no longer in this world, but deserving of my gratitude, nevertheless. I only wish I had taken the time to get to know them even better than the memories I hold of them now. I learnt how to be both compassionate and competitive simultaneously just as a result of playing cards with them.

My mother, whom I still wax lyrically about today as the wonderful independent, educated lady that caused me to grow up holding considerable respect for women. Her enduring patience and kindness with all of us through sickness and health, coupled with her culinary skills, made her a dream parent. My father also. So strong and handsome with a mastery of the English language. Even though I did not inherit his marvellous sporting ability, nor his charm when it came to women, I would like to think that a little of his amazing literary skills may reside also in my DNA.

As indicated, I have tried to convey my life and loves in a series of letters on various subjects with a sense of humour which some may deem puerile, but is very reflective of mine, and hopefully conveys a light-hearted view of some matters and events. But, as with life itself, not all is champagne and roses.

There are sad and happy days, ones of quiet reflection or philosophical cogitation and others of exuberant celebration, some of pensive musings and others of uncontained mirth. In capturing some of these moments, I have relived this rollercoaster of emotions, and enjoyed the journey of reflection and recollection. I hope that whoever reads this, may enjoy it too.

In terms of those who were the providers and recipients of my affections, I would suggest that whatever I consider my successes or failures in matters of the heart, I can think of no better guide than these wise words of the wonderfully gorgeous Audrey Hepburn.

"Your heart just breaks, that's all. But you can't judge or point fingers. You just have to be lucky enough to find someone who appreciates you."

Letter 1 – *First Meeting Calamities*

January 2018

Dear Geoff,

I was thinking how much fun we had at the SexyFish a few nights ago. I had not laughed so much for such a long time.

It still makes me smile when I recall that on first inspection of the menu and prices, we resolved to only order a starter or two and drink water, before leaving for a more substantive meal elsewhere. I am so glad that we decided to stay and make the most of the night there, as it has captured a very special place in my memory. I got the distinct impression the waitress liked us too, as the service was rather attentive and exceptional. It is definitely now one of my favourite establishments in London, and certainly worthy of several more visits. Our enjoyment must have shown outwardly too, as the photograph we sent to H of our time together there drew favourable comment from her.

I am glad you asked me to let you know in greater detail about the events leading up to my falling headlong into an abyss of loving feelings for her. Was it for you to better understand what may have triggered such great emotions? It probably is a worthwhile exercise for me anyway, in order to learn what caused this cliff-edge scenario of moving from largely zero affection to total absorption in an emotional drive at a staggering hundred miles an hour. I have also made note of my feelings at each point in this pandect of events, from the time of our first introduction, to her arrival in London, in order to aid your assessment. And mine!

I was introduced to H by a chap in Zimbabwe, whom I had not known for a long time, but who had become a sort of mentor as well as client and friend. To be quite honest, I felt that I was deserving of something exciting in my life for a change. Turning my business around, only to find my married life in shambles, left me wondering if there really was anything new and rewarding that could happen in my life. I was desperate to meet someone attractive to whom I could turn for some feminine company, and hopefully sexual gratification too. He gave me H's telephone number and suggested that she was likely to satisfy every aspect of my sexual needs. I gladly accepted her contact details and eagerly anticipated a proper re-awakening of my libido.

Also, as you know, I have a very soft spot for French women, and one who promised to lift me to new heights of physical stimulation was indeed someone to eagerly look forward to.

I realise that I may seem callously demeaning in this description, but I can assure you that I have no intention to objectify or denigrate her in any way. And why would I? She is after all someone I have fallen madly in love with since. I am merely reminding you of how a simple, and perhaps primitive interest has inexplicably escalated into nothing less than a divine desire.

I looked at her profile photo on WhatsApp. She looked interesting but did not immediately strike me as a candidate for a coveted place in my Hall of Fame.

I hate cold calling at the best of times but decided to be a little braver on this occasion. I steeled myself and called H. It was mid-afternoon, and I was in between meetings at the construction site of the project I was managing. I believe you know of it.

She took my call, and we talked for a very long time without any obvious or awkward pause. She made me feel so much at ease, irrespective of the fact that this was our first ever conversation. She sounded so delightful. I flirted outrageously with her. I could not wait to meet her and make mad passionate love to her. The people I was due to meet began to assemble, and my attention was sought. I was reluctant to cut short my conversation with H but had to in order to conduct the business of the day. I am sure that the assemblage at the meeting would have been unanimously understanding, had I explained that I was on a call to the most enticing French woman I had yet to meet, but I felt it best not to test their consideration at this point.

We finally ended our call. Very reluctantly on my part, I might add. I felt that I already knew her. I loved her voice. Anyway, I took comfort from the fact that we would speak again soon. I had tried to persuade her to come to London whilst I was there but realised that it was very short notice. She did not seem too averse to the idea, however. She told me that she was heading to Paris but was unlikely to finish early enough to get a flight to London afterwards. I got the distinct impression that she was open to visiting me in London, and that if she did choose to see me here, it would not be for just a fleeting overnight stay. I was thrilled. I felt I had created a good first impression. Not bad for a fellow who had not dated since the Jurassic era.

I wanted to get to know her a little better before we met, and so I kept my word to call again soon and did so immediately on my return to Zimbabwe a few days later.

We chatted often after that initial dialogue, with some of our conversations continuing unstinted for well past an hour. She preferred to speak after leaving the office in the evening which suited me too. The only time we did not speak, but messaged each other instead, was when she was with her mother, watching some Indian movie or television drama. I could not help but like her immensely.

I had taken her telephone number initially with a view to finding an incredibly good sexual companion, which I did not doubt she would be, but I loved engaging her in conversation. We had much to speak about. She was bright, quick-witted, as well as charming, with a good sense of humour. She was definitely someone whose interest I could not hope to confidently win based on my looks, and had to therefore draw on my depleted reserves of charm and whatever other resources remained in my dating armoury.

In my flirtations with her, I offered, and constructed a poem in her name.

Heavenly crafted, she's such a beauty to behold;
Eyes dreamlike, yet sensitive to the depths of one's soul;
Sweet lips of whimsical softness, shaped to Cupid's mould;
Surely a loveliness within to complete her divine whole.

She applauded with my efforts and challenged me to create one with her surname bearing seven letters. I did, and she appeared suitably impressed with that too.

We arranged to meet at the weekend of my next intended trip to London. She organised her trip and secured a booking at a hotel called The Ned. I had not even heard of it, which goes to show how much of London I had no real recent knowledge of. I should really have set aside some time to do more of a reconnoitre of the area and gain a general lay of the land but, I had ploughed ahead heedlessly, and relied instead on my historical knowledge, which would be my undoing.

I did at least have time to buy her a present. I bought a bottle of pink champagne on the flight over, as well as craft gin from Zimbabwe and a bottle stop from Carol Boyes, a rather clever artist who designs and makes tableware with aluminium.

Given our conversations, and hopefully intent, I decided to buy her some lingerie also. I did at least know her bra size having gleaned this information from her in an earlier conversation in which she also informed me about the different attributes of this aspect of lingerie, which was all news to me.

I set off to the Agent Provocateur store in the West End and bought her some lingerie, which I hoped she would appreciate. She told me later that she did indeed like my choice. I had imagined sipping champagne with her as she excitedly unwrapped her other presents, put on the lingerie for my benefit and plied me with a hundred kisses. The sex that followed could only be likened to being taken as close to heaven as possible. That sadly, remained just a thought.

Not having had sex for what seemed like an eternity, (through choice in some instances, as there was not much I wished to commit to), I looked forward, therefore, to meeting her with the predictable eager anticipation. Although more than sufficiently desirable, she did not strike me as being necessarily the type that would immediately propel me toward the nearest wedding planner to secure arrangements with. And now, ironically, I could not get to a wedding planner fast enough!

I had no thought, when I excitedly took note of her number, that it would amount to anything more than a valiant, although primal, cause to seek sexual gratification. And, in my view, the more times this gratification was gained, the better. I was very much in the market for sexual solace and relief from tedious celibacy, so I need you to know that I did not for a single moment harbour at that point, any intention to fall madly in love with her.

She called me as soon as she landed but was happy to make her own way to the hotel, rather than have me meet her at the airport.

It was a pity, as I had great intention to greet her with a bunch of flowers, and wave excitedly as soon as I caught sight of her, i.e., embark on the whole sweep-her-off-her-feet-and-spin-her-around-in-joy routine.

I would have to save that for another time. She suggested that I should meet her at the hotel once she had time to settle in and freshen up. I could barely contain my excitement at the thought of seeing her and tried my best not to scream uncontrollably with joy. A few fist pumps sufficed.

I showered, shaved and spent time grooming myself in front of the mirror as best as I could. The face that stared back at me was certainly not that of a handsome man. It was one that looked like death warmed up. Hosting a nose that looked as though it had been squashed by a pummelling from a crowd armed with baseball bats; eyes that lacked much of their previous confident glimmer; and of a complexion that had lost its taut youthful lambency. The ears were what can I say – just ears. With nibbleable lobes possibly, but nothing more. The lips were not too bad but disguised to some extent by the moustache and goatee. I still had the hair on my head though.

Work on the charm, I mouthed silently at the reflection. It was not convincing. I shrugged my shoulders in resignation, as there was not much more that could be done in confines of the bathroom. My only hope lay in winning the lottery and embarking on major reconstruction in the hands of a highly skilled facial surgeon.

If you have not yet been to the Ned, I would suggest we plan our next meeting there. It is a marvellous venue.

The reception to the hotel was set well into the building, and therefore not immediately obvious. In fact, one was greeted beyond the doormen, by a tea salon on the left, a restaurant to the right and a bar directly ahead.

The reception counter was tucked away on the right beyond which a further two restaurant areas resided. I loved the ambience. It was previously the headquarters of the Midland Bank, which had been tastefully converted into a remarkable hotel with clutch of wonderful associated amenities.

She walked out of the lifts at the hotel reception. The sight of her took my breath away. I realise that many healthcare brands could claim to do the same, but this was beyond even the most miraculous of mouthwashes.

She walked gracefully up to me, dressed like a movie star or fashion icon. I was speechless. My breathing was stertorous at best, and the whole stricken-fish-starved-of-air routine commenced. Thankfully she offered her cheek for a kiss in exchange for the unimpressive limp handshake, which would have been more appropriate when meeting someone from a leper colony rather than one who I had hopes of bedding many times over.

Once I had partly unglued my tongue from the roof of my mouth, a form of babbling began. My knees were the only part of my anatomy putting up a good show of not losing strength. She somehow made sense of my babble and proceeded to thank me for the gift of Lilies, which I had rung the hotel the previous evening, and arranged delivery of to her room. I handed her the bag of further gifts of champagne, lingerie, etc. I later regretted not accompanying her back up to her room, as she may have expected. Instead, I watched her walk casually, assuredly and sexily back to the lifts, leaving me with no doubt that I had just met the most beguiling and beautiful woman in the world.

H undoubtedly has a good figure. I would have given my right arm and probably right leg also, to see her undress and try on the lingerie. I had purchased it with only her in mind, as I had gone to great lengths to explain as much as I could of H's figure, character and taste, to the kind and attentive sales assistant at the Agent P shop. I was convinced that under her virtually perfect choice of clothing there existed a petite and incredibly desirable frame, worthy of worship and a multitude of exploratory kisses.

I used the short time that she was away to regroup, gather together the handful thoughts I had, and decided on a course of action to redeem myself from the uninspired initial greeting. I enquired of the concierge trendy places we could go to close by for an impressive lunch. I was directed to a few within walking distance but had the Caravan City recommended as a desirable luncheon venue.

It started to rain, and she was, rightly disinclined to get drenched. I had hoped to stroll, arm in arm down the West End, culminating our journey's end at Fortnum's for tea, but the weather was not on my side that day.

The problem I was later to discover is that even tea at Fortnum's would not have been forthcoming unless we partook of the same at the tradesmen's entrance, as there was at least a one month waiting list for a seat at a table.

Entertaining her well required careful planning and preparedness, neither of which I had executed with any degree of competence. An errant chicken walking across a blank page with ink on its feet would have derived a better itinerary.

I had trouble locating the restaurant, despite clear instructions from the concierge. H remained patient throughout the application of my hapless navigational skills and walked around with me for a while in needless circles, until we eventually stumbled into the entrance.

Why is it that misfortune chooses to visit me when I need to be at my most impressive?

All I needed to do was to order well, avoid unnecessarily disgorging food from my mouth, and keep to an entertaining script in terms of conversation. Nothing too hard to do, nor out of the ordinary, you would have assumed. Apparently not for me.

My head was still spinning from beholding such a beautiful woman. I tried to remain calm and in full control of my wits, but it was difficult. The coffee arrived, and I inadvertently imbibed more than the intended sip. I had no prior warning that the coffee was exceedingly hot. I felt my teeth melt and my tongue catch fire. I wanted to spit out the coffee and scream in pain, but held myself in check, choking inwardly and feeling my eyes bulge and my face distort in frightful agony.

I excused myself to go to the gents, where I rinsed my mouth with cold water in the hope of re-establishing gainful use of my tongue and teeth. I did my best to regain a degree of equanimity and promised my reflection that I would henceforth aim to do better. Lunch arrived at the table, and I began to regain composure, not serenity, but a slightly more tranquil demeanour.

As we conversed, I grew sufficiently confident to turn on the tap to greater charm. I listened to her intently, knife poised in mid-air, as I hoped to make an intelligent observation or two, as soon as I had swallowed my food. Just when the time came to make my learned interjection, my elbow chose to leave the table and my knife leave my hand. Thankfully, the knife had not pierced her chest nor beheaded any of the occupants at the next table, clattering harmlessly onto the floor.

H just smiled politely, probably mildly amused by my impersonations of an inebriated chimp at a circus. I decided for the remainder of my lunch to avoid trying anything too clever or too coordinated, and merely enjoy the vision of the beauty facing me.

After a rather lacklustre lunch we headed back to the hotel and were all set to relax with tea at Millie's Lounge as an easy alternative.

This seemingly popular lounge was positioned immediately to the left of the main entrance doors. We unburdened ourselves of our coats and occupied a vacant seat. It was short-lived, as we were soon politely guided away by the maître d', on the basis that a firm reservation was required prior to obtaining seating. Even after arguing the point that H was a guest at the hotel entitling her to some preferential rights, he remained unmoved. The subtle offer of a tenner was not to prove very persuasive either.

We found a seat at the Nickel Bar and ordered drinks. We spent an hour or so chatting, and she agreed to dinner but requested a late one so that she could sleep for a while, having arisen very early that morning to catch her flight. Plenty of time to plan a little better. Or so one would have thought.

Unfortunately, it was me. A man who had seemingly last dated in the Cretaceous Period, and had lost all sense of bearing, wit, rationality, and anything remotely corresponding to common sense.

Planning in this instance, especially for entertaining the world's greatest beauty was not easy. Due in the main to my organisational entropy (I refer you again to the erstwhile ink-footed fowl), but in part due to H also. I found her charm and beauty completely disarming.

I had to shake myself out of this nightmarish reverie and offer her some hook of credibility on which to hang her hopes on me.

I took the time on the tube train ride back home to reflect on the afternoon's proceedings and winced in imagined pain with each recollection. If I had been her, I would have arranged for the first flight home, or at the minimum found another (preferably handsome) man at the hotel as companion.

She must possess a heart of gold though, as she was enormously patient with me, and my display of what can only be kindly described as the antics of the unhinged buffoon. This admirable patience of hers was to be put to an even greater test later.

I went back later that evening to take her to dinner. She had made considerable effort to dress for dinner. She looked even more ravishing. I had dressed as best as I could, but I realised from a review of clothing that my wardrobe urgently required very serious updating. It was too late to do anything about it just then.

The concierge had directed me to try a place called Rosa's Thai Café in Spitalfields. We took a taxi and arrived at the venue. Dinner that evening was a consummate disaster. She loved Thai food, and I thought that I would impress her with my knowledge of this cuisine. It would be a wonderful evening, I assumed. Wrongly.

The food was of pedestrian quality. I could have cooked better. The restaurant itself was nothing more than a canteen and certainly did not warrant dressing up for. It was an absolute waste of both time and effort. We headed back to the hotel and had a consolation drink at the Nickel Bar. It was not long before she expressed fatigue and a wish to retire for the evening. I was not in the least bit surprised.

Being a kindly soul, she was prepared to meet me again the following day for lunch with you. The train ride home was mournful. I realised that any prospects of my wooing her to bed had been well and truly torpedoed by the disastrous evening at the Rosa's Café.

I did enjoy the Nickel Bar in the hotel though. It was actually quite a nice place to sit and chat over a drink, as it had a generally good buzz about it – a hubbub of conversations and unobtrusive service. I told my daughters about the bar, and they quietly arranged a surprise birthday celebration for me there, with cocktails, champagne and dinner, some weeks later.

At that celebration, they suggested that I should consider dating again. Their only stipulated condition was that I was not to date anyone under thirty. Providentially, H just qualified. It was all so endearing, especially as I will always associate everything about the Ned with H, regardless of my hapless attempts to woo her there.

They were not aware of H, but I was grateful to my two lovely children for the consideration they showed in choosing a venue that I liked enormously. I have been back to the Ned many times since, always with cerebrations of H, but subsequently also with the added special memory of the wonderful time my lovely daughters created for me there.

The lunch at the Landsdowne made considerable inroads into redeeming my shattered credibility. You were a wonderful host. I could tell from the general merriment that H was enjoying the afternoon. I too could not have thought of a more wonderful way to spend a Sunday. A huge thanks to your lovely Heather also for making us feel equally welcome and for holding the fort admirably with H and I, until you found a parking spot. I hope that she felt that H and I made for a lovely couple.

We took a cab to the Westfield Mall after we left you. I had completely forgotten that shops closed earlier on a Sunday, but we had time for a quick whizz around the shops. We popped into the Prada store, which she told me was one of her favourite brands. She showed me the sorts of things she liked so that I had could develop a better idea of her taste in clothes.

I knew from our previous conversations that she dressed fashionably, and had developed a liking for some designers, much as I did in my *haute couture* days, except that it was on a considerably smaller outlay.

One of her favourite designers was Azzedine Alaia, a Tunisian-born fashion designer who made his name in the 1980s. I also loved his style on women. He knew how to bring out a femininity and sensuality in the women he dressed. H had been dressed in Alaia for our dinner out the previous evening. What a wasted outfit for a lousy canteen.

She tried on various shoes at Prada, which I loved and enjoyed helping her slip in and out of, as it gave me an unexpected but joyful opportunity to hold her exquisitely shapely legs. I only wished my poor budget could have stretched to buying her a gift from the store.

We popped into Tiffany's, which was almost directly opposite the aisle to Prada. Whilst we browsed through the various pieces of jewellery, she told me that she particularly liked the items made from rose gold. The sales assistant who knew me from previous purchases, saw me and welcomed me back enthusiastically. He assumed that H was my wife and began insisting that she tried on some of the bracelets she had been viewing. They looked absolutely marvellous on her.

A crowd began to collect around us, as a few of the other sales assistants also came over to us. I wondered if they assumed we were some sort of minor celebrity couple. She definitely looked the part, not me. Although I was dressed in my suit, for our lunch with you, I am not sure I did any justice to the pairing with H.

If I had the means, I would not have hesitated in making the purchase of a bracelet for her, but I did not and could not. I am sure that the staff at Tiffany were sad to see us walk away, but I believe that my creditors would have been hugely relieved.

I arranged for a taxi to take H back to the hotel and arranged to meet her later for dinner at the Cecconi's restaurant housed in the Ned. She was once again dressed beautifully. This time at least the restaurant was more befitting to receive her. She must have packed so many outfits for this trip, in the expectation of being hosted well. Other than the lunch at the Landsdowne, I felt that I had sorely disappointed her.

The dinner was absolutely superb. We had ordered well, primarily down to her recommendations, and the service was attentive and courteous. The waiters assuming also that we were a couple, which would have raised my credibility in their eyes, for capturing such a beauty. I loved talking to her. She was the most charming and engaging woman I had met in a very long time. She looked so radiant also, I could barely keep my eyes off of her. I was not that keen to eat, as every moment taken to look at the plate of food in front of me was a moment less drinking in her splendour.

We had a quick drink at the bar before she retired for the evening. This was her last night in London, and much as I had hoped to make love to her, the preceding disasters had created a yawning gap in the fulfilment of expectations and there was little likelihood of securing any reward for my efforts, other than a meaningful hug, and a gentle kiss.

She was happy to meet me for a quick lunch before she left for the airport. I was hoping to show her around the project that I was working on, but she was not particularly keen to walk around a muddy construction site dressed in leather trousers and a fetching top. We left her suitcases at a friend's house and sauntered off down the road for a light lunch at a French Brasserie called the Aubaine on the Brompton Road. It was a lovely sunny day, and she was happy to thread her arm through mine as we walked the short distance to the restaurant.

Given the painfully cringe-worthy efforts of the previous days, which I had accepted as irredeemable, I behaved with less intensity and greater normality, and she seemed to react well to this.

I took her across the road to the Joseph shop which was one of my favourites many years ago in my more fashionable days. She was drawn to an Alaia dress but was reluctant to try it on much to the disappointment of the sales lady, and mine too. Perhaps just as well, unless I offered to buy it for her. She did stop briefly at a shoe shop on Pelham Street to try on a pair of boots she saw in the window. They did not have exactly what she was hoping for, but just holding her foot and helping her remove her boots was an absolute delight. I can honestly say that I do not have a foot fetish, but just holding her leg gave me enormous pleasure. Is there something wrong with me?

I gave her a parting gift of the craft gin that I had bought for her as well as the gifts from Carol Boyes, when we got back to her luggage. She had already packed the champagne, I had given her earlier, and as we fought to close her very full suitcase, she remarked that her mother would assume she had become an alcoholic in her short stay here. We laughed together. It was a nice, shared moment. She let me hold her hand until the taxi arrived to take her to the airport. She left. My heart broke.

How could a simple thing like meeting a beautiful woman and making mad passionate love to her go so miserably wrong? Had I become so inept at the dating process? I felt so awful that I let an opportunity to be with such a wonderful woman slip through my fingers so painfully clumsily.

Would it have been the surprise of discovering that she was far too special a person to provide more than mere sexual gratification? I honestly do not know.

I think that I had inexplicably fallen in love with her and had lost all perspective as a result.

Anyway, I trust that I have furnished you with sufficient detail of my thoughts and actions regarding H to allow you some comprehension of my current dire emotional predicament. I shall be looking forward eagerly to your inspiring counsel on suggested next steps. I bid you a fond cheerio for now.

Love,

David

Letter 2 – Seeking French Redemption

January 2018

Dear Geoff,

I realise that when I last wrote to you, I had completely omitted to relay to you my subsequent actions on the matter of my lovely lady.

I felt that it was important for you to gain the whole picture of my interactions with H in order to follow the thread of my argument for continuing pursuit of this goddess. I write again, therefore, to detail the events following that initial disastrous rendezvous.

I should have let matters be after the first calamitous encounter, as we had discussed over a rather sumptuous dinner at the Benares restaurant in Berkeley Square later that week, but my head and heart refused to agree on any form of negotiated settlement, and sleepless nights thinking about her ensued.

By the way, do you realise that we have had some of the most wonderful evenings dining together? You seem to bring out the best in me. I only wish that I could be as witty and relaxed with prospective dates, as I am with you. I think that the lunch at Landsdowne was the highlight of H's trip as we were both at our entertaining best alongside our lady companions.

Anyway, I do agree with you that any sane person would have at that point tendered their resignation from further pursuit and looked back on the initial cataclysmic ordeal as a learning experience. But I was possibly no longer sane. Any semblance of perceived sanity had deserted me the moment I had laid eyes on her. I felt that I had to rectify matters with her. I was so in love, and I could not bear to see her leave my life just yet, and certainly not with a very poor impression of me. I had to go to Lyon to see her, even if it meant that it would be for the very last time.

I called to arrange for an opportune day to see her. She gave me an indication of the sorts of hotels that would be suitable, meaning a proximity to the city centre. I could not obtain a room at our first choice, but did at one called the Hotel Okko, which purported to be trendy, and which I assumed would be similar to the Ned in London. It did not quite live up to expectations but served its purpose to some extent.

The flight on EasyJet was not as difficult as the journey to the airport. I had left sufficiently early to catch the train to Gatwick from Victoria station. With train ticket in hand, I stood on the platform only to hear announcements of severe delays to journeys. I was going to miss my flight, I thought. This meeting was not going to take place and I was going to disappoint her yet again. I would lose her for good. I could not afford to let that happen.

After staring balefully at the display board for a few minutes, I realised that the only way I would catch my flight was to take a chance with a taxi. I approached a well-dressed couple who were looking similarly forlorn and suggested sharing a taxi to Gatwick. They jumped at the chance, and we raced to the entrance to the station where I had arranged to meet the Uber.

It was only at the journey's end that I realised that my companions were Alan Hanson and his wife, who were expecting to catch a flight and an onward cruise with their friends.

As you know, I am more of a Manchester United fan, but remember him as one of the better Liverpool players, who then became a respected commentator later in his career. He was unassuming. His wife was lovely. In fact, they were a sweet couple, and I hope to meet them again. There was no time for selfies or posts with celebrities on this occasion. To be honest my mind was more focused on seeing H again, and I kept looking nervously at my watch, especially when the driver slowed down for traffic on the motorway. The conversation with the Hansons was a welcome distraction, however. When they learnt that I was off to see the woman I loved, they allowed me to be dropped off first, and cheered me on as I sped with suitcase in tow into the terminal building.

I was just in time for the flight check-in. I heaved a huge sigh of relief. I could now focus on what I needed to say and do when I met with H, as I ambled through to the departure gates. A plan of sorts began to form. It was now down to effective execution of said plan.

I arrived in Lyon and immediately fell in love with the town. I had been here before, albeit fleetingly, but there was much more of a *je ne sais quoi* this time around. Everyone smiled, and even the usually surly immigration official welcomed me warmly. It was a wonderfully spirited start to this crusade to win her heart.

Yes, I agree that it is ridiculous and utterly foolish to think so sentimentally, but that is what the irrationality of love does to you. Even the sun, which shone brightly on this cloudless winter's day, seemed to wink encouragingly at me as it glittered brightly off the glass on various buildings. All I could think of on the journey to the hotel was how wonderful it would be to settle down there with H and start a family together. I should really have been kindly put down at that point, as one would a favourite pet who had become painfully ill and showed little signs of recovery.

I unpacked my laptop to work through some project emails and messages. Realising that the day would otherwise speed by, leaving me no time to see the town, I left the hotel hurriedly after learning of the quickest route to the centre. It involved merely crossing the Pont Lafayette in front of the hotel to reach the main thoroughfare of the city centre. I ended up walking right past the building she worked in. I was tempted to pop my head through the door for a quick "hello" but decided to at least arm myself with some flowers first. I had also purchased yet more lingerie for her in the hope that I might be a little more fortunate on this occasion.

I loved the feel of the city. I found a delightful florist amongst a parade of stands in La Place Bellecour, and a sweet convivial lady who put together a lovely bouquet of white lilies with a single long stemmed red rose. She wished me the best of fortunes when I conveyed to her in my feeble attempt at French that the flowers were for the most beautiful woman in my world. Carrying this rather large bouquet, I decided to embark on a little Christmas shopping too and bought a few gifts for Chloe and Holly. I really do not know what it is about the French, but they always make me feel so welcome. The sales assistants at every store I walked into were incredibly helpful. It may have been an aura of happiness I exuded, being in the town of my loved one, but they could not do enough to help, with one very attractive young lady at the Sephora store even holding onto the flowers as she helped me contemplate my purchases.

What is said about adoring every aspect of the one you love appears to be very true. I even worshipped the bank she worked in. As soon as I walked into the reception area, and was greeted cheerily by the ladies working there, I felt inclined to hand over my entire net worth for them to manage. The only snag was that this would have probably amounted to a rather inefficacious sum of tuppence ha'penny.

I told them that I was just leaving the flowers for H and would be back shortly, intending to race back to the hotel and freshen up a little before my evening with her, but they would not let me leave. My plan was beginning to crumble rapidly. Was this not exactly what Robbie Burns had in mind, when he very wisely penned the famous words *"The best laid schemes o'mice an' men; Gang aft a-gley"*?

There were no mice involved in my scheme, but it began to unravel, nevertheless. I decided that the best I could do now was to adopt a cheerful countenance and let the events unfold.

H looked pleased to see me and was thrilled to be in receipt of the flowers. I apologised for my somewhat dishevelled appearance as I was still in my jeans and leather bomber jacket not having changed since setting off early that morning. She suggested that we have coffee before dinner as it was still early.

We walked arm-in-arm to a place called Le Grand Café des Négociants. The sun had bid its adieu and the cloudy skies had begun to generate a light drizzle, so we needed to find seating inside. It was busy, but we managed to find a table almost immediately. The place was abuzz with throng of people and an infinitude of conversations, but we still attracted many looks as we walked in, and I could only hope that they were favourable.

French cafés seemed to carry an ambience difficult for the ones in England to emulate. I was never sure, whether it was due to the seating arrangements, the animated chatter that took place or the courteous waiters manoeuvring busily but efficiently between the tables. I could think of spending much time at this café ruminating over a coffee or two as I waited for H to finish work.

We waited for the drizzle to abate before heading toward the restaurant Le Bistrot d'Abel. H chatted to the manager who seemed to indicate that they would have a table for us in a while. Having an hour to kill, we walked a little further along Rue de la Bourse to a bar fittingly called Le Comptoir de la Bourse for a drink. This was quite a nice little bar too. They obviously have a few gems, in terms of nice venues in Lyon, or I was just in adulation of anything that involved H.

We were sat next to a couple that looked as though they shared a distinct age difference too. It would have been nice to have read minds and determined what it was people thought when they saw us together. 'Lovely couple', I hoped.

I probably ate more than I should have at this bar, as I was rather full by the time it came to dinner. The food at the restaurant was great. H insisted that I practised my French with the waitress, which I was happy to do with some help from her. I was so much more relaxed than I had been during her time in London, and we chatted for a long time.

The only misery was that I was on a course of antibiotics at the time, and could not share any alcohol with her, except for a sip of her red wine, which was delicious, by the way.

It had started raining a little more insistently, and the temperature had dropped several degrees too. She accompanied me back to the hotel, so that I could get changed into something warmer. I would have invited her back to my room, except for the fact that there was barely room enough to swing around the smallest of cats, let alone entertain a delightful lady guest. Oh, how I wished just then for the wonderfully spacious suites I had stayed in on my various business trips. I showered and changed my clothes as quickly as I could and ran down the corridor to the lifts to get back to her.

We took a taxi to a nightclub called the Boudoir on Place Jules Ferry. The place looked a little sparsely attended, so we opted for the Barrio Club a few metres away. It probably was the more popular of venues, as there was already quite a large assemblage there. We handed in our coats and headed to the bar for a drink. She was back onto gin and tonics, whilst I nursed my bottle of water. The music was good. As there was not a lot of room to move, we danced very closely together. It was difficult to disguise my arousal from having her hips and chest pressed up close against me. For most of the time during our dance, our bodies had virtually merged and would have required surgical precision to separate us. I felt at that point that having sex with her would be the most intensely passionate heaven-sent experience I would ever encounter on this earth.

I did not want the night to end, but it had to. She had to go to work the next day and I had an early flight to catch. As we were waiting for a taxi home, she told me that she was happy to see me again, but only after I had finalised my divorce. I was a little perplexed but nodded in agreement, thinking that it was probably only a week or two away from being resolved anyway.

As soon as I got back to the hotel, I messaged to thank her for a lovely evening and told her that I missed her already. She replied with two heart kisses.

I slept fitfully that night, knowing that she was the only woman I ever wanted to be with, but troubled by the mechanics of how best to bring it about. The divorce process I had left in the hands of my ex to procure in

Zimbabwe should ideally have been completed by now. The only thing left for me to do was to pray that no other man would win H's heart in the meantime.

I consulted a close friend, Lindsay, over dinner at a delightful restaurant here called Vic22, on my return to Harare. I did not speak too volubly about the mayhem of my first meeting with H, but merely indicated that I had unintentionally fallen in love. She told me that H's actions and requests seemed entirely reasonable and represented those of a principled person wishing for a serious relationship.

Lindsay suggested that, as a gesture of love, I invite her to meet me at the top of the Empire State Building, an action reminiscent of the movie "An Affair to Remember" with Cary Grant and Deborah Kerr and similarly with Meg Ryan and Tom Hanks in "Sleepless in Seattle". The other alternative, she recommended was something closer to home and a proposed meeting in Venice, which could serve as being equally romantic.

Besides being a very charming and gloriously attractive companion, Lindsay was a font of wisdom that evening, and I was pleased to have consulted her. I am not by any means indicating that your wise words are to be ignored, but this was supplemental advice and sourced from a woman, and you know as well I, that despite sharing similar DNA stranding and structure et al, women and men think vastly differently.

Even after reaching this age after many years of pontification on the subject, I have difficulty understanding the precise means by which the fairer sex deliberates. One theory is that their brains retain information on the basis of a carefully organised filing system, which undergoes a complex and sophisticated process of cross referencing all in their pondering. The brains in men on the other hand just deletes anything that appears too complex or deemed of no further relevance. The thought is therefore just of the moment and has no bearing on previous events or experiences. A trifle primitive perhaps, but it does keep things simple.

I believe that we may both have realised at some point in our lives the futility of engaging in arguments with women, particularly in matters requiring recall of precise dates and specific conversations. Based on my theory, much of this information would have been long deleted from our minds, and therefore inaccessible even from our equivalent of the 'trash' function. They, on the other hand retain every detail!

This allows them to apply guile and cunning more effectively and makes them formidable adversaries. Great partners and lovers, but deadly enemies.

Does this not make you wonder why more militaries do not have women generals commanding them? They have a far greater capability of outwitting foes, probably without the need to fire a single shot. I would assume, that their compassionate thinking alongside strategic assessment would also, more than likely, result in better brokerage of subsequent peace also. A discernible loss in bloodshed, all around.

I do have a second theory also, which is based on the difference in chromosomes, and can be explained thus. I believe that the heterogametic XY chromosomes which define men and separate us from the homogametic XX set in women, indicate clearly that the missing strand from the leg of the 'Y' plays a big part in not just providing elucidation on their capability to make better sandwiches, amongst a whole host of other aspects, but also how our brains process thought. This added strand, I assume, allows women to multi-task more effectively, and think along lines that men had not even begun to conceive of.

In terms of an analogy, imagine a string placed on a surface along its length. It is a demonstration of how a man's mind works – with clear linearity and simplicity. The same string rolled into a ball, results in a tangled object, no longer simple, but a series of concentric and knotted lines, indicating a pattern of great complexity. This theory, I feel may also explain why men are usually able to effectively consider only a single thought at a time.

Anyway, my dear chap, whatever the science, I have accepted the fact that we will never, as different genders, apply similarity of process to thought. We may reach similar conclusions but will never share the concomitance of the process. Forgive me. I digress as always.

I could not read H's mind. I had to be happy with the fact that she was prepared to consider a relationship with me despite all my foibles and the disastrous earlier dates. I was eternally grateful to have at least redeemed myself, salvaged a modicum of pride and obtained a promise of sorts, as a result of my trip to Lyon. All this of course, only as soon as I could demonstrate that I had been truly liberated from the shackles of an incomplete divorce.

We messaged each other a few times after that trip. Christmas was fast approaching, and I soon got caught up in the celebratory sparkle of the season in England. One of my messages was to tell her that I missed her. She sent me a video of Mariah Carey singing "All I want for Christmas is You", in return. I could feel my heart fit to burst, with an enormous amount of love for her.

I believe you know the rest. I will be glad to fill in any gaps in your recollections, should you wish. I look forward eagerly, in the meanwhile to our next chat over dinner.

Until then, my love to you as always,
David

Letter 3 – Visions of a Beautiful Relationship

February 2018

Dear Geoff,

You will never believe what amazing dreams I have had recently about H. I felt I had to write to you immediately about them, lest I forget.

The dreams were so vivid that they seemed almost real.

I could sense touch, feel emotions and witness colours and details with simply amazing clarity. Have you had any dreams that you could recall with any degree of visual acuity? I certainly have not, at least not in recent memory. I have had many dreams, yes, and mostly about running out of time at a written exam, or falling unchecked into an abyss, but never with such continuity and semblance of reality.

I have done my best to note down these dreams as a series of scenes in the chronology of events as they played out in my mind. A lot of content was generated from wishful thinking in my subconscious, I have no doubt. But what if they had been manifested in my dreams in order for me to believe it to be what should take place in my life?

Should I let H know that my dreams suggest that we are destined to a life of blissful marital partnership and production of gorgeous offspring?

Have many major life changing events not taken place as a result of similar visions? Would Joseph have ever hired a camel and scrambled across the desert with his pregnant wife in search of a stable in Bethlehem navigated only by a star, without some divine instruction during the course of his sleep? Would Joan of Arc have ever gained such prominence in the Hundred Year War, and obtained eventual sainthood had she not acted on the visions of archangels?

I feel similarly guided to act. I realise that you have for some time now harboured doubts over my general sanity and consider my state of mind when it comes to H, to being several sandwiches short of a picnic, but I beg you not to hail the men in white coats just yet, and bear with me for the moment, and lend an ear to this tale as recounted by mind's subconscious state.

Scene 1
I am walking up the steps of an aircraft with 2 children. A boy of about 4 and a girl of 2. They both have dark hair. They are both well dressed, and well groomed. The boy is dressed in a grey jacket and shorts with a white shirt and black tie. His hair is perfectly combed with side parting. The girl wears a grey pinafore dress, and a white top with ruffled sleeves and black stockings. Her hair is worn in a top knot.
My son is trying to help me with my hand luggage which I have in one hand as I carry my daughter in my other arm. An airline steward comes to our rescue, and also helps me with the stroller.
We're seated in the front seats of the aircraft.
I tell my children that we'll be seeing their Mummy soon, as I strap them into their seats. My daughter is especially excited.

I am guessing my children's ages from their physical stature, as there is no independent validation of age. They are definitely my children not grandchildren as could have been assumed, as the boy calls me 'Daddy'. I am amazed that I visualised their appearance so clearly, to the point of noting details of their clothing and hair.

I think we were flying EasyJet, if I guess the colour of the steward's livery correctly. It is not my favourite airline by any stretch, but I would have flown atop a stork just to see her, if that were the only means of carriage available. I do not really understand what relevance it has to the story but felt it important to record it as it was one of those details that made the dream seem more real, and somehow more legitimate. Was this the equivalent of Joseph's camel, perhaps? But in his day, he chose wisely, as asses would not have been as enduring over desert stretches as camels.

<u>Scene 2</u>
We arrive in Lyon and take a taxi.
H's parents meet us as we get to our destination.
They are thrilled to see us and make a fuss over their grandchildren.
H's father helps me with the luggage, whilst her mother takes charge of the children.

Although another brief clip, relative to the other dream segments, it was the mystery of visualising something I have no prior sight of, that made this significant for me. We were headed to what I assumed to be H's apartment, which I have never been to, or even had any pictorial presentation of, despite visiting her city. Also, rather peculiarly, I have neither met nor seen photographs of her parents.

Beyond bizarre, it would seem like a story from "The Twilight Zone". Do you remember that series? I used to be transfixed by this programme, when younger, wondering how inexplicable those events seemed. Scary in many instances, but no explanation was ever offered other than the closing narrative advising you that the encounters televised took place in 'the twilight zone'! Mystifying.

I am not suggesting that this encounter with her parents was in any way life-threatening in fact very much to the contrary as H's parents greeted us with such affection, just similarly inexplicable. It was obvious, though, how much love they had for us, especially their grandchildren. H's mother in particular, fussed over them like a mother hen.

It was not just a great thing to see, but also sense and feel. If only it had been real.

Scene 3
H's mum is seated at the dining table with the children and feeding my daughter.
They hear the sound of the key in the door, and I tell the children that it is their mother coming home.
The children leap off their seats and rush to the front door screaming with delight.
Even the dogs yap excitedly.
She walks in with child in each hand smiling broadly as she greets us.
H, wearing a beige skirt suit, is dressed impeccably as always. Her hair cascades in curls on her shoulders. She wears bangles on her arm.
I greet her warmly, thinking how lucky I was to be married to such an amazingly beautiful woman.
She continues to make a big fuss of the children, chattering in French.

It is not clear what the living arrangements are, but the dream suggested that I was with the children in London, (and this only assumed because of the flight over), whilst H resided in Lyon. A rather interesting separation of lives, but definitely a point to ponder. Is this an arrangement we would adopt in reality? But why? We would surely want to be together as a family, especially with young children, would we not?

The dogs are two little Yorkshire Terriers – one grey and the other black & tan. They are H's favourite breed of dog, and I had hoped to surprise her once with a gift of a puppy. I recall one of the first few messages from her, when we were getting to know each other, containing a video of a woman receiving a gift of a puppy sent in a little box with balloons.

The lady recipient squealed with sheer delight for both present and presentation. I hoped to achieve the same for H one day and witness the same jubilation on receipt. A question arises as to why we had two dogs. Perhaps we had purchased one for each of our children, or do I just like symmetry even in thoughts?

I realise that having met her, you do not share my opinion, but I think of H as an amazingly beautiful woman. And, yes, I have had my eyes tested. Many times, I assure you, but I continue to feel that her beauty is one that cannot be easily surpassed. Not only does she dress fashionably and stylishly, but she always seems to look better every time I see her. In this dream she looked as ever the perfect combination of heaven-sent goddess and glamorous supermodel. Even after bearing two children, she appeared to have maintained a figure sculptured by the gods.

But it was not just her external appearance that I am attracted to. I believe she has a beauty within her too. A gentle soul, full of love that she was happy to dispense to all around her with no limit. I know this because of the way she spoke about her parents; the concern she showed for her brother when he was very ill; how she regarded

53

Tunisia regardless of her upbringing in France; being rooted in her culture despite her considerable number of journeys across the world. There are not many women in this world like her.

In my dream, it was obvious from their behaviour that the children absolutely adored her. They could barely contain the excitement when we set off, and it was on greater display when they actually laid eyes on her. She has wisdom, charm, unending compassion and unquestionable integrity that is a delight to see in one so outwardly beautiful also. She appeared to radiate love to those close to her and I could not help but be drawn to her inescapable magnetism.

She laughed easily. Her laughter sounded like the gentle tinkling of the keys on a piano. I assume that she must have married me for my sense of humour, as it would certainly not have been for either my looks or wealth. I realise that this statement will have the team of psychiatrists reaching eagerly for their pens to take note, but I could actually feel the gratitude and joy to be married to her, and to be the father of her children, despite it being just a dream.

Scene 4
H gets changed into a Jalabiya. It is blue with a scattering of gold leaf motifs.
She's just put the children to bed and showered.
I'm cooking something. H comes over and puts her arms around me from behind, resting her head against my back. I can smell the scent of her perfumed skin.
She tells me how much she's missed me.
From what I understand of what her parents say, I gather that they are very happy to see us together.

A Jalabiya is a traditional Egyptian garment, apparently worn by both Egyptian men and women. Its popularity obviously extended across north Africa to H's home in Tunisia too, as she swears by the comfort of these colourful garments.

H had indicated to me in one of her conversations, that she liked to change out of her work clothes into a Jalabiya before sitting down to watch a movie.

She described a particular Indian movie, called "Devdas", which I believe, had her and her mother captivated. I have yet to watch this to verify the appeal. She had since told me of other Indian movies that she had watched, and I presume enjoyed – "Kabhi Khushi Kabhie Gham", "Om Shanti Om", "Jodhaa Akbar", amongst many others.

They all sound to me like items on the menu of an exotic Indian restaurant, but if it pleases her, I unreservedly accept her judgement on what can be deemed good entertainment.

I must admit to never being a big fan of Indian movies, as they all seem to have a very similar plot and follow a mundane theme, with largely over-choreographed song and dance routines. They were not my ideal choice, but I would be quite easily persuaded to even watch paint dry, if it were in the company of my beautiful H.

She told me that she sometimes wore nothing underneath her Jalabiya, which had my imagination racing, and blood coursing through my veins in unquenchable desire.

It was therefore no surprise that this garment would have featured so significantly in my dream. Although she never sent me pictures of her in her Jalabiya, I pictured clearly the colour of the garment she was wearing.

I could feel the sensation of her head pressed against my back in between my shoulder blades. I doubt that this would have been the most comfortable place to rest her head, but it seemed her way of communicating her feelings of love for me. A knee in the groin would obviously have suggested otherwise, so I was thankful for the head-on-back routine. I could truly sense the joy of feeling her arms around me, in a loving hug. I could imagine that her embrace always conveyed much warmth, and thereby no wonder that the children also sought delight to be in her arms.

The smell of her perfume was as pleasant as it was intoxicatingly entrancing and added to her already irresistible sensual allure. It is a surprise that I had contained my desire, and that my dream did not picture me tearing off her Jalabiya and making mad passionate love to her on the kitchen counter. Obviously, her parents being there would have served somewhat as a restraint.

If only my dream had extended to our bedroom later for a little tasteful visualisation of our love making. I think you know exactly what I allude to. The scene of a couple undressing each other slowly and deliberately, the focus on each other fixated, their kisses hungry with passion.

The streetlight and glow of the moon combine to provide an ethereal illumination within the room. They lay down together naked, the curtains blow in the gentle breeze, silhouettes of their bodies closely entwined, moving rhythmically, the music builds to a crescendo. And then, … waves crash against the rocks on the shore with some ferocity. Ah, yes! If only one could edit dreams.

Scene 5
There's lots of excitement as we get our luggage together with suitcases lining the corridor in preparation to travel.
H's parents are as animated as our children!
H looks lovely in her trousers and top. She is carrying our daughter in her arms, taking charge of tickets, passports and generally directing matters.
Her father and I begin taking the bags out to the car.

I presume that we are all packed and headed to Tunisia. Though I am not sure of our destination at this stage, merely our preparedness to travel. There appears to be an inordinate amount of luggage suggesting that we were travelling *toute la famille*, grandparents included! I enjoyed watching H take charge and orchestrate matters, and in this instance to be reduced to the role of caretaking only the manual element of this intended journey. I think that it was the manner in which H appeared to conduct herself – showing control and command without appearing dictatorial in any way, which held great appeal.

Scene 6
We're at H's parents' home in Tunisia.
We are sat outside on deck chairs with our Gin and tonics and watching the sunset.
I tell her that I wanted to make love to her a million times. She laughs and tells me that we have made love a million times already. And that we have two lovely children as a result.
"You might get lucky!" she says smiling, as she squeezes my hand.

I assume that we were at H's parents' home in Tunisia. Again, I have never been to, nor seen any photographs of their residence, but assume it a likely destination given that we had included her parents in the itinerary. H has since, described her home to me by capture on video, but at the time of my dream, I had no idea of its architecture or interior layout.

I have every intention of visiting Tunisia at some point to experience first-hand the magical allure that she describes. It is the same magic I felt existed in my dream when we sat together outside to watch the sunset. It may have been a setting drawn from a memory of a maudlin scene from a movie I had seen, but it obviously represented a deep-seated desire on my part to share as many lubricious moments as I could with this true love of mine.

With regard to her suggesting that I would get lucky, I could almost sense the heavenly pleasures that awaited me in bed with her later. If, as she, by her own admission, felt that we had made love a million times, we must have had an active sex life, though how this was conducted when we lived apart remains a mystery.

Her sensuality continued to entice me endlessly. Even in a dream!

I could never find sufficient words to describe her sensuality. It was neither overt nor coarse, thank goodness, but just something she seemed to just exude in copious quantities unwittingly. Just in her deportment alone. I never tired of watching her walk either away from, or toward me, from the first time we met.

Scene 7
I'm seated at a desk in front of my laptop. My mobile phone pings.
"No 3 is on its way!" is the message I get from H.

I can't believe how thrilled I am on receipt of this news. I immediately respond to tell her that I would be home soon.

I'm on the phone with the florist trying to organise some flowers for H. I get very frustrated at the inability of the florist to understand my particular request and decide to take matters into my own hands.

I'm now headed to the airport with a big bunch of white Lilies, and a bottle of Pink champagne.

There is a little issue as to whether or not the flowers or champagne would be allowed through security.

I explain that they're for my newly pregnant wife and that I'm already late for my flight.

I'm helped through promptly, and cheered on by the airport personnel, as I rush to the departure gate to catch my flight.

I assume that I was back in London for this segment of my dream. I was alone on this occasion, and at a desk in a home in London. Again, this assumption is validated by the airport scene which came later. How wonderful that I now appeared able to afford lodgings in London, which did not constitute a cardboard box under Charing Cross Bridge. Would I have provided sufficiently for Chloe and Holly in the meanwhile? Had they now become women of independent means themselves? They are both incredibly capable and bright girls, so I have no doubt that they would be successes in life.

I understand the flowers being Lilies, as these were her favourite, and I sent these as bouquets to her together with red roses on a few occasions, but I am unclear as to why I would dream of having a little contretemps with the Florist. Was I bothered about its availability or its arrangement? What significance does this have as a message to me? No matter for this tale, as all appeared well in the rush to the airport.

I have travelled reasonably often and had never in any of the journeys challenged the security staff at the airport as to which items they would deem acceptable to carry through as hand luggage. Perhaps it was underlying hope on my part that the people who manned these stations could sometimes actually show understanding and compassion, but I was grateful that they were not just understanding, but fully supportive of the excited prospective father I was in my dream. It mattered not to them that this was my third child with H, they responded to my display of feverish delight, by not only being agreeable to my luggage content, but in cheering me on my way!

Scene 8
I'm with H. She looks even more beautiful than I remember! She now looks noticeably pregnant.
We're taking a walk, hand in hand.
She tells me that our first child was conceived in London, the second, in Paris, and this one during our last holiday. She's not sure, but she thinks that by the way she is carrying, that our next child is another girl!
"This one's special for you, isn't it?" I say placing my hand over her tummy, as we stop to look at each other.
"Yes. Very special." she says putting her hands over mine.
I mutter something about her being special too, as I reach forward to kiss her.
I feel her love for me in the warmth of her kisses.

I am not sure exactly where we are. We were possibly back in Tunisia, judging by the landscape surrounding us. Interesting is it not that the segment of the dream of us in

Tunisia would be the precursor to the conception of a third child there? Such speculation matters little though. It is sufficient for me to accept that our lovemaking had resulted in three amazingly beautiful children.

So, my friend what exactly should I make of these dreams? Would it not suggest to anyone that these dreams must be acted on? As you are aware, H and I had discussed children, but not specifically that they would be ours. I knew also that she wants three, but we had never discussed their genders or sequence. What would have caused me to dream of having a boy and two girls, and in that particular order?

Is this what destiny intends for H and I? I had always wanted a son but was more than delighted to have had two lovely daughters and had long since dispensed with any notion of having more children. Had dreams of H awoken a deep-seated desire? Is it even vaguely possible that I would marry her and have three wonderful children to add to the two delightful girls I have already fathered? Five does seem such a wonderful number.

These dreams were so real, Geoff. I could feel her head truly resting against my shoulders. I felt the silken texture of her skin when we touched. The softness of her lips against mine could not have been more authentic. They were so many magical moments. My heart could not have been fuller with love for her, and our beautiful children.

The sheer delight on the faces of the children when they saw their mother was not anything that could be merely imagined, surely?

You will realise from my previous correspondence how troubled I was about my feelings for H and concerned about how best to manage them. I feel that these feelings have been further compounded by my dreams.

Why would thoughts of a possible infatuated relationship escalate so quickly into considerations of marriage, and having children with her?

My logical mind points to the likelihood that she had a multitude of men to choose from. So, why on earth would she ever pick me? I have been in love several times. I have never ever felt the sensation of being inexplicably in love with a woman, divine thoughts of whom prove consistently impossible to exorcise from my mind. And one with whom to have children with. My heart continually refuses to accept that they will remain nothing but dreams.

As I had mentioned in conversation with you some time previously, I had also consulted a therapist/healer on this matter. I am not sure what exactly Margaret considered herself by way of title, but I had gone to see her with a view to getting an understanding of my feelings for H. Yes, I admit that even I felt at that stage that my feelings would warrant interest from psychiatrists the world over, but I hoped that Margaret would provide the required rationality, and failing that, guide me gently down the corridors toward the white padded room with no windows.

Margaret was of the opinion that my love for H was not imagined and very real, and clearly demonstrated what I was capable of emotionally. I indicated that it was unrealistic for me to believe that anything would come of a relationship with a woman considerably younger than me, separated by geography and practicing another faith.

Margaret felt that the sort of love I described as feeling for H and complimented by my vivid dreams of her, suggested a recurring love from previous lives. I was not then, nor even now, able to fathom such conjecture. Was H someone I had loved many times in past lives? How so? What happened to our lives then? Were they unfulfilled romances too? She suggested to me that even if a relationship with H was never realised in this lifetime, I was to be grateful for meeting her and believing that I was once again capable of feeling and showing great love.

I had applied my mind to the concept of being able to love again, and it makes eminent sense. But if not with H, then whom? As mentioned to you previously, since knowing her, I had dated other women, or at least expressed interest in some, who seemed compatible, companionable, and had generally been very pleasing to the eye, but had failed rather miserably to capture even the smallest piece of my heart.

I have kissed quite a few too, but again their lips lacked the softness and warmth of H's imagined kisses. Falling in love with her has been a curse, I fear, as there is unlikely to be any woman who comes close reaching to the inordinately high standards set by H. And I know that I would unintentionally but subliminally forever compare.

I find it hard now to look at another woman and appreciate her for her beauty, as she more often than not pales in comparison to H. Why do I undertake comparisons of H against any future prospective date, anyway? I met a girl recently, called Zarah with whom I got on famously well.

So well in fact that we ended our date with a few passionate kisses on the lips, but even at that moment I could not help but close my eyes and think of H. Zarah's kisses were tender and sensual, but all I could imagine was having my lips pressed against H's and feel her tongue play inquisitively in my mouth.

I would honestly accept your view that this is nothing more than a strong infatuation, and a very persistent one at that, but if that were the case, why have such vivid dreams of her? Why were they so indubitably tangible, almost suggestive of a real future rather than one of a trifling little dalliance? If anything, it would suggest that my love for her is very real. If Margaret were correct in her speculation that ours was of an enduring nature, our hearts must have been entwined for centuries.

I just need to have some coherent and plausible explanations for the dreams, or act upon them. The alternatives are either to resign myself to offering some token affection to a deserving lady seeking solace in the twilight of her amorous endeavours or quit this love race altogether and enlist at one of the last surviving monasteries.

I think that, providing I have my music, a few changes of clean and comfortable underwear, and excused for keeping the hair on my head, I could possibly cope with the frugality of living in sackcloth with bowls of gruel for sustenance.

I hope that it does not come to that, and would therefore welcome your views, or suggestions as to how I may make the dreams of a life with H a splendorous reality.

Love,

David

Letter 4 – Coping with Deadly News

April 2018

Dear Geoff,

H messaged me today.

It was a bright sunny day and I had just completed a viewing with an estate agent.

Yes, and I am back in London and flat hunting as before all the hysterical news broke out about my condition. After many consultations with family and given the possibility of continuing to work on the projects in London, it was felt best that I should have my operation and undertake recuperation here. The fact that I could provide a base for Holly as she started University here and the confidence I placed in the capability of the surgeon undertaking this delicate procedure, played significant parts in this deliberation too.

Anyway, I was sitting at the Estate Agent's office, when I heard the ping of the phone. I assumed it was a message I could respond to later, but was as always, curious to know. I saw her name. Despite wanting to forget her, you cannot imagine the sheer delight I felt at that moment.

As you are aware, I had been trying to avoid communicating with her if I possibly could so that I could attempt avoiding thoughts of her, and carry on with other considerations. This, particularly in light of the awful news with regard to the diagnosis of cancer. And would have, one assumes, driven the final nail in the coffin as far as a possible future with her was concerned, but nagging thoughts of her persisted. The dreams of our future together could not be that easily dismissed. I had to, on many occasions, try arduously to stop myself from climbing rooftops to shout out declarations of love for her. Why does she affect me so?

Anyhow, there's me trying my best to move on, and just a message from her makes my heart leap with unadulterated joy. The thought of her made me smile. I lost a sense of where I was for a moment, wrapping myself into this cocoon of tender feelings for her. I responded quickly, not wanting to miss an opportunity to communicate with her.

I guess some, including you, would have advised me to wait, or respond with less enthusiasm or urgency, but you know better than most how my mind works when it comes to H. Unless on my deathbed, with impaired vocal cords, severed fingers, and generally unable to do so, any message from H warranted an immediate response.

H had heard through a mutual friend about my condition and messaged to convey her concern. I was touched. I only wished that she loved me enough to want to be by my side and be my emotional crutch at this difficult time. I told her that I was a little anxious, but otherwise ok.

In reality, I was terrified! I was fearful of hospitals at the best of times. Thoughts of popping into a surgery for a mere injection would have my heart in palpitations. I have managed to put a brave face on this whole matter but was inwardly scared witless. I could not tell her that. I would not want her to think that I was such a wimp. I wanted her to know that I could be strong.

I think that I am generally strong and certainly must have been to have coped relatively well with many of the difficulties I have had to face in my life. When times are tough, I am to generally able to avoid panicking and running around like a headless chicken. I may get a little shirty from impatience, but my head is usually abuzz with possible solutions for problems to be faced or mechanisms to trigger comforting sensations. News of my diagnosis was beyond my mind's ability to comprehend, process or offer solutions.

There were times of outright denial. I kept telling myself that it was a misdiagnosis. They had made a mistake. I was getting healthier; this was not a disease that had plagued our family from either my mother's or father's side; and my sister, Isabel's death from cancer, though painfully tragic was not a genetic trait.

The information on the internet suggested that there was a high recovery rate from this particular form of cancer, which should have provided some comfort, but did not. The surgeon had indicated that it was small and was unlikely to have spread substantially but cautioned also that there was much that was unknown.

My lovely screen idol, Audrey Hepburn had succumbed to it. I had been in love with and worshipped her throughout my life, and my only consolation, if one could term it such, was that I shared with her a common enemy.

It was an awful feeling, Geoff. I was surprised that I wished to arise every morning to face the day. I had lost some dear people to this dastardly disease, including an ex-girlfriend at the young age of twenty-six; and another dear friend, who had been so supportive during some of my difficult days, in his early thirties. Cancer was cruel! I had somehow never thought that this would plague my life.

Yes, I had considered my own vulnerability and mortality, since losing many members of my family over a short period of time, but I felt that there was much life still to be enjoyed and experienced, especially as I had, from an emotional perspective, just begun emerging with a new lease of life. Would life ever be 'normal' again? Or would I feel the sword of Damocles forever swinging just above my head as a constant reminder of my life's fragility and unpredictability?

I was also caught rather by surprise. Both my parents had lived relatively long lives. I was young in comparison. I felt young. I had just survived some very difficult times and I was beginning to regain some financial stability and some confidence with it. Why now? It was hard enough that the price I had to pay for the previous years of hardship, was my marriage. Was a major ailment in my life now the additional tribulation I had to endure?

By this time, I lost all faith in God. Had I not been punished enough? I had lost my siblings at a relatively young age. I felt that I had already put my children through the torment of a broken relationship and financial difficulty, and I was about to heap additional emotional burden upon them, for no clear reason. It felt grotesquely unfair!

I sometimes could not help but feel a little concerned about possible unsuccessful outcomes. In case anything happened to cause my demise, I wanted H to know that I loved her, and would continue to do so for an eternity. I wanted her to know that if I had completely destroyed any prospect of a future with her as a result of any delinquency, in this lifetime, I promise to do considerably better in many others to come.

I loved my daughters too. I loved them as much as my heart could repeatedly fill with feelings for them. They were my future and legacy. I could not bear to let them, or anyone else in my family for that matter, know that I feared for my life, as I did not wish to lay yet a further layer of emotional burden upon them. I was comfortable in the knowledge that my girls were better provided for upon my death from the insurance cover, and just hoped that they fared well in life.

I believed the whole matter of my illness to be unfair, but I became more concerned about my children. I hoped that they would continue to exercise the values instilled in them. I wished also that they would fall madly in love and continue to believe in their happiness, despite the unhappy ending they witnessed in their parent's marriage.

It was tough time, but I grew more accepting of my fate, and focussed my mind on likely courses of action should I live.

H's call, and the sound of her voice triggered joyous thoughts of her.

I went for a run the next morning. It was another gloriously warm day, but not as sunny as the day before. I was feeling good. My breath was regular, and I could feel an energy surging through me as my feet pounded the streets in regular stride.

I listened to the "Starboy" album by The Weeknd as I ran. There was something about the melancholy in his lyrics and yet an upbeat tune that appealed to me. It was reflected my oxymoronic feelings for H – a sad elation.

The music and his voice were therapeutic. I allowed my mind to drift. I was accepting of death, but my feelings for H gave me the desire to fight to live. I smiled as I thought of her waiting for me at home after my run. It was delightful thought, especially as she would be holding our child in her arms as she opened the door for me on my return.

I got back home, to Carole's house, where Holly and I were resident for the time being. I was panting from my efforts but delighted to note that I had covered a good seven kilometres, an improvement from the five I had done previously. I had been thinking during my run about how touched I was by H's concern and felt that I should thank her for it. I arranged with the online florist I had used previously for some flowers to be sent to her with the following message:

"Dear H,
Thank you so much for your message. I really appreci-ated your concern. I just wanted to let you know that thoughts of you do make me feel so much better. Look forward to seeing you at some point in the near future.
Love, David x"

Do you ever sometimes define women into three dis-tinct categories? One being those you simply cannot wait to get into bed with, the attraction being purely one of fulfilling a sexual desire; and the second being those whom you enjoy the company of immensely but regard as friends; and the third being those you wish to marry and have a dozen children with, as they appear to offer fulfilment of every other desire beyond the sexual?

I sometimes do.

Could women fall effectively into all categories? H fulfils every wish I could possibly have – sexual, emo-tional, spiritual, mystical, physical, metaphysical, chem-ical, biological, and every other positive 'al' you could imagine. I wanted as much to hold hands and watch the sunset with her and talk to her "til the cows came home", as much as I wanted tear her underwear off with my teeth and make mad passionate love to her. Even thoughts of my pending operation could not blight my loving or sen-sual thoughts of H.

Why do I love her so much, is a question I cannot help but ask myself repeatedly? Why her, and not the several other attractive women I see, especially the ones that seem to exist by the million on a lovely sunny summer's day in London?

I have never wanted to be with someone so badly. All I can think of is having her as my attentive friend, passionate lover, lifelong companion, supportive wife and loving mother of my children. Perhaps this was my mind's way of coping with the horrific news of my illness. Providing hope for a future which I could not otherwise tangibly identify with. Some motivation to survive, perhaps.

Other forms of therapy included throwing myself wholeheartedly into dating activity. This was partly also to take my mind of H. I met several attractive women. Some of whom, at least on the surface appear to give H a good run for her money. But I was captivated only for a short time. I would invariably dismiss them, or they may me, for that matter, after a show of very little follow up enthusiasm. Whilst I could picture H's beautiful face at any instance, trying to recall what these other dates looked like was a struggle.

I would have applied myself to obtaining some retail therapy, had that been practical. I had already bought some clothes to replace the regulation plain chinos and baggy shirts I had grown accustomed to as standard attire. I had also lost some weight from exercising regularly and was in need of clothes to fit better, but it was pointless buying anything more at this point, not knowing what the outcome of my hospitalisation and surgery would be. I tried to cheer myself up with some window shopping to identify items I could treat myself to upon discharge and recovery.

I was glad also that I had my building projects to work on and occupy my mind actively. I enjoyed being busy, particularly on projects where the outcomes were ones I could visualise easily. I could see the outcome of this house that was being built. It was going to be a stunning building, the talk of the town for many years to come, I believed. I was so happy to be championing its realisation.

My operation is due in the next few days. I am understandably troubled, and face this with the greatest trepidation, but I shall keep my hopes up for success. Should anything untoward happen, I believe that you will know what it is I wish to convey to H and my family.

To cheer myself up and avoid thoughts of pain, I shall think of all the times you made me laugh hysterically and accept my sedation and whatever follows thereafter with a brave smile upon my face. Wish me luck, nevertheless.

Goodbye for now, and God bless.

Love,

David

Letter 5 – More Vivid Dreams & the Helios Life

May 2018

Dear Geoff,

H continues to haunt my thoughts.

Why do I find it so difficult to dispel thoughts of her? I have met beautiful women before. I have even made love to a few, so why would I be particularly obsessed with this one? I have tried thinking rationally about my feelings for her, but they are far too bizarre to comprehend. I keep reminding myself that she is much too young for me.

The geography certainly does not work for us. There is such great disparity in her expectations of a 'boyfriend'. Not that I am a particularly fastidious Christian but, there is also a mismatch between us in terms of choice of religion. Most important of all, she probably does not feel the same way about me. Why oh why do I continue to apply considerable mental energy pursuing such unrequited love?

As it proved, my subsequent visits to Margaret were less to do with H, and more with how I could manage emotions related to my cancer treatment and all the resultant logistical and financial complications that ensued.

Nevertheless, H would arise in conversation, and I was advised to focus less on her and more on the renewed faith that she had created within me of the capability to show a deep love again. I suppose she was right; I could well imagine myself otherwise becoming highly cynical, and highly mistrustful of any other seeking my emotional commitment.

I applied myself to consider all other matters of import in my life, reflecting with gratitude the many people who had contributed to making my life richer and sweeter, especially my daughters, for whom my love was boundless. But still the last thing I remembered on my hospital bed before being sedated beyond thought was H's face and the touch of her hands.

It is obvious to me that, despite the rational intervention of thought, my mind subconsciously works overtime with respect to H, as I continue to have vivid dreams about her. I recall writing to you previously about the very clear visions I had about a relationship with her. Well, you may or may not be surprised to learn that I have now further dreams, or visions, or whatever one should call them, to add to the ones I had communicated to you previously.

Scene 1

We're at a clinic. H is heavily pregnant with our third child.

My son sat on one side of me and my daughter on the other. H on the seat beyond her. She asked my daughter to move to the other side of her so that she could sit next to me and hold my hand.

My daughter was reluctant to move, as she wanted to remain sitting next to me. I could see H getting upset. I suggested to my daughter that she sits on my lap so that H could move next to me.

My daughter beamed in delight.

H smiled too as she moved to the seat next to me. She took my hand in hers and squeezed it. I turned to kiss her.

I had one hand around my daughter's waist, the other holding H's with our fingers intertwined. My son rested his head on my shoulder.

The waiting room and the arrangement of furniture is almost exactly what remembered of the Harley Street Clinic where I had checked in for my operation earlier this month. Why I dreamt I was there with H is not clear. It would seem, given H's nervousness that we were there to see a specialist with regard to her pregnancy, rather than my condition. But would we have chosen a clinic in Harley Street for a routine check-up with a gynaecologist? Unless this was merely meant to be representative of a 'clinic' and bore no significance to the purpose of the medical consultation. Let us assume that for now.

We probably looked the perfect picture of an ideal family. Other than the minor fracas between mother and daughter over seating arrangements, which were amicably resolved, we had indeed created the picture of a perfect family. Two children and one very obviously on its way, given how heavily pregnant H appeared.

It was nice to feel that whatever had agitated H, I was able to provide the necessary reassurance. I did wonder though if this had anything to do with thoughts of what happened with hospital appointments relating to the birth of my children.

I was once delayed at a Board meeting and arrived late to an appointment with the gynaecologist. Was this a result of the guilt I was suffering from a previous late attendance, or a warning to me that I needed to make up for any possibility of malfeasance with my future wife? Intriguing, isn't it?

Scene 2
We're on a beach.
*My daughters, Chloe and Holly are with us on a family
holiday with H and our other children.*
*Chloe and Holly are in animated conversation with H
and they laugh together over something.*
My daughter Chloe is playing with the baby.
H is wearing a chocolate brown swimsuit.
*I look at her admiringly wondering how amazing she
looked so soon after giving birth to our third child.*
*I can't believe how lucky I am to be married to such a
sexy and attractive woman.*
*H and I are strolling down the beach with two of our chil-
dren.*
H is holding our son's hand.
I have my daughter on my shoulders. Her name is Sara.

I have no idea where exactly we are in terms of a precise location, or for that matter imprecise location as the
beach is not referenced to any specific country. It is a
sandy beach and less crowded than the ones to be found
in Europe, so perhaps one to be found possibly in the Far-
East?

From the interaction, it would appear that Chloe and
Holly had a great relationship with H. She had indicated
to me in a conversation we once had that, given the age
disparity, she would see herself more as an older stepsis-
ter to my daughters rather than a stepmother. And I would
concur. If I married again, I would not be seeking a
mother for Chloe and Holly, as they already have one.

I am not sure what to make of the brown bikini. I had
not made any particular note of what the others wore,
other than patterned swimwear. I did note that Chloe and
H wore hats to shield themselves from the sun, and that

Holly wore very similar sunglasses to H. I do remember buying H a swimsuit from Agent Provocateur, but I thought it was of a burgundy hue rather than chocolate brown. It was probably this purchase that prompted the image in the dream.

Anyway, she looked exactly as I would imagine in swimwear. From her appearance it was difficult to imagine how much more amazing a woman can look after having three children – still perfectly formed, and every bit the sensual soul I had first married. At least, in my dreams!

None of the children had names in my dreams, except our first daughter, who H referred to Sara. It is always difficult to determine whether one truly and accurately recognises a conversation from a dream or infers it from its visual enactment. As I had indicated to you in my previous dreams, it was only a snippet of a conversation that I retained. In the dream at the clinic, there was no distinct conversation to be remembered but the sentiments expressed were clear.

In dream of us together at the beach I have no memory of the specific conversations the girls had with H, only that what was said inferred much affection and gaiety. However, the one word that resounded was that of our first daughter's name, Sara. It was particularly interesting, at least to me, because I had once teased H that given her love for wine, she should name her children after references to said substance – Rosé, Chardonnay, Syrah, etc. I wonder if the name Syrah stuck.

Did you know that I hard as I tried, I could never regain continuity to these or the previous dreams I had? I hoped that by re-thinking these thoughts and trying to re-visualise the dreams I could gain some further insight into a future with her, but to no avail.

Should I act upon these visions on the assumption that they were provided by some divinity, even if my feelings are not reciprocated? Or should I opt to ignore them at my peril, and pursue the mundanity of my current existence?

The more these dreams of H continue, without an ability to determine what course of action I should pursue, the more inclined I feel to contact the relevant psychiatric authorities myself.

All I ask of you in the instance that my thoughts and dreams are no longer deemed rational, and I am indeed carted away for further evaluation and incarceration of sorts, is that you convey to H my profound sentiments.

You may wish to avoid mentioning to her of my dreams for fear of appearing a little deranged yourself for even entertaining any recount to you of them, but you could perhaps stress the depth and verity of my feelings for her. I had hoped that during my period of recuperation out of the hospital, I would have less time to dwell on thoughts of her. No such luck, I am afraid.

I am now out of the hospital, after spending two weeks longer than was anticipated. I hate to think what my final treatment bill will be and shall just pray that the medical insurance will cover the bulk of it.

Holly and I stayed for few days with Carole before moving into our own flat.

I had found a flat in the Helios building, after viewing what seemed like a million other two-bedroomed apartments. I was shocked at the number of flats which were in almost uninhabitable state, or in need of urgent cosmetic uplift, but still held a high asking price. This flat was priced at a little more than we had originally budgeted for, but the girls offered to chip in some extra monies from their meagre student earnings so that we could afford to take it on.

I am not usually a great fan of newly built apartments, and I have a definite preference for the charm of period properties but thought that this re-development of the old BBC offices and studios, into a series of apartments and convenience retail had been rather well planned and constructed.

I did not realise until we moved in that the Helios, in which our apartment is housed, is a Grade II listed building and is considered a culturally iconic piece of modern architecture. It was developed as more a lifestyle offering than just a living arrangement, as the buildings enjoyed a beautifully landscaped communal garden, a large forecourt where they showed sport on a large screen and served as a great place to spill out onto for *al fresco* dining from the various restaurants, including lovely little café and bar easily accessible by a lift from our apartment. We even have the luxury of a 24-hour concierge service.

The girls were overjoyed by the prospect of entertaining their friends at the resident's private cinema and various lounge areas. As residents, we were also allowed access to the Soho House gym in the basement, and I shall, as soon as I am able, be making the most of this facility. I have been reduced to a skinny seventy-three kilos, and I could really use some training to regain my old strength.

The only drawback I see to our location is the proximity to the Westfield shopping centre. I personally am not a great fan of shopping centres, despite having been actively involved in building two myself, as I prefer the idea of strolling down a high street, preferably arms entwined with those of a pretty lady companion and peeking into various shop windows as opposed to wandering around in circles in an artificial mall environment on my own.

The quainter the streets and parade of shops, the better the appeal to me. Very much like the memorable shopping I experienced in Paris and Florence.

I love shopping anyway, but I really do not know why. I think I may have inherited this trait from my father. I would be so much happier had I inherited his good looks, charm and sporting prowess, but I just seem to have absorbed his love for music and shopping. One cannot have it all I guess, so popping in and out of Westfield will have to do for now.

Thankfully, I have the work on my project to keep my mind mostly occupied, as no matter how delightful our new premises are, I can imagine going 'stir crazy' from continued confinement without some worthwhile undertaking.

I do also need to distract myself from continuing thoughts of H. It is really not helping my cause, particularly as in this current state, I am even less able to convince her that I would be an attractive proposition for her romantic considerations.

I hope that we may have occasion to get together again soon to partake of a glass of wine or two at the delightfully cosy bar downstairs, so that I can pick on your wonderfully perceptive brain in the review of these continuing visions. I shall bid you a fond farewell in the meanwhile.

Love,

David

Letter 6 – Sporting Favourites

July 2018

Dear Geoff,

I am still feeling disappointed after England lost their semi-final match to Croatia.

I was already rather sad to see Roger Federer lose his opportunity for another Wimbledon title by losing to some fellow he had beaten numerous times before. He was 2 sets up and at match point when I headed to the shops, thinking that the match was in the bag and did not require more of my attention, only to learn from my daughter Holly, on my return, that he lost the next 2 sets. I got home just in time to see him lose the final set.

Feeling rather exasperated, I went to the gym and vented my frustrations on challenging exercises, until it was time for the England match. Thinking that this game would lift my spirits, I got home and settled down to an easy supper of tuna fish rice, and a refreshingly cold glass of white wine. The girls were out on babysitting errands, so it was just me in the household to cheer England on.

The team were soon 1-0 up and looked as though they would cruise to a convincing victory. I decided to post a photograph of the England flag, suggesting as much on Instagram, such was my confidence. I intended to message H to tell her that it would be great to see England play France in the final. Alas it was not to be. We lost the match 2-1. Defeat had been snatched from the clutches of assured victory, as some might have suggested.

If the Federer loss had been disappointing, this left me entirely distraught. I almost wished they had lost their match to Tunisia to instead, as I would at least have gained some comfort from knowing that it would have made H happy. What a miserable day, it was turning out to be, despite the glorious summer weather outside. I just wished I could have laid my head on H's lap and felt her run her fingers gently through my hair as she sought to comfort me.

Why is that we sometimes feel such abject dismay when the teams of players we support lose their games? In both of these matches the disappointment ran a little deeper as there was a good chance that each of whom I was supporting had very good chances of reaching the final and securing the ultimate trophy in each of their respective featured competitions.

England had assembled a team of young, spirited players who exhibited skilled play but a show of humility too and were considered by even their severest critics to hold a very good chance of winning the World Cup. This, after several previous lacklustre attempts to capture it for a second time in the history of the tournament. It was not to be. We had to shelve our dreams for another four years.

Roger Federer was one of the greatest players the game had ever seen. I loved watching him play. He had a grace and elegance about the court which not many of the others could emulate. Theirs was almost a game to win by exercise of sheer grit and determination rather than the unperturbed fluidity that Federer displayed. And to top it all, he was very humble, generous to a fault in his charitable efforts, and was generally a very good egg. But he was getting older, and I was one of several I am sure, who wanted him to acquire as many wins and unmatchable records as he could before he hung up his racquet for good. This was a great opportunity for a win in a relatively open field. The disappointment at his loss was therefore all the more acute.

It was the sort of disappointment I used to feel as a youth supporting my favourite football team, Manchester United, or 'Man U', as I alongside many others refer to this glorious of all English football teams.

I realise that your support is for some team local to your area cobbling together the butcher, baker and candlestick maker, which is all very charming, but never quite offering the spectacle of a fast flowing and gloriously skilled performance at a Man U game.

I do remember once coming to watch one of your local games, which was very enjoyable, but to be truly honest, I was more entertained by the fact that we had the luxury of viewing the match from the Director's Box; indulged in continual topping up of our champagne flutes and partook of an unexpected but sumptuous spread of *hors d'oeuvres.*

I am truly sorry if I had not exhibited sufficient support for your team that evening, as I may have spent too much time busily gorging on the delicious food and throwing back enough champagne to drown the entire British fleet. I promise solemnly to do so at the next occasion, support, I mean; the gorging shall be tamed.

I love these hospitality events. Is it just the offer of free food and drink that sets me off and makes me act like some pampered child unable to resist the open jar of cookies? I would like to think that I behave with the utmost decorum, but I do feel my inhibitions completely vanish in such environments, especially in good company.

For someone who is disturbingly shy at the best of times, this is quite a change in character. I feel completely at ease, charmingly confident, effusively witty, and could happily stand up to make an impromptu speech or even dance on the table tops too, if called upon to do so, preferably after consumption of a great measure of champagne. It is the same I feel at weddings.

Put me in a morning suit with a fetching waistcoat, and I become a new man. Is it the suit? Does the attire provide some transformative effect, not quite as superman perhaps, as he undoubtedly possesses superhuman ability even in his underpants one assumes, but maybe a little confidence derived from being suitably and formally attired for the function?

It may have been the combination of exuding confidence by the bucket-load (which I do not normally wield incidentally), and the sentimentality of the occasion, but I often left a wedding arm-in-arm with one or other of the lady attendees. I once found myself with someone's mother, I think. I say that 'I think', only because she was considerably older than me at the time. A very attractive blonde and a passionate one too, but much older. Yes, weddings were definitely one of my happy hunting grounds, but sadly only existed in my twenties. The only problem with these romances, obtained at weddings is that they tended to be very short lived. In the case of the older recipient of my wooing, thankfully so.

I am due to attend my niece's wedding in a couple of months, but I am unable to wear a suit properly with a stoma bag to contend with. No matter, I shall look forward to the joyous event, regardless of the fact that I may not look as smart as I would wish, nor have the possibility of an amorous encounter.

Returning to the subject of Man U, however, I was an ardent fan, as you may have already gathered. I had followed the team to some extent whilst in Brunei but not as indefatigably or perseveringly as I did when I arrived in

England. Thanks in large part to my brother John and his resolute support for the team, regardless of success or defeat in any particular game, he remained devout and dedicated to tracking their overall performance like a highly committed zealot.

I too, began to follow their performance with a spirited intensity, either on the TV if we were allowed to at school, or on the sports pages the following day. I began to enjoy the jubilation of a win and feel disappointment at a loss. Major trophy games were watched mostly on edge of our seats.

When Man U was relegated from the First Division once, I moped around inconsolably for days. The insult to injury in that determining match was in the fact that the losing goal was scored by a player previously a great in the Man U team. I sought the company of fellow supporters for empathy and camaraderie, which was very forthcoming, and provided unstintingly. Under the watchful eye of Tommy Docherty, we regained our position in the Top Division the following season. As you know, we achieved even greater glory under the stern stewardship of Alex Ferguson.

Man U appear to have completely lost direction since his departure, and a lot of the passion with which I used to associate with the club has been largely eroded with it.

Besides watching Man U football games, the World Cup games were an absolute must. As a family, we all were keen supporters of Brazil too, especially my parents. The wonderful days when they played with such considerable flair and skill, and more importantly as a team, reading each other's position on the field almost telepathically. They currently seem to be more of an ensemble of prima donnas, who spend more time play acting after a foul than providing a heart-warming performance.

Understandably, given their sporting backgrounds, my father and mother were keen spectators of most sport. Watching any game with them was highly entertaining, as my father would sometimes resort to harsh commentary in Tamil, if the game was not being played as he would have wished. My mother, being a gentle soul, would offer some sympathetic corresponding comment such as the team were probably doing the best, etc., which would infuriate him more and cause even further denigrating judgement.

They loved watching everything from football and cricket to athletics, and hockey of course. I used to cringe when watching a hockey match with my father. Remind me at some point to relate to you my attempts at this sport whilst at school, which will explain the cause for cringing.

Athletics events, be they at the Olympics or World Championship arenas, would absorb our undivided attention, mine especially. I loved the sprint events on the track. Stars such as Edwin Moses, were a joy to watch. I still think that his twelve confident strides between hurdles in the 400m event are a joy to behold. There has not been such a consistent champion like him at this event since.

Speaking of joys to behold, one of the most beautiful sprinters ever born must surely be Allyson Felix. She runs with the grace of a gazelle. Long legs planted one in front of the other in poetic motion. Did you know that she is now the most gold medalled athlete in athletics history? I look forward to watching her compete for more acclaim and medals in the next Olympics in Tokyo.

It has been such a lovely summer here too. The weather providing seemingly endless days of sunshine and a gentle warmth to lift one's spirits as well as the length of one's trousers. I have lately been spending much of my day in shorts. I had left most of my shorts in Zimbabwe, not expecting to stay in England quite as long, and had to buy a few new pairs. It probably has worked out well, as I am now a notable waist size lower than before.

I love warm and sunny summers in England. The weather really brings out the best in everyone. It is hard to feel despondent for long when the sun streams down blissfully to warm one's shoulders and one is often generally greeted with a smile from every passer-by. What a delight to see all the wonderful ladies in their summer dresses too.

Are they not a joy to behold? There just seems to be a considerably larger number of pretty girls around. Or is it mere illusion, and the impression that they look better for their cheerful lighter attire and smiles? Whatever the cause, the summers in England are wonderful, providing the weather behaves as well as it has this summer.

I recall well and fondly the many weddings, balls and other functions that tended to take place in the summer months, to which I was invited, and the enormous enjoyment I derived at each and every one of them. It is such a pity that there do not appear to be too many of those to attend these days, especially when I could do with much more cheer in my life. I should not really complain, as I have my daughters staying with me, and sharing time with them during this glorious spell is pleasure enough.

The long days of summer are such a joy to spend in London, in my opinion, for there is much to do, and see – art exhibitions or street shows. Whilst it is nice to enjoy the countryside on summer days, I must admit to preferring the metropolitan environment. In an ideal world, I would shoot down to the country for a long weekend or two, and be back in the action-packed, fun-filled teeming metropolis for the week. What a life that would be.

I sometimes now just enjoy just being out and about, after slowly recovering from my operation, and sitting out at one of the many streetside cafés or bars to just enjoy watching people.

According to some research on the various Myers-Briggs types, ESFJs can sometimes enjoy people-watching because they like to observe and understand those around them. For such types, paying attention to how people behave can supposedly help them to understand their own needs and desires better. I am an ENFJ more accurately, but still enjoy the study of others.

I have also lately taken to observing my dates with greater scrutiny, without appearing to stare, as I attempt a derivation of her personality type and thereby her suitability as a partner. I am not sure I am well skilled at this, at the best of times, but this observatory exercise is made especially difficult as thoughts of H seem to intervene.

Sunny days, pretty girls, interesting conversations with prospective dates, and yet all I think about is H. And worst of all, I feel that any examination of a lady companion is largely for comparative purposes. I am trying to wean myself off H, but it is proving difficult. Very difficult.

I hope that we may see each other again soon. Would you like to visit me here again? The café downstairs is rather delightful, and I have now come to know the staff there better too, which allows for even superior service to that we enjoyed previously.

All the best for now.

Love,

David

Letter 7 – Soothsayers, Art & French Fancies

July 2018

Dear Geoff,

Why am I so gullible?

Do I advertise the fact that I am perfect prey for even the lamest of confidence tricksters? I wonder if there is an aura about me that signals to anyone wishing to deprive me of cash, that I was the sort who would cheerfully part with whatever sum was asked of me.

These days I tend to go out of my way to avoid anyone I see in front of me with a sales pitch or hand-out on offer, sometimes taking a slight detour from the straight line I would otherwise tread in my journey. The only reason for deviating from this routing, would be to take up a free beverage on offer to quench a thirst, or when a busker plays a song that strikes a chord with me, as has been the case with anyone playing "La Vie En Rose", or any other noteworthy tune.

I was on my way to a private viewing of paintings by an artist friend of the family. Paramjit Singh was one of my favourite Indian artists, and one of his landscaping scenes on canvas used to adorn a wall at home. He was in London again this year to showcase some of his works and appeared to be going strong even at the ripe old age of 84.

I was merrily strolling along Jermyn Street on my way to the gallery on Duke Street stopping occasionally to peer into a shop window, but otherwise minding my own business as usual. I had arranged to meet Aurelie there, as she had an hour or so before her dinner engagement. It was the last time I was going to see her before she left for Paris.

Aurelie, despite already possessing beautiful eyes was quite keen to have surgery to make them more almond-shaped. I could not really understand her motives for doing so, but she was quite adamant about having it done.

I did not know her well enough to argue to the contrary.

Before I could cross the street, humming away to a tune I had in my head, and thinking all the while of H, this bearded Indian chap in a turban came around the corner and stopped to tell me that I was a very lucky man. I should have at this point, smiled politely, thanked him and wished him well as I walked on. Instead, I stopped and asked why.

He told me that I was troubled and carried too many concerns in my head, but that they would soon be resolved, and I would enjoy happiness by September of that year.

The first thing that sprung to mind was H's birthday on the 8th of September. My niece was getting also married on the 1st of September, and I was expecting my stoma reversal operation date to be announced anytime soon with recovery shortly after – possibly in September. I wondered if that month was indeed going to be the turning point in my recent life. How joyous it would be, I felt if I could be back to good health and have H meaningfully in my life again by that time.

If I still appeared to be harbouring misgivings, he soon convinced me of his authenticity by naming my favourite colour and providing correctly the answer to the number of children I had. I had reached a point in the conversation where, had he suggested he was 'Bob's much acclaimed uncle', I would have believed him, and sought to assist as much I could.

Although I generally considered myself as rather perspicacious, I was unable to see through the antics of what now appears to be a confidence trickster at play, as it was only when I walked away that I realised that I had been duped. He must have been scanning the other passersby carefully until he set upon me as perfect prey. I had ended up parting with the entire contents of my wallet which contained a solitary 100 Euro note. I hoped, he'd choked on the expensive curry or whatever else it was he treated himself to at my expense.

I ought really in future to carry no cash with me whatsoever, or preferably be locked up for my own safety. I clearly need to be kept at a reasonable distance away from anyone with either a sad tale to tell, or one aimed at gaining my confidence and depriving me of all my possessions.

I shall forthwith desist from any interaction with these so-called soothsayers and put this down to the fact that I was at my most vulnerable, and therefore anyone with a hint of good news to foretell was made welcome. I also was a little taken by his apparent sincerity, which I had been told by a good friend does exist in some people, as she used to be of similar ilk. No, she was not a confidence trickster.

She actually called herself a 'white witch'. Suzanne was a lovely young soul, albeit a trifle eccentric. We met at a party, through another good friend of mine Kate, and we soon grew attached, but on a completely platonic basis, I must add.

Suzanne tried explaining to me on a few occasions, what she deemed to be her 'gifts'. I had my doubts, particularly as I had grown hugely cynical about most matters in life since my relationship with a girlfriend called Luisa ended. I think you remember Luisa, don't you? My delightful Dutch lover whom I used to wax lyrically about on several occasions, and subsequently shed numerous tears over when things were unexpectedly terminated.

I can remind you of her on another occasion if your memory fails you, but for the moment, all you need to understand is that I was rather disaffected and dispirited about the whole untimely end to a seemingly perfect relationship. Despite having the odd unfulfilling relationship or two since Luisa, I was, for the most part mistrustful of anyone and anything. Pity this turbaned fellow had not turned up at that point in my life, as he would have been at the receiving end of a swift punch in the nose rather than a 100 Euro reward.

Back to Suzanne. I was about to tell you how she convinced me that not everyone with soothsaying ability had evil intent. She was aware of my cynicism and told me she was going to do something out of the ordinary to prove a point. We were having lunch in Camden, during one of my weekends down from Cranfield, where I was studying for my MBA as you know. She took me into a Bookmakers, where she asked me to pick any horse in any race. As a test I picked the most unlikely winner and felt comfortable losing the pound bet. After placing my bet, all she asked was the name of the horse I had picked. When the race started, she gazed fixedly at the screen, as I did. My horse won! Amazingly and completely unexpectedly.

I could feel my hands shaking as I collected my winnings, unsure about what it was that took place in the few minutes that passed from horses bolting out of the starting gate to my horse crossing the finish line ahead of others. I did curse a little for not placing at least a fiver on the race, instead of the miserly and solitary pound, but gallantly procured a sumptuous dinner for the both of us, as had been promised.

I had, since that day, always given her the benefit of the doubt. Suzanne read my Tarot cards when I finished my studies, and correctly predicted that I would meet with my ex and also take up job offer in Zimbabwe. But I am now back to being extremely wary. So have no fear, my friend, if I had been cynical before, it was probably only half-heartedly, for I am now a fully-fledged member of the club for cynics and expect to be elected President of said society in due course.

I told Aurelie about this chap's prediction later, but not letting on about H. She felt that September was key because of her birthday on the 20th of September. I wondered then that this turbaned fellow may have had a point about this particular month after all. We shall see if anything happens in the next few weeks to prove that I may have wrongfully vilified this purported soothsayer. I do have my doubts, though, as I feel that I was well and truly fleeced. Like a 'lamb to the slaughter' is a phrase that comes to mind.

Aurelie spoke English with a light French lilt, which sounded like congenial music to my ears. I must admit to being very attracted to most European accents, but French and Italian just always seem a little ahead of others in the league table of attractive accents. I am especially drawn to women gifted linguistically. Did you know that Audrey Hepburn spoke five languages fluently? Anyway, to my great delight, and besides her charming accent, Aurelie seemed to have a genuine appreciation of art.

I do not really know what it was about art that attracted me. Yes, I am sure we all did colouring by numbers when children, but was that my sole foundation for an appreciation of colour and form? My earliest love for art probably began when I arrived at boarding school in England. I could barely draw well enough to save my life, but I loved it. To my guardian's disappointment and that of the headmaster too, I forsook Latin in favour of Art as an exam subject. I remember the Art teacher so very well. He was exactly as one would imagine an art teacher to look like – bow-tied, but slightly bedraggled. In fact, he could have been a latter-day Cézanne himself coming to life, and stepping out of the canvas, except this fellow had a slightly fleshier figure and more hair to his name.

He took as much of an instant liking to me as I did to him and was very encouraging of even my most dire of artistic efforts. According to him, it appeared I had a greater affinity for recreating still-life imagery than work requiring imaginative composition. It is a pity as I could see clear and wonderful pictures in my head, but I could never translate these images sufficiently attractively either in water colour or oils no matter how dogged the struggle.

He thought that I spoke English very eloquently and having decided that I should bear a princely moniker to reflect this, chose to share his inspirational moment with the entire class, declaring subsequently, that I was henceforth to be known as 'Chocolate Charles'. A nickname, which amidst several guffaws and especially amongst those who struggled to pronounce my surname, unfortunately stuck with me throughout my time at school.

Sadly, Art was the one subject at my 'O' Level examinations in which I scored a failing grade. Perhaps as a result of my own failure, I have grown to respect the skill of artists even more and am in constant awe of their beautifully inspired works at exhibitions and galleries.

My interest in collecting art began with learning of erotic art. This, by some strange quirk of fate, first came about in a gallery on High Street Kensington, which happened to be one of my favoured stomping grounds, as it also played host to possibly my favourite and much-frequented clothing store. I had popped into this gallery to see some of their Japanese prints, as I wished to purchase an anniversary gift for John and Maureen. Having acquired a rather appealing print as the gift, I decided to treat myself also. I acquired a couple of Japanese prints of geisha women, which I thought looked very collectable. I was told by the gallery owner, that I had chosen well, and had selected pieces which fell into a style of Japanese artwork known as Shunga and in this instance a signed work by a renowned artist, Utamaro. Sensing that she aroused my curiosity, she proceeded to tell me more about the art.

Shunga, is apparently an erotic artistic tradition that emerged during the Edo period in Japan (covering the 17th to 19th centuries, I believe), depicting graphic images of couples expressing joy and satisfaction in their sexual endeavour, and featured exaggerated genitalia on both men and women. I suppose it must have been the equivalent of Penthouse magazine on steroids, in that day and age. Although explicit in content, it did not seem in the least bit pornographic, but rather tastefully artistic, I would say.

This very helpful lady at the gallery explained that while Shunga is generally known for nudity and explicit sexual situations, there were less audacious iterations, which featured only elaborately dressed courtesans, such as those in the prints I had purchased that day.

Having developed a keen interest in this form of erotic art, I used to go hunting for these works with Rachel at the Saturday morning antiques market on Portobello Road. Rachel spent her time scouting around for home-wares, costume jewellery, or items of clothing, whereas my concentration was entirely focused on works of erotica.

I mentioned this interest to my friend Dieter, and he immediately insisted on introducing me to Robert, who owned an antiques store on the Fulham Road, specialising in art from the Far East.

I had met Dieter as a result of his frequent visits to the restaurant called the Singapura that John and Maureen owned on the Fulham Road. He would often stay on after supper to share a few Tiger Beers with me, and we soon became very good friends. Dieter, who spoke English faultlessly, albeit with a noticeable German accent, was well-versed in most subjects and I was always a very happy listener to his many discourses on various subjects. Dieter was also a frequent visitor to Robert's antique shop.

I got to know Robert quite well myself and we soon became friends also, with a shared interest in antiques amongst other things. We would often meet at a wine bar called the Crocodile Tears, which was one of my favourite haunts too, or at the Singapura. Robert would call me relatively frequently and let me know of pieces of erotica he had acquired or come across, and I would go trundling off to his shop to review these pieces over cups of coffee and hour-long chats.

Through Robert and other purveyors, I began to develop a collection of sorts – everything from paintings on ivory to scrolls, woodblock prints, cricket boxes and rice bowls. I even bought a beautiful bronze sculpture by a

French artist, which is rather rare as it carries a signature by the artist.

I will never forget an incident with my niece, Francesca who was a cute little four- or five-year-old at the time, and very curious about this collection. One day, while jumping up and down on my bed, in her eagerness to help me hang the little ivory paintings which had just been framed, she asked me what the people in the pictures were doing. I was stumped. I stopped what I was doing and looked at her somewhat bemused. As I struggled to find a suitable response, she looked directly at me with serious expression on her face and asked if they were 'doing exercises'.

I smiled in relief. I could not have come up with a better answer if I had mulled this over for a million years. It was so wonderfully descriptive and apt, without being in the least bit offensive. "... out of the mouths of babes...", as the bible so rightly implies!

I am still grateful to her to this day for that appropriately perceptive, yet innocent interpretation. I offered my own children the same explanation when they made a similar enquiry many years later. I still have this collection, which I hope will be appreciated by my girls when it passes into their possession.

My love for works of beauty deepened with the discovery of contemporary Indian art. I had travelled to India to spend time with my father who was alone in Madras, or Chennai as it is now known. My mother was in England at the time recovering from yet another operation. She had undergone so many major operations and still managed to retain good humour and spirit, unlike her youngest child who trembles at the mere thought of needles.

This was the first time my father and I had been alone together, if that makes sense. He was the most amiable and generous host, as well as the caring parent I had always considered him to be. Despite being somewhat elderly, he woke me every morning with a cup of coffee, having been up earlier to read and then wander off to the market for fresh produce for the day. I had many times chastised him for going out on his own, promising to accompany him on the next occasion, or at least leaving instructions with the maid to make the necessary purchases. He accepted neither my company, suggesting that I would be unforgiving of the smell and crowds of people at the market, nor the maid's assistance, indicating that she would more than likely be overcharged for any purchase.

Carole had been to Madras earlier and procured some paintings from the Victoria Technical Institute of Art. When my father and I went, however, there were more crafts to be had rather than inspiring art works on canvas.

We were advised by one of the staff there that we were better off seeking such works at an artists' village a few miles out of the city centre, or at some of the private galleries, and offered us the names and addresses of two in particular. Thus, began our voyage of discovering Indian contemporary art in Madras.

We decided that our interests would be best served by heading to the artists' village as a first stop, as we would not only get to see works of art, but hopefully meet the artists too. The Cholamandalam Artists' Village was almost exactly as described – a collection of various structures and little rondavels with interconnecting pathways across an area of sparse vegetation and a scattering of trees. There were obelisks and several sculptures around the general reception area.

We found a young, bearded gentleman, himself an artist, who looked a little undernourished but of cheerful countenance, and very keen to assist. He explained the make-up of the village, which appeared to cater primarily for the young aspiring artists hoping to create a saleable masterpiece or two. Our newly found artist friend was so taken with how my father looked that he insisted on drawing his portrait for free.

I must admit that my father did cut a rather remarkable figure with his white hair worn long creating a striking contrast to dark skin and the strong angularity of his features. It may have been as a result of his past and training, but he had always adopted a verticality of posture, and thereby accentuated his height. I remember him clearly requiring it of us too, especially at church when he would constantly check to see if we were not just mouthing words to the hymns as we tended to do, but also standing similarly rigidly upright.

He was so thrilled at the prospect of having his portrait drawn, that he gleefully accepted, and with almost childish delight walked briskly and with added bounce to his step, back to the artist's studio/residence.

As we were leaving, we met an artist called Adimoolam, who told us that we were best headed to one of the galleries as this is where the works of the established artists, including those of his, were often exhibited for local and international interest. He kindly invited us to his home a little way down the road from the village, and arranged for us to meet with his colleague, Achutan. We got to know both these artists well and have, within the family, purchased many of their works. Unfortunately, two stunning pieces by Adimoolam and Achutan, offered at a discounted price to me as a pre-wedding gift were lost on the way back from another visit to India.

Pleased as I was to see the works at the artists' village and those of Adimoolam and Achutan, I felt that I had only scratched the surface of what was to be enjoyed in viewing Indian art.

We headed to the first of the addresses provided and were delighted to be shown some wonderful pieces of work. I was astonished to see so many amazing paintings and hear of the many skilled artists from various parts of India. Many of the paintings were not on immediate display, but brought out of storerooms by the enthusiastic gallery owner (Bashir, if I recall correctly), subject to the specificity of our search – portraits, landscapes, abstracts, etc.

The paintings I loved most were well beyond my frugal budget. As I had just left full-time work to enrol for my MBA, I had no means of justifying any purchase no matter how great the temptation was to secure at least one piece.

We went on to the next gallery, which seemed a little harder to find as it was nestled inside the depths of crowded residential area. Again, the gallery owners generously offered their time to show us several works by established artists, and I once more witnessed some amazing works by Manjit Bawa, Yusuf Arakal, Anjolie Ela Menon, Ganesh Pyne, Arpita Singh, Ram Kumar, Laxma Goud, Raza, Bhattacharjee, amongst many others. Rachel and Carole followed up on this discovery and between them acquired several beautiful works, admired by many of our friends and colleagues since.

Beyond the joy of these paintings was the delight of seeing a stunning Indian girl, who worked there. Besides her seemingly unlimited knowledge of the artists, she was so very pretty too. So much so that I found it very hard to concentrate on the paintings, being more inclined to take in every aspect of her delectable appearance. Yes, I was captivated by the large eyes, like pools of the most invitingly delicious gravy, a cute nose (which I hoped any children with her would inherit), and marvellously shaped lips, which were promising of the sweetest of kisses.

Lightly toasted brown skin, draped in a fetching red sari, with bared midriff providing only a subtle indication of the slim and delightfully curvaceous figure beneath.

My father had been very keen to find me an Indian bride. I had no intention to get married then, but I eventually yielded to his badgering and indicated that I would be happy to meet any bridal choices whilst I was there on holiday. There was no harm I felt, giving in to a simple request, as it required no firm commitment on my part other than to leisurely review various of these prospects. And if it made him happy, why not?

The girl at the gallery ticked so many boxes, that it seemed foolish not to pursue this one as a worthy prospect. Not just truly ravishing but so wonderfully accomplished and engaging with it. When she left to fetch another painting for us, I indicated to my father that she was exactly the sort of girl I would definitely consider for a bride.

I should have kept those thoughts to myself, at least until we got home.

Barely able to contain his excitement, he decided to strike whilst the iron was hot. And, as soon as she returned, he began to ask her a series of searching questions on her education, parentage, etc. What is it about one's parents in their inability to understand simple behavioural protocols when it comes to finding suitors for their children?

Their intentions were always invariably saintly, but their execution was extremely poor. I was so embarrassed that I wished the floor to open up and swallow me whole, there and then. I could tell that she too was getting progressively more embarrassed, and I did my best to refocus attention on our primary objective of viewing art.

I loved the various paintings I was shown and learning more about each of the artists, but I felt it best to come back to this gallery on another occasion without parent in tow.

I was relieved to finally leave, as she must have equally been to see us go. I told my father that if he wanted to assist in securing a suitable partner for me in my presence in future, he needed to exhibit far greater subtlety. When we went back, she was not there. Understandably, perhaps! I never saw her again.

Following my enthusiasm for this girl, I could see that my father now began his quest for a bride for me with added vigour. He was convinced that if he secured anyone bearing similarity to the Gallery Girl, I may be persuaded to commit to being betrothed before I returned to England.

He consequently beavered exuberantly away at this task with phone calls and meetings along with some of his recruited help. I could not help but be amused. Sadly, no such lovely lady could be found, and I returned to England, empty-hearted and embarked on my studies.

After completing them, I bumped into Shingai, a college friend, and also met my ex, as foretold by Suzanne. The rest, as they say, is history.

I was really enjoying my time at the exhibit with Aurelie. She was by far the most attractive woman there, and I think I had a lot of men rather envying me, as she linked her arm in mine whilst we sauntered through the gallery.

We must have caused some chatter, especially as Paramjit chose to spend a lot of time talking with us, perhaps conveying an impression to others that we were some exotic couple seeking art for one of our exclusive nests.

We did exude an air of self-assuredness in the way we made our way from one painting to another, stopping just long enough to make a meaningful remark on each work of art.

I must admit I had a thoroughly enjoyable evening, except for smarting slightly from being cheated out of a 100 Euros. I suppose I should not really complain too much and write it off as the cost for sharing a delightful time with Aurelie.

There was not much about her appearance that I could fault. Her eyes were large, as was my desire. Her lips were perfectly shaped to kiss a thousand times over, and a well-crafted nose, beautifully centred on her face of unblemished light complexion. She had long dark hair worn with a fringe above her forehead, framing her face dramatically, and making her look like a modern-day Nefertiti. She was tall – I would assume standing five foot ten inches on her preferred footwear of ballet flats. Her choice of clothes contoured the shapely figure beneath.

Was I just attracted to Aurelie, purely because she was French? Very possibly. We had met through a dating site and appeared a compatible match. As with H, she was also considerably younger. We met a few times and appeared to have similar interests and a congruent outlook on life too. She was in an unhappy relationship with an equally older man and sought an alternative.

I never like getting involved with women actively involved in other relationships, but I seem unable to avoid them. A retrospective review of my life shows a past littered with relationships with girls or women who were in other relationships when I met them. I am just gratified that most gave theirs up for me. I was possibly contemplating the prospect of Aurelie doing the same, but felt it was very unlikely given our conversations about her feelings.

I was quite happy though for nothing to occur between us, given my feelings for H. Unfortunately, Aurelie does not even begin to create the depth of feelings I currently and stubbornly retain for H.

At best it would be a wonderful fling. At worst a continued platonic relationship with a rather attractive lady.

I know that you would prefer that I began to wean myself off thoughts of H, anyway. And to be honest, although I harbour the most profound of feelings for her, I am a realist also, and therefore remain open to whatever transpires with anyone else.

I shall no doubt be seeing you again shortly to discuss this and other possibilities of interest further.

My love to you for now,

David

Letter 8 – Harrods, Fragrances
& Holiday Romance

July 2018

Dear Geoff,

I recall you commenting on the Harrods bag I was sporting when we met that afternoon.

I was actually on my way to the meeting with you and those consultants for a project we hoped to work on together, when I decided to pop into one of my favourite departmental stores in London. Probably in the whole world. At least the one I know.

I have tried Galleries Lafayette in Paris, Bloomingdales and Saks in New York, and Tangs and Takashimaya of Singapore which all have their various draws and charms, but still rate Harrods at the top of this particular league.

I do happen to like Harvey Nichols, Selfridges and Peter Jones, in Sloane Square too, mind you.

On my way, I took a detour into a shop called Divertimenti, as the window was dressed so fetchingly, and I could not help but be drawn inside. I have always enjoyed shopping there even if it was to buy a token item for the kitchen. Sadly, there was nothing to meet my immediate needs. My eyes were drawn to the crockery with seafood designs on them. I had seen these items before when I had passed by and was very keen to take a closer look. I made a mental note to procure these, if the need ever arose.

I was not sure when the need would arise however, given how many plates I already had. Probably sufficient to service a Greek wedding or two and still have few remaining after several rounds of Zorba dancing. When it came to crockery, cutlery or anything to do with the kitchen, I tended to veer toward Emma Bridgewater's style of the country cottage feel, or the clean white look of crockery associated with fine dining experiences. It may have something to do with the fact that I loved period properties, but modernised ones. What appeared to draw my eye to this particular cache of items on display was the fact that it appeared to combine the fine dining's stark white with images of food enticing enough to warrant both comment and appreciation. I was not in the market for crockery at this point, and left the store providentially, empty handed. Who knows? The need could arise with the possibility of sharing a life with H, if my dreams were to come true.

I could imagine us walking hand in hand as we sauntered in and out of shops making choices for our home together.

This thought prompted, no doubt, by my love for shopping, especially in London, as Harare has a pitiful offering in this respect. For an avid shopper like me, being in Harare is like being in purgatory, as other than grocery shopping, (which has limited appeal), there is very little else on offer. Shopping in London was therefore a little like pointing a thirsty man in the desert in the direction of an oasis.

All the visions of delicious food had made me feel rather hungry, especially as I had just taken my medication, following yet another long and exhausting bout of meetings at the project site. I stopped at the Marks & Spencer but soon marched on seeing the number of people packed in there like sardines and had no interest in joining that very long queue just for the sake of a sandwich. But I had to make sure I complied with the strict dietary orders and eat something however small, so I decided to pop into Harrods for a *pain au chocolat* instead.

Perhaps it is unfair to judge other departmental stores against Harrods merely on a shopping experience, as it really is the only one where fond memories came about for me.

An example of one such fond memory is the recollection of a working stint there one summer and meeting a rather lovely girl called Karen. It made me smile to think of her again. My sister Carole had obtained an opportunity for me to work there during their busy summer sales. I had by some good fortune obtained a posting to the Ladies' Fashion floor, where I was initially appointed to be no more than a look out for shoplifters, but soon got elevated to helping man the sales tills.

The shoppers acted as though all their Christmases had arrived at once, and business was blisteringly brisk. There was a ceaseless flow of women wishing to spend an enormous amount of money on the assumption that they were amassing substantial bargains. It was an incredible experience to just watch the till constantly chiming with every purchase made, and trays fit to bust with reels of cash.

I enjoyed every moment there, not just watching the cash till, in case you ask, but the general buzz of a shop brimful of eager patrons.

The days passed quickly with enjoyment drawn from everything from chatting to Karen at every possible opportunity, and understanding various purchase choices being executed, to watching many Arab women handover large bundles of cash without a word. That alone was an interesting experience.

Unable to speak English well, these women would signal for me to peel off the required amount for their purchases. It was quite unnerving having to count out the precise amount of money from these bundles of cash and subsequently hand back the remaining equally large bundle alongside any change.

To add to the joy of working there, I also got to meet Roger Moore. To be more factually accurate, when I say I met Roger M, it sadly did not involve a formal introduction with a handshake and the proffering of an invitation to drinks. It was just that I kept looking at him wondering why his face looked so familiar, but out of context. It was Karen who informed me later that it was indeed him. Thankfully, RM did as least nod in my direction, and smile.

Karen was so pretty. Petite, with ringlets of auburn hair framing a very admirable face, boasting bright and piercing blue eyes. She told me that she had a boyfriend, but was clearly not averse to my flirtatious attention, often catching my eye with a seductive smile. She would sometimes signal me to join her on the pretext of taking items of clothing back from the tills for the girls to rehang on the racks, just so that we could talk. We also lunched together.

I longed to kiss her, but sadly our relationship did not develop any further. It could possibly have, had I not left for Malaysia shortly after that brief stint at Harrods. Given that no romance blossomed with Karen, you may wonder why I mention her, but I do so because this aspirational interest in her actually allowed me a brief romance with a childhood flame, Jasmine, later that summer.

My parents had paid for my sister and I to fly out to Malaysia and Brunei to spend some time with them. I had just finished school and had a long summer ahead of me before the start of university.

It was wonderful to see my parents. Given that most of their children were in England, it was easier for them to visit us than for us to find the means to go there, and this was a rare treat. Also, although we exchanged letters reasonably often, it was not quite the same as being at home with them.

Carole and I worked for a few weeks prior to leaving, to provide ourselves some additional pocket money for our visit. Armed with gifts, we began our journey with a visit first to Malaysia, where my father happened to be working at the time. Beyond introducing us to as many students as he could as proud parent, he was intent on making us revisit some of the places of historical interest and provide us the opportunity to immerse ourselves in this culture and that of delicious street food also.

I must admit to being all the more appreciative of these sites on this occasion viewing them as a grown teen rather than the child I was on previous visits, when I was probably more interested in hanging onto a pocketful of marbles and considering what plans had been made for supper.

It was during a tour of one of the forts in Malacca that my father and Uncle saw two European ladies and made some comments about them in Tamil. Their amusement soon turned to full embarrassment, when one of the ladies turned around and responded, with wagging finger waved in their direction, fluently in the same language. Although at the time we could only look on in astonishment, it was delightful to see two grown men being properly chastised for what must have been disparaging remarks made about them. Their embarrassed faces left a lasting impression.

We played lots of games of three-nought-four, an Indian version of bridge I may have mentioned to you at some point previously. It was pairing of the younger generation against the seniors. Hard as they tried, my father and uncle could not find the means to beat us, especially when Carole and I played together. We both had a very good card sense and could play together well. Holly and Chloe seem to have inherited that trait and now create a formidable pairing at this game and most others too!

Whilst it was a joy to catch up with parents, uncles and cousins, and others of that ilk, it was an absolute thrill to see Jasmine again after so many years. I had a formidable crush on her whilst at school in Brunei, but felt only able to worship from afar, as she was the most sought-after prize at school at the time not just by the boys in my class but definitely in the classes across the age range.

I was also rather keen on another girl called Fawzia at the same time, so competition for Jasmine's affections was best avoided. She was stunning though, and hard to miss. Just thirteen at the time, she had the face of a seductress and the body of a goddess. I was astounded that she was interested in meeting up with me after all this time.

She had heard through the grapevine that I returned from England and expressed curiosity to see me. I may have cultivated my skills in charming conversation over lunch or it may have been my choice of aftershave, but she seemed particularly drawn to me that afternoon.

I usually find it hard to read signals of interest from women, unless clubbed on the back of the head with a blackjack and advised of it. But on this occasion, it was hard to miss, even for me.

I had taken her to lunch at one of the better restaurants in Brunei. Or at least it was one of the ones I remember as being better, because it had air conditioning. Thankfully, they also held a few items on the menu which could be eaten delicately whilst conversing. It became progressively more obvious from the conversation over lunch that she seemed very interested in me, as she looked at me with undivided attention. Those beautiful brown eyes staring seductively at me, as she moved close to me, and reached out to touch my hands often.

That interest seemed to develop even further when I mentioned Harrods and the possible missed opportunity with the attractive girl I had met there - Karen.

I may have been a trifle economical with the truth at that point and possibly conveyed the impression that there was more to a relationship with Karen, than truly existed. But did I unintentionally make myself more desirable by creating an issue of jealousy? Do women prefer men who appear to have drawn interest from other women, especially an attractive one? Why is life not simpler in matters of attraction between boy and girl?

I cannot believe that our cavemen ancestors agonised much over these matters, and it was more a case of 'your cave or mine?' being queried after establishing their mutual interest at the watering hole.

Given how hard I had to work to stop myself from drooling at the prospect of kissing her, I was not inclined to over analyse this, as it appeared obvious that Jasmine liked me. It was more a question of when, not if.

She invited me over to her house for dinner the next evening. Her mother left us alone after dinner to converse. We had much to talk about and I found her charming as well as attractive. She was sitting next to me but drew her chair even closer. She could not have moved any closer without taking up residence on my lap. If she was intent on seducing me, she was making great strides. I was ready to surrender at any point and have the shirt ripped off my back.

I found her approach deliciously flattering, but also a little unnerving as I wondered why it was not I who was taking more of the initiative in this seduction process. She then proceeded to ask me directly what I thought of her. I told her very candidly how I used to worship her from afar whilst we were at school, and that her beauty had an alluring quality, which was now further enhanced with a large degree of sensuality.

She was eighteen, and even more beautiful than I remembered. Olive complexion, large brown eyes, and cupid lips that almost begged to be kissed. Fervently and many times. Her figure, shaped by an artisan of the female form, was now even more curvaceously defined. Her blouse seemed to pop a button as I looked down at her chest. I could almost feel those beautifully shaped breasts aching to be released from the captivity of her bra.

She leant toward me as she placed a hand on my thigh. This was a point of no return and an invitation I felt unable and unwilling to refuse. I leant my face forward to meet hers. This was no mere antiseptic pressing together of lips. Her lips yielded to mine, eager to engage. The kisses simultaneously tender and passionate.

Although we did not undress completely and indulge in full blown sex, we came close as we could, partly clothed! We had moved to the terrace to obtain further privacy, but we could not have necessarily made love that evening with her mother within hearing distance in the adjacent room.

Nevertheless, I was overjoyed that I had kissed one of my teen idols. It gave me a boost of confidence to think that beautiful girls were indeed attainable. I was doing something right for a change, I thought.

I looked forward to seeing her again and finally having a more meaningful sexual experience. I was comfortable that she would help develop my inexperience in this area, not having had a sexual partner since losing my virginity in a rather bizarre foursome in a hotel room some months previously.

Whilst this would undoubtedly aid my experience, I felt that she and I would make for caring lovers also. We enjoyed each other's company and clearly were attracted to one another. I was not in love with Jasmine, nor her with me, but we seemed to be rather drawn to each other, perhaps out of some nostalgic desire. I was never to find out.

As soon as my mother learnt of my seeing Jasmine, she admonished me tirelessly, and forbade me from seeing her again as Jasmine purportedly had a reputation for being a little sexually indiscreet. I did not doubt that Jasmine had been sexually active, but I never believed she was the promiscuous woman the originators of gossip assumed her to be.

It was dreadfully unfair on both Jasmine and I, but given her living circumstance and mine, i.e., neither of us having anywhere to go to consummate our passion, and the fact that Brunei was a very conservative country, which provided us with no option of being amorous in public, we had no option but to maintain a longing but unfulfilled relationship.

Although in a capital city, the social environment we occupied was more typical of village where gossip mongers seemed to exist for the sole purpose of destroying credibility with gleeful abandon. I could not afford to bring rumoured 'shame' upon my mother, given her prominence in the country. I felt sorry for myself for missing out on a wonderful sexual opportunity, but I felt even sadder for Jasmine having to endure the unspoken but inferred humiliation.

I am sure that had the circumstances arisen in England, Jasmine and I would have enjoyed a glorious friendship with a wonderful sexual orientation. What is the term to describe these relationships? 'Friends with benefits'? The benefit was clearly mine, though. She was very pretty, great company, and had an absolutely marvellous figure to compliment her assured intelligence. Every man's dream.

Without wanting to be too self-deprecating, I truly wondered what she saw in me, as I had really only just turned up and bought her lunch. Perhaps my company had become more scintillating, and a combination of boarding school discipline and having older sisters tutor me into gentlemanly behaviour. Whatever attracted her to me on that occasion, and despite neither of us admitting to being in love, those kisses remain highly memorable, and hopefully now recorded for posterity. I have not tasted many lips so soft or sweet as hers, before or since.

There was something more captivating about Harrods, beyond memories of Karen and the trajectory of those further onto Jasmine, I thought as I ambled into the store.

I had sometimes just enjoyed strolling through the store with no intent to make a purchase, but to enjoy the 'window shopping'. When I did previously have some disposal capital from pay rises, I would invariably spend some of it at Harrods. When I took up horse riding for example, all of my equestrian needs from my boots and gloves to crop and riding mac were all well considered purchases at this wonderful store.

We did not have the luxury of the internet, at that time in order to make comparisons on prices, but I felt that any premium paid in Harrods was justified on the basis that these were lasting purchases. Other than the gloves and crop, I still have in my possession to this day the boots and mac. They look as good as new many years later. So, they were indeed, lasting purchases!

Harrods drew me like a magnet or like an unwitting consumer fly to a cunning retailer's web. I loved almost every part of it, from the barber's shop in the basement, the food hall with a range of exotic purchases, and the jewellery concessions on the ground floor to the home-wares departments in the floors above.

Actually, it was from Harrods, not in Zimbabwe as you may have assumed, that I had my first taste of croc-odile meat. After procuring a recipe from the helpful staff at the butcher's counter, I decided to treat my friends to a dinner party where I served it as my *piece de resistance*. It went down rather well. If you have never tried it before, it has the taste of white meat – a mix of chicken and pork. It is not something I would partake of regularly, given my distaste for anything reptilian, but it was a good culinary experience, nevertheless.

I also once lost my Filofax at Harrods, but had it re-turned to me at their very helpful customer service desk. I received it completely intact albeit with a small sum of cash missing, which I assumed the returnee felt obliged to keep as a reward. The service provision at the store was exemplary. I knew this from having once been a small part of it.

Harrods has over the years, through some means or another, played a part in my life. Whether it was for an equestrian related purchase, meandering through the Food Hall in search of an exquisite and exotic offering, or just walking past the various jewellery concessions, it continued to hold an inescapable draw for me. Having brought many a prospective or secured girlfriend at some point in time in my life to its vaulted chambers of therapeutic retail, just meandering through the store on this occasion awoke many fond memories.

I made the requisite purchase of the *pain* with the promise of oozing *chocolat*, but not without first looking for a fragrance within the Maison Margiela range, which being French added a very comprehensible draw to the counter.

My two favourites in their range were Jazz Club and By the Fireplace. The fragrances were also presented in attractive packaging, and more importantly, sat lingeringly well on my skin. An absolute must, I felt, as most of the fragrances I used were from the Aqua di Parma range, which I loved and suited me very well but never held their scent remain for any extended period.

Ever since I was introduced to the joy of fragrances by my brother John, I had grown progressively more conscious of the variety of fragrances available and wanted always to smell good. Not just when preparing for a date but really at any time.

As I grew older, I began to distance myself from fragrances that were highly popular and worn by almost every other man. They say that fragrances tend to be different on different skin types, but there are very few that are truly unique. I would sometimes conjure up a mix of fragrances, carefully though, to avoid being over-scented and smelling like some low-life gangster's boudoir.

I am sure we have both encountered many men, particularly of the gold medallion brigade who insist on emptying the contents of the entire bottle onto themselves before stepping out, and whose smell precedes their presence by some distance.

Therefore, beyond wearing a commonly unrecognised scent, a subtle application is what I generally sought to achieve. Receiving the compliment of an "mmmm... you smell nice" when a lady is close enough to exchange a fond greeting is always a welcome reward.

For some strange reason, I discovered an allergic reaction to some fragrances depending on the alcohol content, so my choices were limited by this consideration also. It did not stop me from wandering through the various other concessions trying an assortment of old and new offerings.

Unable to decide at that point, I opted to remain with the fragrances I liked from the Aqua di Parma range, particularly the Essenza, which always evokes sweet memories of Italy, and the Colonia, which I have associated with happy times with my family. Strangely, or perhaps not, one of my favourite scents is Jasmine.

I bought a few chocolate biscuits for the girls as well as some pasta sauce for supper that evening. As the lady at the sauce counter was describing the best way of enhancing the proposed pasta dish, I pictured myself preparing supper for H, as I had envisioned in my dreams of her.

I thought of her returning from work, dropping off her handbag and kicking off her shoes before giving me a big hug and a passionate kiss as I toiled away in the kitchen. It was a sweet thought. Utterly and ludicrously demented, but sweet.

I was now ready to leave the store and re-focus my mind on work. I made my way through to what I felt was the best set of exit doors onto Hans Road. I walked past the Fabergé counter. I am not sure why, but I could not help but be attracted to a lovely egg pendant and chain on display.

I was tempted to walk quickly past as I had no intention of buying anything, but the charming sales lady, Rachel, could see my interest. There was no harm in making a cursory enquiry or applying closer inspection of the article, I thought. She kindly brought the item out from the locked glass case, and it looked even more appealing on close scrutiny. She told me that it was one of Kylie Minogue's favourite items of jewellery and she apparently chose to wear it on several occasions. I had no means of verifying this, but I love Kylie M, anyway, and the sale could have been secured on that fact alone. I felt that it would a great piece of jewellery for H, as she loved rose gold. I realise that my wish to ply her with gifts may appear to you decidedly maniacal at this point, and it is indeed a valid explanation, as only someone a little unhinged would contemplate supper with a precatory love when purchasing pasta sauce or procuring expensive gifts to service unrequited love.

But, sane or otherwise, I hope you realise that the moment I stumble upon some wealth, I shall be making the necessary beeline to the Fabergé counter at Harrods to make this purchase. Rachel, who manned this counter admirably was quite convinced of this, as she insisted on giving me her card, with an indication that she would write to inform me of other possible gift ideas too.

Please do not misunderstand me, for I am not suggesting that H's love could be bought. She is far too principled for that. It has more to do with me, and my wish to demonstrate my profound feelings for her. I long to ply her with endless kisses, flowers and gifts, write her several reams of poetry, stand atop a mountain and call out her name. In fact, do anything I could to convince her that I am a worthy recipient of an investment of her emotions.

Forgive me for these continuing indulgences in thoughts of her. I feel like a lovesick adolescent most times, but until I can dismiss these musings, and successfully retract my head from its irretrievable nesting in the clouds, I will be continuing to plague you with such tales of H.

I bid you farewell for now.

Love,

David

Letter 9 – Beaches & Kisses

July 2018

Dear Geoff,

I felt I had to write and let you know that I got a message from H with a link to an article about Sidi Bou Said – a lovely seaside town in Tunisia.

It was a well-written article and described the town beautifully. I was not sure why she had sent me this article, however delightful it was, but I messaged back indicating that I thought it sounded absolutely idyllic. She responded with a video of herself with the breeze blowing through her hair. I watched the video completely mesmerised. How could anyone look so devilishly seductive and yet bear angelic countenance at the same time? She is so utterly and exquisitely beautiful. All I could think about was how I wanted to marry her a thousand times over. I stopped myself from proposing marriage outright, but I did indicate in the reply that I thought she was amazingly beautiful and that words failed me in describing her undoubted appeal.

Why Geoff, would she send such things to me if she did not harbour even a modicum of affection for me? You can imagine the sheer euphoria I felt on seeing her message, and interpreting this as some subtle indication that she liked me too. I longed to hop on a plane and whisk her off to Sidi Bou Said, where I would make love to her a million times under the starry sky.

I went to bed that night with my heart brimming with love for her; my head filled with every image of her that I could conjure up; and my soul full of hope that our love was destined to be fulfilled in this lifetime as well as the next, and the many that followed.

I love beaches. From the time that my parents took us to the various shores in Malaysia, I have had a fascination for beaches. Not so much the sea, as I fear any depth of water beyond the reach of my feet and carry a perpetual paranoia of being dragged to a watery grave by an unforgiving and menacing shark. A fear that surprisingly existed long before the advent of "Jaws". The film however only served to propel this fear stratospherically to one bordering on frenzied paranoia. So much so that if anything were to brush against my legs even when immersed only waist high, I am very likely to scream hysterically like a little girl who's had her favourite ice cream wrenched from her grasp (in all probability shriller and louder than said little girl) and make a mad scramble for the safety of the shore.

Prone to sea sickness also, I remain happy to be grounded on sandy terrain.

Since childhood, I have been on many beach excursions. Deriving endlessly enjoyment, from constructing ever more elaborate sandcastles to simply lying comfortably on the sand, preferably with a drink in hand, and a good book and a pretty lady for companionship. Despite the inconvenience of finding sand sometimes embedded not just between toes but in the most intimate of cavities, most of my beach experiences have been very happy ones. My children have a similar love for beaches, following several memorable vacations to France and elsewhere.

The only beach we derived little enjoyment from was the one in Durban. The waves were tall, and the children too young and insufficiently sturdy to withstand the strong currents. We had gone with Kurt and his family of children of similar age. As parents we took it in turns to keep beady eyes on them, as they played on the water's edge. It was only memorable because of the odious behaviour of some of the town's locals on the night of New Year's Eve, when we had taken the children out to watch the fireworks but were confronted instead by several couples fornicating rather openly on various sections of the beach.

I had always considered making love on the beach a romantic undertaking, but these uncared-for accidental sightings left me scarred for life. The beach the following morning was littered with evidence of the rather vulgar undertakings witnessed the previous night. The added disappointment to this beach holiday was that town had no sights of interest, nor any dining venue of note.

Our experience as a family with young children in Vilanculos, in Mozambique was gratifyingly different. We had gone with the Dawson family. The children had become firm friends as we had with the parents also. This was just one of several holidays that we shared together.

Delightfully fresh seafood awaited us each evening. Prawns and crabs that were not as easily available in Harare could be enjoyed almost daily. We were greeted every day with a pour of blissful sunshine during our vacation there and enjoyed stretches of sandy beaches very much to ourselves. We once set-up camp and lunched on a small island called Bengui, which had remained uninhabited, except by us for most of the day. Not another soul to be seen for miles. It was rather a selfish occupation of space, as there was plenty of room for many more, but it was with great dismay that we viewed a boat charting a course our way carrying others toward this beach. The magic was lost, and we packed our bags to head home shortly thereafter.

Can you imagine the luxury of such vacant space on a beach in Europe? I just remember having to arrive terribly early to lay out towels in lieu of peeing out a grid to demarcate one's occupation of only a minuscule section of the crowded beaches of La Tranche-sur-Mer, Guérande, etc.

We had a marvellous time in Vilanculos, irrespective of that minor incursion, and the only fly in the ointment in that particular holiday was the very long drive from Harare, and the navigation along sections of hopelessly poor roads that it entailed.

The best of our beach holidays was that at the Datai in Langkawi. This was the first family trip to Malaysia. We had the most delightful of stopovers at the Raffles in Singapore at the start of this holiday. If you have not yet stayed at the Raffles, it should be a definite inclusion on your bucket list.

The Raffles provides the ultimate treat in sumptuous luxury in every aspect from superb accommodation to very courteous and discrete service provision. Should fortune ever come my way, I shall always continue to regard it as my first choice of abode in Singapore.

We travelled on to Penang so that I could show the family my place of birth. There was little of anything I could truly remember, as I was very young when my parents moved from there, but there was still much to be enjoyed, particularly giving my daughters their first taste of street food and enjoying them marvelling at the goods on offer at the late-night market. Besides many tee-shirts, bags, and flip-flops, the girls bought the entire DVD set of the "Friends" series, which they watch to this day.

We carried our trip onto the island of Langkawi, and the Datai hotel. Although this was not strictly a hotel for families with young children, we were made to feel especially welcome, and the girls immersed themselves in all the hotel had to offer. The beach was especially charming. Secluded and emerging from the dense vegetation that skilfully hid the buildings behind it. Attendants followed us at discreet distance, and only made themselves apparent at our side to provide sun loungers, towels and refreshments when we had finally chosen a suitable spot to rest and for the children to play.

Such unobtrusive but attentive hospitality is such common place in Asia, but so seems rare in Africa.

The children occupied themselves for hours and I would have to carry them into the water to cool off from time to time. The water remained shallow for a considerable distance, so there was never any fear of losing oneself and one's children to a dorsal finned brute with voracious appetite and sharp teeth.

I hope that by this time, I have firmly established my credentials as a lover of beaches. But not any seashore, mind you. I am not a fan for example of pebbled beaches. Difficult to walk or lie on, they carry little charm *pour moi.*

Sidi Bou Said, from the information H had sent, better represents the type of beach that I could spend gaily skipping along with my hand in hers. What a delight it would be, on moonlit nights, to stroll along on the shores of Sidi Bou Said with her, feeling the water lap gently against our feet, and stopping to kiss those tantalisingly sublime lips of hers. Her lips and mine softly and wordlessly communicating a deep and endless love for each other.

I have yet to kiss H's sweet lips, but I can imagine what a divine experience it would be when I do. I cannot remember if I told you about my date with Zarah and kissing her? If I had failed to mention this encounter, here goes. I met Zarah on a dating site and arranged to meet her for a coffee. The date went well, and she was keen to see me again.

As I leant forward to kiss her farewell, she presented her lips. All I recall vividly is closing my eyes and imagining I was kissing H. Our kiss was intense and lingering. I felt a little guilty, as although Zarah was quite attractive, I had closed my eyes and thought of H in her place.

I do not usually close my eyes when kissing. Is it standard practice to do so? Supposedly women lift a leg too if the kiss is suitably passionate. Do men demonstrate similarly? Perhaps there is more to learn about kissing than meets the eye, or should I say lip?

On the matter of not closing one's eye, I am of the view that it may have been as a result of an experience when I was a teenager. If I had not told you the story of the time, I had delightfully kissed this girl for almost the entirety of a school dance, only to shockingly discover her lack of aesthetic appeal in the cold light of day at a meeting sometime later, I must digress for a moment to do so.

Once a year, as boarders were allowed a school dance, and girls were shipped in from one of the girls only schools in the same county. I suppose it may have appeared a little like the film "Dirty Dozen" when a few ladies of the night were brought in to service the men before their mission into enemy territory. Not that we were being rewarded for any great achievement or being prepped for a major tournament at which the school's reputation was at stake. I think it had more to do with the consensus amongst the teachers, that they should allow some release of the build-up of testosterone over the year.

I was in the Lower Sixth Form year when I met this girl, who after a few dances, was happy for me to kiss her for practically the whole of the remainder of that night.

So good was the kiss (with my eyes shut, I might add), that I felt impelled to seek out this amazing tonsil tickler. I told my good friend Simon about my amazing find, and he recounted a similar fate that evening.

We decided that we needed to track these girls down together, and jointly hoped to re-engage in the pleasure of many more of such devilishly exciting oral exchanges with them. This was an expedition that required both strong moral support and good companionship. Besides, the girls had indicated to us that they were very good friends, as Simon and I were also at the time.

We were so taken by these two girls we met, not just for the numerous passionate kisses that they bestowed on us, but by the way they pressed their bodies so seductively into ours as we danced, promising many more pleasures to be enjoyed. Such was our naivety that I think we would have gladly promised marriage in exchange for more of such kisses and prospects of further gratification, as we both felt that we had met our partners for life.

Off we trotted to meet them in Ashford after prolonged negotiation with Form Masters for the required release from school, and arrangement with the corresponding school to ensure the girls' joint availability. The train ride was one of nervous excitement, during which all we could talk about was how wonderful the whole kissing experience was, and even began to describe to each other rather competitively how attractive our respective 'girlfriends' were. Upon arrival at the station closest to their school, we stopped only to purchase chocolates for the eagerly awaited forthcoming meeting. When the girls came to the gate to meet us and looked so unlike the beauties we had imagined, we were, quite understandably, in a state of utter shock.

We were both disturbed and dismayed by the fact that neither of them was even vaguely pretty. Our first instinct was to scream aloud and run as far and as fast as our legs could take us, but being the gentleman we were, we extended our greetings and our gifts, as well as an invitation to the promised tea. All through the tea, we tried our best to seek any comforting aspect in their personalities and appearances to warrant further attention or cause a resumption of interest, but there was nothing that we could pin our hopes on. Not even a glimmer of a smile when we attempted humour. We were rather surprised, as Simon and I were usually a frightfully good humorous combination, especially when we sat together to discuss sketches for school shows. We did maintain the civil conversation as would have been required of us. We were both well brought up and attended a school that expected each and every student to uphold every virtue and tradition of gentlemanliness. We could not afford to let slip values held so dear by many of the previous scholars, through any laxity in our behaviour.

After walking them back to school and issuing the necessary formalities of cordial farewell, we raced back to the station and hopped on the first available fast train back to Canterbury. We vowed to never again follow up on a kiss after the first date, or even kiss unless we had very clear and prior sight of their physical features. The girls may very well have felt the same about us. We have no way of telling.

It was a tragedy in many ways as the kisses were memorable and heartfelt. There was no cause to create hope in their hearts if we could not rustle up interest on our part. We solemnly agreed that to avoid the injustice of possibly misleading any girls in the future, and to adeptly preclude any possible follow up meeting taking place with those we were uncertain of, we would claim to have enlisted in the Foreign Legion and left the shores for good.

You will now perhaps understand why, I have since abided completely by this rule, as I would say in generality that the sight in the cold light of day rarely justifies the intensity of effort in the preceding evening. I have no reason to apply this to the many girls I have kissed since, but guided by this previous horror, I have always tended to keep my eyes open ever since. Out of habit.

There is some perplexing wizardry in the quest for a kiss, isn't there? The ceaseless drive to find a suitable member of the opposite sex, well in my case at least, with whom to delight in the heavenly pleasure of pressing one's lips against theirs. Ever since I discovered girls, and the ebullience they created in one's senses from their winsomeness or vivacious companionship, I have sought their kisses. The more desirable the object of one's affections, the greater the ultimate pleasure to be derived. I loved kissing. I think I could possibly forsake everything, even my favourite food or an article of clothing in exchange for kisses.

I went to great lengths to obtain them. Wise words on this matter were once obtained from a good school friend, Tim. Yes, it was unusually not Camel (my usual guiding light, particularly on matters of the heart), but Tim on this occasion who served as my oracle. He had suggested application of what he called the 'suicide tactic' at a party.

Be rest assured that it did not involve a sharp implement or self-harm in any way. The approach, rather, involved looking rather despondent and cheerless whilst all around you were making merry at a party. It was of great importance that this was done at a location in the room which would command optimum view, and understandably so as it would have been rather pointless faking such melancholy without another soul in sight. This despondent look would hopefully then draw the attention of one of the ladies in the room to whom the maternal urge of providing comfort to the disconsolate overtook any other consideration. In the process of providing supplication, a kiss could be earned. I must say dear chap, that this tactic worked like an absolute treat. It is almost completely without likelihood of failure and should actually be written into widely distributable literature. For teenagers anyway. I never tried it as an adult.

An example of its success was at a party I attended with a mix of friends, mainly those of Carole and John, as they had similar friends, but gladly, older. I positioned myself strategically at one of the windows at the front room where others were busy leaping around with raucous felicity, whilst I gave the impression of staring vacantly into a cavernous void. More specifically I was staring out of the window, and I fear I often give the impression of staring vacantly anyway, especially in the presence of a pretty girl, but my assiduous efforts to create the vacant gaze may have provided added authenticity in this instance.

I felt a tap on my shoulder. It was a very pretty Indian girl called Louise, a close friend of Carole's who I thought was very attractive but beyond my ability to attain. She persuaded me to dance with her, hoping to revive me from the dejected state I appeared to be in. I gave in after some mild and hopefully convincing protestations. We danced for a while, and she felt gratified that her efforts caused me to flash an occasional smile. The music changed and it was a slow song. "Samba Pa Ti" by Santana, if I recall correctly. She placed her arms on my shoulders, as I did mine around her waist pulling her close to me. Our cheeks touching whilst we rotated on the same spot repeatedly, as was the manner of dancing slowly at the time. Our hips pressed together in a gentle sway.

I believe she asked me how I was feeling, and I must have muttered something in the equivalence of "this is so good". Almost in the very next minute I found myself in a tighter embrace and our mouths locked together. Our lips never lost contact through the entirety of the song nor for the remainder of the evening. The only pity of it was that no relationship developed from this kiss, but the song remains a favourite, inspiring similar encounters with other girls. I saw Louise a few times after that but from her reticence I felt it prudent not to take matters beyond that memorable evening, especially as she was one of my sister's closest friends.

At school, I proclaimed Tim a master strategist, and we would share many a tale of success. If there were any failures, notable or otherwise, no one seemed inclined to speak of them. But Camel, not to be outshone on the subject of kisses came up with some equivalent wise words of his own and suggested that we should adopt the 3-date rule.

Regardless of the original source of his wisdom, it seemed like a good principle to adopt and utilise in my life. It was simple and applied in the following manner. One merely offered three dates to any prospective girl to offer up her lips for one's amorous attention. Failure to do so by this time would necessitate the diversion of one's attention and effort, and for that to be bestowed instead on other more readily willing prospects. On very rare occasions one had a girl succumb to one's advances on the very first date, but these occasions especially in the darkened space of a disco or school dance could seriously backfire, as I have mentioned to you earlier, and generally best avoided.

A kiss by the second date was very achievable, so a cut-off by the third date seemed eminently sensible. I wonder if Camel had gone on to achieve fame as an eminent philosopher of our time.

It is a pity that we have lost touch. He imparted much wisdom during our friendship, and I shall always value his contribution to guiding my teen years when it came to matters relating to interaction with members of the opposite sex. Although derived as teens, I practise this three-date approach to this day.

Do we as adults place less import on the greatness of the kiss? Do we cease to treasure the appeal of the kiss we once tortured ourselves as teens to obtain from the targets of our affection? Yes, there is the reasonable regular contact, and brushing together of lips, but do we do so with the same degree of fervour we once did? Do the once roaring flames of seemingly unquenchable desire die down into a dull regular glow of embers?

I never grew tired of kissing Paulette, Madeleine, Ravinia, Luisa or any of the women I had been in love with. In fact, when I saw Paulette again after a long time, and despite the fact that we were both in other relationships, at the time, our kisses were meaningful and fulfilling. The lovemaking that followed was sublime, sensual, tender, fervid, coveted and appropriate all at once.

Do we sometimes get to a point in our lives where the kiss becomes a mere precursor to sex? Do we lose sight of the magic of the kiss? It would be nice to think that there is such a person for each of us that causes one to continually rekindle that wish to sometimes just kiss. And do so without release from dusk to dawn.

Have you sometimes just gazed at a woman's lips and wondered what it would be like to kiss them? Does the shape of her mouth determine desirability? It does for me. No matter how attractive a woman may appear to be at first glance, her lips are one of the features besides her eyes, that I tend to focus on. Thin lips, or thick for that matter, provide little appeal to me. It is a strange trait, on my part, I understand, and one which I have failed to understand the root cause of, but the shape of a woman's lips remains an integral part of her appeal.

Friends would sometimes ask why I had expressed no interest in one individual or the other. To me it was very simple. I had no desire to kiss her lips, but for fear of appearing too shallow, my proffered excuse to them would involve the suggestion of an incompatibility with other of her traits.

Kissing Zarah, whom I mentioned earlier in this letter, passionately would have been perfectly admissible as I had ample opportunity to review her attractiveness in the cold light of day. However, keeping my eyes open had become such a habit that I would have normally done so, except for the H factor. My mind had seized control of all my senses and made me imagine that I was truly kissing H. Zarah was merely now a surrogate. I realised that it was Zarah's lips I enjoyed having mine attached to, in such a pleasurable manner, but peculiarly my grey matter would register only visions of H's face.

I have been on several dates in a quest to find a special someone, or at least someone capable of replacing thoughts of H, and kissed many women in the hope of feeling some magical connection, but to little avail.

I accept that I should not expect the same youthful exuberance in the kisses I used to experience when younger;

but do they have to be devoid of any spell binding allure, and provide only momentary and superficial satisfaction?

Being the hopeless and helpless romantic, I shall continue to seek the one with whom I shall kiss for an eternity or at least until we are both completely breathless. I am sure, as poets would record, that when the soul rises to our lips, we will feel the kiss that we have longed for.

I strongly believe that the provider of this soulful and heartfelt pleasure for me, may be H.

I sometimes cannot think, eat or sleep without her constantly in my thoughts. The absurdity of my sentiments is that even if I were to somehow win her affection, I could never expect her to select me as her marital choice, nor could I provide the comfortable lifestyle she enjoys currently.

As you are aware, recent economic catastrophes have left me with substantial financial burdens, including but not limited to university fees, medical and divorce costs as well as several personal obligations, from which I can only recover slowly.

Why do I therefore aspire to win the love of a woman who I will not be able to feed or clothe, at least not for a while yet? Utter insanity, I would agree, but I cannot stop loving her. I think that she is the most beautiful woman in the world. Her skin is of flawless silk, her eyes pools of the richest chocolate, and her lips of cherubic charm with softness I long to feel in a million kisses. I want so much to kiss H, that I think my heart will expire on the day I actually do. Her lips, I am certain, would taste sweeter than the sweetest of wines.

Beaches and kisses are subjects which we will undoubtedly have much further discussion on in the future, but for the meantime, let me know what you think of these delightful words from the poet Rumi, which I would love to send in a card with flowers to H.

"In the orchard and rose garden I long to see your face. In the taste of sweetness, I long to kiss your lips. In the shadows of passion, I long for your love."

Love to you as always,

David

Letter 10 – Thoughts of Renewed Fatherhood?

August 2018

Dear Geoff,

What strange things our minds do when allowed to meander across various arising thoughts, without limitation.

I sometimes wonder if I really have lost the plot.

I don't really know what went through my mind, as I walked through the mall and after staring awhile at the window, walked into a shop selling prams. They looked like they were a top-of-range retailer of prams. They were in fact the Rolls-Royce of prams, and the sort of retail outlet that H and I would possibly venture into for paraphernalia of this nature for our children.

The sales assistant at the shop greeted me enthusiastically and began telling me all about the prams and highchairs, which the company specialised in. They held a range of products to suit all sizes from newborn babies to the toddler years. I was totally engrossed. He asked me if I was looking to make a purchase for my child. I told him that I was, and, so as not to cause any offence, he readily suggested that I was not too old to be a father again. He proceeded to show me other models that would suit my indicated requirements better, as I imagined travelling back and forth with the kids between France and England. It was almost as though I were re-enacting my dream.

They were wonderful products, but what on earth was I possibly thinking of to make these enquiries. Yes, my dear fellow, I agree that it was bordering on madness, but I could not stop myself from delighting in the moment.

I should have headed straight for the psychiatrist's couch, but I went instead to collect my dog tag pendant and chain from the Tiffany store – my favourite jeweller incidentally. I could barely wait to wear the recent purchase. I had popped into Tiffany a few weeks previously, as I had been contemplating a purchase of a silver dog tag pendant which offered sufficient space on the back to inscribe words of love to H. The idea being that this would sit comfortably against my chest and remind me of her all day and every day.

After considerable deliberation, I did make the purchase and submit to an inscription on the back of the tag. The chain and pendant felt heavy, but I liked the feel of the cold metal against my skin. The bright silver looked especially lustrous against my dark skin. Although I eventually chose to make the inscription read "I love H & C" to register my love for my children, it did have the effect of making me think even more often of H. As a child, I sometimes lost many marbles, and now, as an adult, I was in danger of losing considerably more - of the intellectual variety.

The lady assistant, Kristina who had served me originally was not there. I had the attention of a fellow called Oliver instead. He was very polite and helpful, but I would have preferred seeing Kristina, as she was much easier on the eye. Besides, from the way she flirted with me, I did consider asking her out for a drink. I wondered how she would react, though, knowing that I was somewhat of a regular customer.

My next stop was the O2 shop. I was there to enquire into the possibility of adding Holly to my contract line, as she rather clumsily had dropped her phone and cracked the screen, needing a replacement handset. I thought it an opportune time to upgrade my phone too.

I was given the usual sales drivel, which I listened to with scant attention until he touched upon the subject of Facial Recognition technology as one of the selling points, when I could not help but break out into a big smile as I thought of H.

Yes, thoughts of her do bring a smile to my face, but in this instance, it was because of a phrase that had both H and I laughing during one of our many previous conversations. H had found it very difficult to pronounce the term 'facial recognition' and I used to tease her about it. I can still hear the tinkle of her laughter each time the subject came up.

Oh, my goodness, Geoff, I miss her so much. I miss talking to her for ages on the phone. I miss her attempts to teach me a phrase a day in French. I loved the sound of her voice, and I long desperately to hear her wonderful French accent again. I would give anything to be with her at the moment.

The phrase she gave me to practice is *"Je ne sais pas pourquoi, tu me rends fou"*, which translates to *"I don't know what it is about you that drives me crazy."* And it happens to be so true of my feelings for her. To this day, I really have no idea of what caused me fall so deeply and inescapably in love with her. Whilst I accept, now that I may never win her heart, all I wish to do is to die trying, as I know that there is no other woman, within my current social orbit at any rate, who can even vaguely compare to her in brains or beauty, sense or sensuality.

If I were to secure her affections, I have to think seriously about a renewed fatherhood, as she has made her wish to have children of her own abundantly clear.

Is fatherhood something I would be prepared to go through all over again? Do I choose to remember only the good times in jointly raising my children, forgetting all the difficulties associated with the day-to-day requirements of childcare? There is much to ponder.

I remember very clearly the day my children were born, especially Chloe, as the first child. I had not previously given much thought to how life altering fatherhood could be as married life had already demonstrated a considerable impact already on all of my thoughts and actions. For instance, one had no longer any need to embark on thoughts of the next expedition to find an amorous escapade, nor ponder the where or whom one hoped to obtain, and reciprocally provide, emotional succour to.

I had remained relatively calm throughout the whole process of waters' breaking; the midnight journey to the hospital; a frantic search for the attending gynaecologist; and even the final nerve-racking moments of extraction; despite my usual squeamishness when it came to anything related to medical facilities, particularly those involving needles and pain.

But there is no more special moment than witnessing the birth of one's child. It mattered not that some may liken the appearance of a newborn to that of a drowned rat. She was my child and the most beautiful creation to behold.

When the nurse handed her to me to hold for the first time, all I wished for was to hold this delicate child in my embrace for a lifetime. No book I read prepared me for the sheer volume of sentiment that surged through my entire being at that point. My heart swelled, and the eyes bore tears, as frantic thoughts coursed through my mind on to how best to keep this delicate little being wrapped in cotton wool such that no harm could ever come to her.

I had not grown in any way complacent when it came to Holly's as the second childbirth to witness. If anything, this was going to be the one of slightly greater concern as there had been suggestion in the prenatal ultrasounds that she would be a small gestational aged baby, and thereby one with the possibility of a heart and other conditions associated with this form of anticipated birth.

What an incredible relief it was therefore, beyond the usual ecstasy, that she was born with no defect whatsoever, obtaining an Apgar score of nine. As high as that for Chloe. And what amazing girls they have turned out to be.

Although we had maids on hand to help, I did partake in some of the aspects of nappy changing, bathing and feeding. The feeding I quite enjoyed, especially once they were weaned off the breast and I could cradle them in my arms as I fed them bottled milk. As they grew older, feeding became more of an art form, as the aim was to keep them amused and interested in the whole eating process.

To be fair, both girls were very good about eating most things, except when they insisted on trying to feed themselves and most of the food ended up on the floor, pressed against the tray of their highchair or dispersed somewhere on their person.

Bathing was not too difficult a task, once I had mastered the art of juggling the multitude of actions involved including interesting them in the bath toys (for educational purposes); washing them gently (for hygienic purposes); whilst holding them upright (for the purpose of maintaining neck posture); and with all of this conducted in bath of tepid water to shallow depth - to avoid any occurrence scorching or drowning.

When they were slightly older, it was much easier to shower them together, but doing so in a manner suited to keep soap out of their eyes, which Chloe would testify to the fact that I was not the best at. They did enjoy the post bath procedure of applying cream though, as I did that rather well. I applied their body creams, as they lay across my lap, with a flourishing motion of scaling fish and commands in Tamil of *"Kaya Thuku"* or *"Kalla Thuku"*, meaning lift your arm or leg. These simple instructions had them highly amused.

The napping changing was the worst task ever devised by man. Despite the frequency with which I tried, sometimes thinking I could perfect this measure, it never got any better. The ghastliest was seeing them smile or giggle wickedly when they saw me grimace in abject horror. The worse the faecal deposition, the worse the look of total repugnance on my face, but the greater the amusement on theirs. There was obviously something about having their bottom cleansed coupled with my reciprocal disgust that appealed to them and caused their amazing childish display of innocent but slightly irreverent delight.

Getting them to sleep was, at times, not the easiest of assignments, particularly when they were babies. But when they fell asleep on my chest, it was one of the most blissful of experiences. Feeling their tiny arms and legs move until their heads found a comfortable spot on my breastplate to nestle into, whilst exuding that soft baby smell and an aura of total tranquillity. I swear in those instances that I could feel their little hearts beat to the same rhythm as mine, giving much felicity and gravity to the saying 'two hearts beating as one'.

As they grew older, so did the demands for bedtime stories, and providentially, there were many to hand – "Pumpkin Soup" by Helen Cooper, "The Rainbow Fish" by Marcus Pfister, "Guess How Much I Love You" by

Sam McBratney, "Where oh Where is Kipper's Bear" by Mick Inkpen, "The BFG" by Roald Dahl, "The Very Hungry Caterpillar" by Eric Carle, "We're Going On a Bear Hunt" by Michael Rosen and Helen Oxenbury, together with stories of Winnie the Pooh and Peter Rabbit, being some of their favourites. They were at the age when their thresholds of boredom were extremely high, and repetition could not be exercised enough times. Perhaps, if I had written the story of my life at the time to read to them, they may have fallen more swiftly into a deep sleep, even if it were with a look of befuddled anguish on their pretty little faces.

Any recollections of difficulties with child rearing have largely receded with time. I recall only how hard I tried, especially during the long commutes in London, to get home to spend a little time with them before they slept.

I believe we were lucky as parents to have been gifted with children who were not just bright, but generally well behaved. Yes, there were tantrums and tears, but nothing that caused concern or hand-wringing grief. One seemed to spend more time holding discourse on efforts to keep them educated, entertained, and amused, beyond the bathing, feeding, etc.

On the matter of clothing, it was a primarily simple function, as they were for the most part very easy to please. Holly, however, from the age of four had developed her own inimitable style and was clear on her preferences both for clothing and hairstyles.

It was not all fun and games, though. The enduring worry, for me at least, was never only all the aspects of making their lives as happy and well-guided as possible but keeping a promise made to them as babies that I would ensure that no harm befall them. This was so much more difficult, given how accidents occur. The pain I felt when they hurt themselves is something I can feel with great empathy in recollection even to this day.

Holly was six when she fell badly in playground and cut her lip.

I had taken them both out to a playground just yards away from the house. The irony was that I cautioned them against climbing the trees there in case they fell and hurt themselves on the stakes driven into the ground to secure them. I ushered them instead to a supposedly safer play area with stepping stumps. She fell and screamed in pain.

There was an abundance of blood, mostly on my shirt as I picked her up to cradle her. I still feel her pain. The poor girl had to have her lip stitched and spent her sixth birthday with a badly swollen face and a cancelled party. Happily, she has recovered from that ghastly injury with no permanent disfiguration to her very pretty face.

Chloe had also injured herself at a playground, but it was relievedly not serious or long-lasting other than abrasions to the skin. Her more serious injury was sustained when she was sixteen, when she suffered considerable harm in a horrendously painful fall off a skateboard on a steep slope. I was with her at the time and could not think of a more horrific moment than being witness to this fall. Her injury, although primarily on the surface, was severe and took a long time to heal. She was exceedingly brave, especially as it was in the middle of her international exams and had to sit through hours of pain to complete her papers.

I constantly think about how these accidents may have been avoided, as Chloe's injury caused me much of the same excruciating mental agony as when Holly was hurt as a six-year-old. I would have preferred to have endured their physical pain in their place, if it had been possible.

These were the little babies I never wanted to see hurt in all of the time that they lived. The pain of their children's suffering is not one any parent should experience. I am grateful that they did not suffer lasting harm, and just hope that they never will.

Unfortunately, the emotional pain they suffered when my marriage failed is something that I can do little to remedy. Is there anything that one can do to ensure that this emotional damage is contained? I would hate to think that it affects their choices when it comes to the selection of their future partners in life. I believe it may but pray that it does not.

Given all of this, would I still want to entertain prospects of a future marriage that will undoubtedly include having children? I realise that over the years, some of the grey cells in my head have irreplaceably perished, but I can assure you that my brain is not completely addled, and still functions with reasonable agility.

It would take me being veritably, consummately and unreservedly in love with someone to recommence the process of fatherhood of young children all over again. And H seems to fill that requirement rather well.

It is a difficult decision, I accept, and I hope that you will trust me to make it with a degree of rationality. You may argue it is one of the resources I have I have demonstrated with scarcity thus far, but I shall find some means of convincing you nearer the time, should it ever come to pass.

In the meanwhile, I look forward to hearing your thoughts, as always.

Love,

David

Letter 11 – *Zimbabwe Beckons*

August 2019

Dear Geoff,

I am now back in Zimbabwe.

It was quite a shock being back here after all that time away in London. I felt rather disoriented at first. Although there were many familiar things – dogs, staff, home, etc., it still felt a little peculiar. I knew that it would take me a little time to settle.

The things I did immediately appreciate greatly upon arrival, were being offered some delicious food by a friend, Reyhana, the warm welcome from my staff at home, Dunmore and Sarudzai and the unconditional love shown by the dogs, in their effusive greeting.

I realise that it has been over a year since I last wrote to you, but I hope that our telephone conversations and a few meetings have kept you reasonably informed and up to date on the goings on in my life. I shall try my best to provide you a pandect of events over the period since my last letter to you, nevertheless.

Unfortunately, the lease on our flat expired at the end of June and our plans were very much up in the air, as I had still no clarity on likely sources of income to maintain a home in London. Had it not been for the charity of family, primarily Carole, I am not sure how we could have coped. We had to try and find alternative accommodation in a little bit of a hurry until a more permanent arrangement could be derived. The girls took refuge, sharing a room in Carole's house, whilst I found myself shuffled from one obligatory family home to another.

Homelessness is such an awful feeling, and I vowed that no matter how humble or meagre my future residence was, I would cherish it as my own home. I believe that at one point even the cardboard box under Charing Cross bridge, I had mentioned in an earlier letter, began to appeal.

I hoped that I could find some means of helping the girls, and myself for that matter, through this difficult period in our lives. I decided it was best for me to return to Zimbabwe but hoped at some point to realise my ambitions to create value in a business proposition for property development projects in London. I thought that I had developed a rather clever business concept which could have been wonderfully successful there. I had partnered with Dimitri, a really nice half Greek, half English fellow who had undertaken various property refurbishment projects in London over the years.

As you know, I had done that reasonably successfully in Oxfordshire, when we were back in England for a spell between 2001-2007. Anyway, the idea was very simple, instead of undertaking projects one at a time we would undertake them on a multiple basis. This would allow us to gain great economies of scale in terms of materials purchases, and economies of scope in terms of better utilisation of highly skilled but highly priced labour. The properties we would purchase for refurbishment were what we termed the 'mid-market' opportunities priced between £400,000 to £1m, for which there seemed to be a vast market of potential buyers.

The buyer market comprised many first as well as second home buyers of period properties. We would avoid competing with developers of modern blocks by focusing our attention solely on period properties. Geographically we would also channel our attention to areas we could easily access and assign labour too. They were areas in London that we were often familiar with ourselves. I still think that it is an absolute wizard of a plan, and only wished that I had the capital to commit to this myself. I am so disappointed in the lack of investors willing to back me on this, claiming that Brexit would create uncertainty. I wish I could prove them wrong. If I did not have to rely on others for capital, I am sure that I could have already garnered a fortune for myself and Dimitri by undertaking this endeavour.

The plan was, and still is, to get this project off the ground so that Dimitri and I could earn a fee out of managing these investments on behalf of investors. We would eventually, after a year or so be in a position to reinvest our profit share back into the property fund so that our own earnings would grow exponentially, alongside that of the investors.

I remain hopeful of finding property-minded investors who will believe in us and our capability to manage and grow such a fund.

In the meantime, I hoped that my business in Zimbabwe would also regain some traction in the development market, which would provide an income sufficient to clear my financial obligations and begin to recreate some wealth to support a comfortable retirement future.

I do not really see myself retiring however, as I enjoy working and building things too much to give it up for the sake of pottering around a garden. By retirement, I meant that I would build a business to a point where I could continue creating new developments often but also take more time off to travel, read more extensively and learn new things - another language, playing a musical instrument, or new recipes to broaden my culinary skills. The most important aspect of owning a business rather than being an employee, in my view is having the ability to leave a legacy of sorts for children to benefit from. It is my wish to leave something more than a memory for the girls.

I set about re-establishing my presence at the office, which appeared to have acquired a demoralised presence. Thankfully many of the staff were pleased to see me return and provide some confidence in the future of the business and thereby, their continued employment. It was good to contact clients and receive their warm welcome also.

I began to feel a sense of relief that there was a possibility of resurrecting the business to the point, where it could start generating substantial value again. It was unlikely to grow swiftly enough to be at the point it was before I left for London, as the general economy in the meanwhile had begun to crumble badly, and we once again faced the difficulty of enticing foreign investment and therefore access to foreign currency was seriously limited. With some care and attention, I could nurse this business back from its intensive care status to a relatively good degree of health, providing the macro-economic, and to a certain extent the micro-economic, environment did not impede this endeavour too greatly. All I needed was for the gods to smile upon me a little more kindly.

With some tweaking of the way the office was run, and decisions taken, it was soon back to business as usual. It gave me a renewed sense of purpose, as well as re-establishing a determination to succeed, in journeying to the office each morning.

I realised after a day or two of settling in, that the house needed to feel more like a home. I missed being with the girls of course, but there was not much I could do to re-create their presence. Chloe was always loud and untidy, so it was difficult not to miss her presence. Much loved as this first-born child of mine is, I remain continually mystified as to how she manages to be untidy even when offered closet space and a maid to help. Holly on the other hand, could never be faulted in this regard and is always meticulously tidy.

The house needed a re-injection of life, and the dogs seemed very happy to contribute to this new venture. They had been, for over a year, limited to the pantry, and now rejoiced in once again being allowed to roam the house freely, at least on the ground floor, as the upper level remained strictly out of bounds to them. Nougat was just happy to have me home, so he loyally followed me everywhere. The other two merely jostled for space on the sofa, which I had to find coverings for, to avoid them being ruined with dirty paw prints.

I set about rearranging furniture, paintings and furnishings. Unfortunately, I had to make do with the remnants of these elements left to me. In some cases, a mishmash of curtain colours and lengths, but I had no spare budget to undertake any major make-over, at this stage. The plan was to make it feel welcoming not just to me, but also to prospective buyers. My efforts appeared to reap some reward, as it soon began to feel more like a home rather than just a large house. As I had mentioned earlier, the purpose of all of this was twofold. i.e., it was not just to suit my comfort but also to stoke the interest for any potential buyer coming to view the property. Comments from friends would suggest that I had achieved some success in this exercise. Perhaps if all my other business endeavours failed, I could sell my services as a specialist of shoestring budget home makeovers!

There was still an immense amount to do. I left things like packing away things for storage for another time.

There were many things that the girls wanted to keep for their respective futures. As storage space was not an issue currently, I was quite happy for them to keep as much as they sought to, for the sake of kindling good childhood memories. I too, had many things that I had no immediate need of, which could be packed, but I found it hard to get terribly motivated to do so, as it would have involved the purchase of all the packing paraphernalia that I was loathed to make into a priority.

I did, however apply my mind to rummaging through my wardrobe and other cupboards to find things for sale. I really had to de-clutter, regardless of any move as I was sure we had accumulated much more than I would ever actually get around to making gainful application of.

Much as I was disinclined to sell or throw out shirts and other items of clothing that I had clung onto desperately in the hope they would come back into fashion, or at least kept to be reminded of the days when I was fashionable, I sought to be ruthless. I identified many items which I hoped would be of greater value to someone else and created two separate piles – one for sale and the other to give away. My staff at home had first dibs on the 'giveaway' pile and helped themselves gleefully to whatever was there. It gave me enormous pleasure to see their delight. How wonderful it is to give to such grateful people. They continued to express their gratitude for the items, despite my thanking them in return for taking these unwanted items off my hands.

The kitchen cupboards were also emptied of all the items I was prepared to sell. I was very pleased to have completed the first phase of my de-cluttering plans. I now had to hope that the items set aside for sale would realistically generate some income with which I could apply some minor repairs to the house. There were a few other things I needed to do in the house, like filing personal paperwork and sorting through the girls' schoolbooks and files, but I felt that these tasks were best undertaken when I had oodles of time over the Christmas holidays. Given that I was spending this mostly in a companionless state of sorts, it would be a way to pass the time.

Having undertaken the key tasks of addressing business and home, I turned my attention to that of re-constituting my social life. There were many people with whom I had not been in touch for over a year. I realised that some had already taken sides, as a result of my marriage ending, and that I could not expect to re-establish that cordial relationship unilaterally, but although saddened, I had anticipated such behaviour. What I felt was more disappointing was to be told that some friends in particular had no wish to see me again, for what they felt I had supposedly done to them.

I felt obliged to clear the air with them as soon as possible. They were some of the first people I called. The surprise was to learn that they had no issue with me at all and were delighted that I was back in touch. I was happy to see them again, especially as I was the sort of person who valued friendships greatly and would be distraught to lose friendships needlessly.

Throughout my life I have placed greater value on friendship than I did on monetary benefit, which may have caused some financial discomfort at times, but it is a system of principles inherited through generations of our family, and not something easily cast aside. Thankfully there were some friends who were happy to welcome me back into their homes and hearts. I looked forward to reciprocating their hospitality shown as soon as I was able to.

The final aspect I had to put in place was my exercise schedule. I missed going to the Soho House gym at the Helios, and with all the shuffling around homes the only muscles gaining exercise were those over my brow creased in anxiety and those around my mouth, which had been drawn in a perpetual frown.

It was time to rectify that. Thankfully, in that regard, Givemore, my previous personal trainer was more than happy to pick up where he had left off.

Givemore, and as his name so beautifully suggests, always expects a little more out of me than I feel sometimes capable of giving. His favourite expression being "Let's go. Let's go …." even when my aching body kept wanting to reply with "Let's not! Let's not!"

He is a really nice chap, though. He was Mr Zimbabwe (as in bodybuilding) a few times, so I do believe he knows what he is doing, and I trust him to bring about the sculptured look in me that I crave!

It was going to be David version 3.0!

If all goes well, I shall be residing happily in my home, be in the process of resuscitating a flailing business, reviving a social life of sorts, and getting back a degree of fitness and muscular improvement.

I shall let you know how I get on with these aspects in my next letters.

Love,

David

Letter 12 – Losing a Devoted Companion

August 2019

Dear Geoff,

Even as I pen this letter to you, I can feel my eyes well up with tears. I lost Nougat a few days ago.

I am still reeling from the shock. I feel such a searing pain in my heart. Why Geoff? Why do things like this happen to me? Every time I feel that I am re-working my life to adjust to a new normality, another dramatically damaging event occurs to throw me off my feet. It sometimes feels like I have been written into a very sad Greek tragedy, where the protagonist stumbles from one tragic occurrence to another without even the smallest of breaks. Why is my already troubled life compounded with further grief? I am not sure my heart can bear any more pain, particularly that of losing a beloved pet.

It all seemed to have happened so quickly. Despite my having been away for more than a year, Nougat had obviously not forgotten me. He followed me around everywhere. It was almost as though I had never left, as that was his practice when we had first rescued him from the dog sanctuary and brought him home.

At the time, we were not in the market for another pet dog as we had recently lost Cous-Cous and bought a pup, whom we named Bamboo to take his place. Not that dogs could ever be truly replaced, as they seem to obtain an immovable slot in one's heart.

I had taken Holly along with me after seeing Nougat's picture posted on Facebook seeking anyone who felt inclined to adopt him. It would do no harm to just see him, I thought.

The conditions under which the dogs were being kept in the sanctuary were sadly very poor, but the workers there did as best they could with limited funding. They had to provide a home and food for the many dogs who had been abandoned and would have likely perished without their timely and charitable intervention. Nougat looked so emaciated but still stood proud as was becoming of his pedigree of golden Cocker Spaniels. Apparently, he had been given up by the previous owner because of his inclination to attack his neighbour's fowl.

He seemed to take to Holly rather than me, at first, as he clung devotedly to her side as we both walked him for a short while in an adjacent field. Although we made the point of discussing seriously the pros and cons of taking him home to add to the two dogs we already had, I knew that we had both already decided that he was too lovely a dog not to adopt.

I called the sanctuary the following day and made arrangements to collect him. I took Dunmore as trusty companion to fetch him. Nougat was not in the best of moods and appeared to snarl at one of the keepers at one stage. I began to wonder if we had made the right decision to take him, as we could not afford an ill-tempered dog to join the bedlam that prevailed at our home. After reassurances from the lady who managed the facility that he was generally good natured, we signed the required forms, attached a new collar to him and led him to the car.

Nougat seemed resigned to his fate as he walked obediently with us to the car. I wonder if he felt that his life was about to get worse rather than better. I did not realise at the time, that the dog sanctuary would have seemed a godsend to him compared to the treatment I believed he suffered under his previous owner.

If Nougat was wondering what lay in store for him, Dunmore and I were similarly considering what reception awaited him, both from the dogs and my ex. Ollie and Bamboo, were cautiously welcoming. Although little Boo growled a little, no fights ensued. If my ex had uttered anything disparaging, it never reached my ears. Nougat was well received overall. Holly took to him in an instant as he did to her, but he seemed to grow a special affection for me and refused to leave my side. Even Dunmore who was wonderful with all the dogs we had, experienced a difficult time with Nougat to begin with, and I was the only one he allowed to attach a lead to his collar, and be led out for a walk.

For a long while, Nougat slinked around the property, fearful of being close to anyone, and spending most of the time outside awaiting my return from work. As time progressed, he became more comfortable with his surroundings. It was then, that we realised he must have been very badly mistreated previously. We no longer believed that his being given up had anything to do with his behaviour with the fowl. Nougat had no inclination to chase anything with wings.

The other two dogs would bark incessantly and chase any bird, or any creature for that matter, that landed in our garden uninvited, but Nougat showed no such interest. He barked at nothing and no one, at least until Bamboo and Ollie showed him that it was required behaviour in our household. Bamboo would sometimes take barking to an extreme and even applied her vocal endeavours to shadows.

Nougat must have suffered so much under the last owner. Browbeaten, I am sure to the point of total submission. Why do people act so cruelly? Is this the sort of behaviour they exhibit towards humans also? Or is it something they reserve for animals thinking they are lesser creatures? Why then have a pet? Why take a beautiful pedigreed dog and treat it with such unbelievable contempt? I cannot help but be generally drawn to support the underdog, which Nougat literally was in this case, and I cared for him even more as a result.

Chloe, when she came to visit us during her university holidays, was equally taken with him, and soon adopted him as her own. She had taken the loss of Cous-Cous (her previous pet Spaniel), as badly as I did and proceeded to shower Nougat with all the affection she had held in reserve. It was so lovely to watch.

It may have started as Holly's love, but Nougat was soon usurped by Chloe, partly also because Holly had become totally absorbed by Bamboo in the meanwhile. Those two now seemed to have created a special bond as Bamboo would sit quietly with no one but Holly. Chloe and I would try to show Bamboo affection but whilst she enjoyed the attention, she gave the impression she had something else more pressing to attend to. Whether it was to bark at the front gate or chase birds she always seemed impatient to get out of our grasp. With Holly, on the other hand she would sit on her shoulder, or by her side completely unperturbed, and with the demeanour of a dog at complete peace with her mistress.

Nougat may have sensed that Chloe's affections could only be enjoyed temporarily and took to me as his more permanent attachment. Apparently, whilst on one of my business trips away, he stood guard outside my bedroom door, and would not be moved even with the lure of a treat. How I would love to have seen that! I was so touched to hear of his attachment.

I had no real favourites amongst the dogs. If pushed, I would have admitted to having a soft spot for Cous-Cous. He was gruff with most people, but he reminded me so much of my father, who sometimes appeared brusque and uncaring, but bore a deeply loving heart. I had grown accustomed to Cous-Cous's constant and unwavering attention to me, particularly after we lost Waffles, another of our golden spaniel pets. I avoided having favourites, even between my children, but I could not help but love him dearly. And now that partial favouritism began to apply to Nougat.

Whilst in England and away from the dogs, I was more concerned about Nougat than I was about either Ollie or Bamboo. It was not because I favoured him, but out of concern for him, given his attachment to me. I was not sure that he would cope without having a central figure to anchor his sense of security. I need not have been concerned. Dunmore was so good with him. Bearing in mind Nougat had once actually bitten him in the hand whilst attempting to put him on the lead when giving him his first bath, Dunmore showed him no grievance whatsoever, and treated him with as much care as he did with all the dogs we had, both previously and currently. I must admit that Dunmore was a real godsend when it came to looking after our needs or those of the dogs.

Dunmore, who, as is name would aptly suggest, has singlehandedly done more in looking after all our needs as a family than most of the staff we have employed. He has been with us for over twelve years and had been by far the most honest, loyal and faithful of domestic staff. If he ever broke anything or mishandled an implement, it was never through negligence but an over zealousness. We had saved him from starvation and grave illness once, and there was nothing he would not now do for us as a family. Why is the world not populated with more Dunmores? Nougat was in very good hands.

I had wondered how the dogs would react to me on my return. The girls thought that they would greet me with great enthusiasm. I hoped so. Having been through hell and back with the scare and treatment my cancer diagnosis had caused whilst in England, I could do with some display of constant and unwavering affection.

The girls were right. They barked at the friend's car that dropped me off, but as soon as they realised it was me, they leapt about with joy. Ollie was the usual springing self and could barely contain his excitement. Bamboo spent the time darting in and out of my arms whenever she spotted a gap in my attention, and Nougat was truly overjoyed. I tried to record this enthusiastic greeting on my phone so that I could send a video to the girls, but the dogs were too excitedly leaping about and all I captured was a fuzzy blur. I was equally happy to see them. Is it only dogs that can express such total devotion so beautifully? They sought nothing in reciprocation. They display such expressive joy in the unconditional affection they hold. It was just the tonic I needed.

They had been confined to the pantry previously, but on my return, they were delighted to revert to their old ways. They now roamed the sitting room with unfettered access to select their choice spot on the sofa. Bamboo, though the smallest amongst them ruled the roost. She had the first choice. The other two had to make do with whatever other space she did not wish to occupy. Women! Or should I say 'bitch' in this case?

Nougat seemed so happy. I could see even in his gait that he had a renewed spirit about him. I was beginning to quite enjoy Nougat's constant presence next to me. He had such a calming attendance. Not ever nagging for attention, just a wish to provide quiet companionship. Every time I think about his absence now, I can feel my heart fill with such unbearable sorrow.

I am still not sure what truly occurred that evening. I had gone out for drinks with friends. It was not even such a great evening, as I arranged to meet a couple at a wine bar I used to frequent previously called the Blue@2, but the venue no longer bore the same ambience and after a couple of drinks we called it a night.

I got home to find that Nougat was not just following me around as was his habit but was whining continually as he did so.

I assumed at first that he was merely crying for attention, and I would reach down and pat his head occasionally as he sat by my feet. I sensed that something was not right after a while, as he seemed to get progressively more agitated.

I took more time to comfort him, but he now appeared to be in some distress. I knocked on the door to Dunmore's room hoping to awaken him to find out if Nougat's behaviour had been apparent earlier in the evening. Dunmore was nowhere to be found. I discovered later that he had popped out to his church for midnight prayers. I decided that I would take Nougat to the 24-Hour Vet down the road as a precaution. He hopped into the car without any difficulty, and I took heart that it may be just a minor ailment plaguing him. On examination, the Vet felt that he could have a stomach upset of sorts and gave him a painkiller to ease his now very obvious discomfort. He offered to keep Nougat overnight for observation, but I thought that Nougat would prefer to be at home with me. I also wished for him to be under my observation.

I brought him home, but he could not even make it out of the car. As soon as I placed him on the ground he could not move and ended up with his legs comically splayed. Cous-Cous sometimes ended up similarly splayed when suffering one of his seizures, but generally recovered quickly. I put Nougat in his basket and carried him inside.

He laid there in great discomfort. His breathing was laboured, and he kept throwing his head back into an abnormal angle. I tried my best to soothe him and put his head back into a more restful position, but in vain. I was not sure that Nougat should continue in this posture overnight.

I called the Vet and asked him for advice. He recommended a return to the surgery for re-examination and overnight care. I had to carry Nougat back to the car as there was no way that he could stand, let alone walk. Ollie and Bamboo were in utter confusion and sought some attention, which I could not offer as my entire concern was then focused on Nougat's condition.

The Vet calmed him down, gave him a further sedative and offered to put him on a drip. He seemed fairly optimistic about Nougat's recovery and suggested that I should pick him up the next morning. I drove home with great unease. The nagging feeling at the pit of my stomach would not leave no matter how much I tried to tell myself that he was in good care.

I remember the same unease I felt when we had left Waffles overnight at another Vet's when she was unwell and looked forward to collecting her the following day, only to be advised of her demise. Holly was particularly distraught, as she was as attached to Waffles, as Chloe was to Cous-Cous. I can remember the pain I felt at losing Waffles being compounded with the sight of children crying inconsolably.

I felt the same apprehension and called the girls to advise them of Nougat's condition preparing them for the worst. They wanted to know more and persuaded me to call the Vet again for an update. It was close to three in the morning, but I called anyway. I was assured by the Vet that Nougat seemed calm, hooked to an IV drip of medication, and appeared to be responding to treatment. I was to check back again at seven that morning.

I was awoken by a call at six. I had only three hours of very disturbed rest. I hoped with all my heart that it was a call to collect him but was instead advised of his death. I was numb.

There were a hundred questions I wanted to ask, but all I could utter was a muted 'thank you' to them for their effort and hung up. My mind was racing with a repetition of an unanswered query. Why? Why him? Why not me instead? Why now? Why, oh, why? I wanted so hard to cry!

I hoped that the tears would have brought me some relief, but no tears appeared. All I felt was a sharp stabbing pain in my heart, which continued without any applicable remedy. If I were to have been struck down then, I would have welcomed it. I would have gladly joined my beloved Nougat. I felt no wish to continue my life. I had suffered physical pain, emotional anguish, financial distress, unabated worry, but this pain was by far the worst.

I called a couple of friends – Reyhana and Monisha to tell them of my loss. I could not bring myself to go to the office. I just wanted to sit quietly somewhere, close my eyes and wish it all to have been just a very bad dream. I could not bear to not have him by my side. He was in my heart, but I needed to feel the reassurance of his physical presence. To stroke his head of beautiful fur again. Ollie and Bamboo seemed a little puzzled by Nougat's absence and, in their own way, offered some consolation.

The ladies came over later in the morning to offer their sympathies, and I did appreciate their company, as I really did not want to be alone in my grief. I had little appetite, but they insisted that I eat. Monisha made me an interesting brunch of scrambled eggs, onions, and tomatoes on toast. A dish with a name that has slipped my mind but sounded very much like one of the high-rise buildings in Dubai. It was delicious and a served as a perfect temporary distraction from my sorrow.

I went with Dunmore to collect Nougat's body from the Vet. I had many questions for him. I was struggling to understand how a perfectly healthy dog could suddenly give up his ghost. The Vet, a more senior one in for the morning shift, suggested that he could have ingested some fast-acting poison.

There had been burglaries in many areas where the *modus operandi* was to hurl meat laced with poison over the gate at properties where owners had dogs, in preparation for robbing the residents who had been deprived of their canine protection. I assumed that this must have been the case, and blamed myself for leaving the dogs unattended, and also for not considering poison as a possibility when discussing the matter with the Vet the previous night. I felt considerably worse for thinking that my negligence played a part in Nougat's untimely death. It was not a nice feeling.

Poor Dunmore. He was calm but his grief was obvious.

He hated losing our beloved pets as much as we did. We discussed plans for Nougat's burial. We decided on the place in the garden he always seemed drawn to, which incidentally was where we had buried both Waffles and Cous-Cous, and therefore so appropriate. We agreed on the type of tree we would plant over his grave.

Monisha had mentioned an Indian tradition, (Hindu, I believe), of scattering salt over the body to aid the departure of the soul.

The grave was dug and prepared. We laid him in his bed and placed him carefully in the ground. He did not have a favourite toy, so he parted only with his lead. It was a similar ritual to that we had performed with Waffles and Cous-Cous previously.

I hated burying pets. I remember the sadness even when as children, my parents would help us make crosses and stood with us as we lit candles and uttered prayers at a graveside vigil whenever we lost a pet.

My parents were so wonderful at helping us understand the loss and grief we suffered at the time as children. They even once allowed me to make a great fuss over burying Henny, my pet hen.

I was completely grief stricken and very close to tears, but none flowed.

Here I was, a man who could usher tears at the drop of a hat, and who found himself with eyes watering at even the slightest hint of sadness watching a B-rate love story or hearing a sad tale, unable to shed a meaningful tear when confronted with the loss of a beloved pet. I think I was just much too sad to cry. The tears, I was sure, would come later.

They did, eventually. I fight back tears now as I pen these words to you, thinking of his saintly presence, which I can neither enjoy nor benefit from any longer.

It was sometime later, when at drinks with some friends that Justin's wife Jacqui suggested an alternative theory for the cause of Nougat's death, and that the symptoms Nougat displayed could have been caused by 'twisted bowel syndrome'.

Apparently, it is something that can happen to some dogs without prior warning and often proves fatal. Unless the Vet had been able to detect this and immediately performed surgery, there was very little prospect of survival. It was little consolation. I still felt guilty for not doing more to protect Nougat from his painful demise.

It is at times like this that I wonder if there is a God.

I was brought up as a Christian and still call myself one. I even took great pride in advertising the fact that I was confirmed into the Church of England by the Archbishop of Canterbury no less. But I no longer feel that I hold any true faith. Despite all the grief my parents suffered, I know that my mother in particular continued to hold unshakeable faith. Not so for me. I finally gave up in despair a year or so ago. Science would suggest that there really is no room for a divine being. If one existed, would it not be beyond any God to listen to a prayer from any one individual, given the vastness of the Universe? I don't understand why any God would allow such gross injustice to prevail in our world. And it continues to worsen. Even the biblical plague of locusts would have been easier to combat. So much unnecessary pain and suffering in this world has been caused in the name of religion, in my view.

I do not know what to expect anymore, Geoff. How could such a beautiful animal, who had nothing but an enormous amount of love to give meet such a painful and untimely death?

He asked for nothing. He was grateful for the one meal a day, a soft and warm place on which to rest his head, the occasional treat and daily pat on the head. It is so true that some people and animals can enrich you by being part of your life but take away a part of you when they leave or die. Nougat enriched mine considerably, which is why I grieve his loss immensely.

I miss him so much. I wonder when this particular pain will ever ease.

I apologise for having to write to you on such a sorrowful subject. But I know that as a friend, you will stand by me no matter what the circumstance, be it the heights of joy or the depths of despair. I value such friendship. It is akin to the wonderful comfort that Nougat offered me.

He was at my side no matter my pain or elation. He was a wonderful companion for the short time he was in my life.

I bid you adieu now, and hope that the next occasion I write to you shall be a happier one.

Love,

David

Letter 13 – Brunei Beauty & Childhood Crushes

September 2019

Dear Geoff,

So much has happened in my life in the last few months, but I am still having a devil of a time dismissing thoughts of H. She appears to be ubiquitous, and I am reminded of her no matter what I do or where I turn. I even think of her in the midst of punishing exercises set by my personal trainer. I have very fond memories of past loves, but never with this degree of consistency.

I cannot remember if I ever told you about one of my first loves ever. You probably think that I have been in love with almost every pretty girl that I meet. But it is not entirely true. I would, without any need for torture admit that I do lust after many, but the sustainable love interest I do actually reserve for the special ones. The fact that I still think fondly of my first childhood love, after so many years would suggest that I was indeed truly in love with her.

Fawzia was a very pretty girl. Not just in an immediately obvious way but also rather in a shy reserved manner, which was also very representative of her character. She was therefore oblivious to her beauty, which made her appeal even more enticing. She would have been very surprised to learn that I would have placed her at the very top in any and every beauty competition held.

I met her when I had just started at senior school.

I must have been thirteen or so at the time. We had been in Brunei for about six years by then, having moved from Malaysia.

My parents had been head hunted for jobs in Brunei, whilst teaching in a town called Ipoh. Even though I was quite young at the time I recall the excitement when my parents shared the information with us. My father had nomadic tendencies anyway, which must have frustrated my mother immensely, but as ever, she disguised it beautifully as she always successfully made a home of wherever it was that my father chose to lay his hat. In this instance they appeared to be mutually excited at the prospect of moving to substantially better paid jobs.

My siblings were older, particularly my elder sisters who would have entered their teens and may not have been as keen to move, leaving all their friends behind. Again, if they had been disappointed to move, they managed to throw themselves wholeheartedly into this new adventure.

The move was a good one in hindsight I think as we seemed very happy there, at least we were until my mother suffered an illness, from which she would never fully recover. We all made new friends very quickly. Some of the family friends we cultivated there remain friends to this day.

Fawzia was not the first girl I had met in Brunei that I had fallen for. I have no idea as to what the move there caused, but it was an introduction to girls, I assume. All I remember of my childhood in Malaysia was that it was a series of happy days, free of any responsibility, many beach holidays, trips out with the entire family squashed into a car together with our pets. Adorable pets too, some of whom I understood from my parents I relinquished the comfort of my bed to lie down next to on the floor. I felt an enormous sadness when I was told that one particular pet dog was so concerned for me that she once followed the car she assumed I was being abducted in and was accidentally run over as a result. At the time my parents had, in order to protect me, just mentioned that it was her time and that she had gone to heaven. I do remember her well now, and still mourn her passing.

The food was memorable too. We ate out quite often. The street food culture exists to this day and is something I introduced to my girls when we all visited Malaysia in 2007 and 2008. Of course, everything was now terribly sanitised and housed within large shopping malls, which did not really exist when I was little. There were malls certainly, but not of the scale one sees today. They were mainly double or triple storeyed structures playing host to a multitude of retailers, with some operating from space as little as two- or three-square metres. My parents loved to shop and dragged us everywhere from clothing shops to jewellers and retailers of cameras and curios. My father had mastered the great art of bargaining. His skills at negotiation would warrant at least a few chapters in a book on best business practice.

Some of those street markets, thankfully still prevail. My daughters loved the fact they could choose from a myriad of stalls and try a multiplicity of freshly prepared dishes for a paltry sum. Although many years ago and probably one of many instances when we ate out, one memory in particular stands out. We had gone out as a family and ordered to our various wishes. I was in the middle of my meal when I turned around to chat with a friend. When I turned back to resume tucking into my food, I found that my plate was gone. It had been cleared away.

My siblings were rolling around in uncontrollable laughter at my misfortune. They could be absolutely merciless at times. The more upset I became in my remonstrations, the more they erupted in mirth. I tried hard to fight back the tears, but they flowed. I had saved some of the best bits of food (probably prawns or some other delight), only to find the much-anticipated remnant of my meal no longer where I had left it, assuming its sanctity.

Much as I was comforted by my parents with a reorder of food, I felt cheated. Overzealous waiter at fault or not, and although I was only five years old at the time, I felt that there was no greater betrayal than having something special taken away directly from under one's protective care. I am sure that my father was more understanding. He was a very slow eater and hated anyone beginning to clear way until all had finished, meaning him in essence. So, we would all, therefore, sit dutifully at the table and avoid placing our elbows on it, until he had finished and declared it time for his plate to be removed.

Girls did not really feature as one of my greatest priorities at the time. I was more concerned about winning at marbles, a game which my sister Carole tended to monopolise with her unerring skill; calculating how many sticks of satay I could safely consume without feeling terribly ill; making sure I did not miss any episodes of Batman; chasing butterflies; fishing, which in some instances included capturing tadpoles into glass jars; looking forward to the next trip to the beach to construct ever more ambitious sandcastles; playing board games with my siblings; improving my swimming; and completing any homework, if any. To some extent, this list covered almost everything and is largely in the order of importance they featured in my young life. Completing homework was conducted under a strict regimen and given that both my parents were teachers, this was completely understandable.

Fishing was less of a comprehensible lure for a past time. We never possessed any fishing paraphernalia at that age. Ours comprised sticks with some string and a pebble tied on as a sinker. I remain unclear as to what exactly we used as bait. Probably nothing, which is why we were never successful. Sadly, I must admit that even with bait in my more recent fishing endeavours I have not been hugely triumphant. I certainly would not capture the attention of any reporter from an Angling journal, as other than catching a reasonably sized tiger fish at an outing on Lake Kariba with some friends a few years ago, there is very little to indicate my abilities as an aspiring fisherman. What the attraction fishing had for us as children remains a mystery.

John, Carole and I once played truant from school to go on a fishing expedition at the river some way from our house. We did not realise how frantic my parents were when they discovered us missing and playing at fishing in a river known to provide a habitat for crocodiles. If we were at all scared it was only after the event, as at the time we were having the time of our lives. We continued this interest in fishing even when we moved to Brunei and spent many a day at the side of the river, which flowed past the one and only hotel in Brunei at that time – aptly named the Brunei Hotel.

This was our home for a while until they could provide us with the promised teacher's quarters. It was an old building of uninspiring architecture, hosting a series of steel framed windows and located at the end of a parade of shops in one of the few 'high streets' that existed at that time. The interior was equally uninspiring with a bland front desk in front of a set of tired and creaking lifts, and the restaurant set off to one side. The rooms led off long corridors lined with threadbare carpets. Although a major oil rich country, the wealth was yet to show in retail or hospitality representation.

It could not have been the most comforting set of circumstances for my parents, but as children we loved the time at the Brunei Hotel. Beyond playing along the corridors, racing the lift against the route up the stairs, and being told off many times by the staff, we spent our time fishing and playing hide and seek at a nearby clothes shop appropriately called the 'Glamour Store', run by a friendly Sikh family. We spent so much time there, that I think my parents came to regard the Sikh patriarch and his children as *de facto* babysitters, primarily for John, Carole and I.

The hotel was close to stores and a nearby food market so we would shop often, particularly for soured prunes and other typical Malaysian treats from the Chinese shop a few doors down as well as Malay cakes (Kueh) from the market at the weekends.

There were so many types of Kueh, but my favourites were Kueh Dada, Kueh Kosui, Kueh Salat, Ondeh-Ondeh and Kueh Lapis. I am salivating at the thought of tucking into a few of these right now. I am sure I could happily eat a truck full of them. You must try these, if you have not before. I shall make it a point of introducing these delights to your palate one of these days. My daughters also now love these Kueh, particularly the Ondeh-Ondeh, and I obtained them in London as often as I could, but they lacked the authenticity of the ones I remembered from my childhood.

We ate out quite often as a family, mostly at Chinese restaurants, but found the heavily air-conditioned restaurant on the ground floor of the hotel, which was supposedly the finest of Brunei's restaurants our least favourite dining experience. We dined at friends' houses, but it was not until we moved into a house that we could reciprocate in kind. My parents were great hosts and entertained often. They employed a Chinese Amah, who delighted us with some amazing food. The key was not to ask what it was that we were eating and just indulge. Prawn heads, for example, were items usually discarded, but she would not just keep them but trim the feelers, marinate them in something-or-the-other and deep fry them. They were delicious and one of my father's favourite snacks with his glass of beer.

So, it was primarily food, marbles, butterflies, board games, sandcastles, learning to swim, fishing and school that occupied space and time in my young mind, in that rough order. Girls, clothes, art, etc., were yet to gain greater prominence and devotion of effort and time in my life. I think it was not until we moved to Brunei that my eyes opened to the beauty of the opposite sex. Suddenly girls appeared far more beautiful and enchanting than the butterflies I attempted to entrap in my makeshift net.

Prior to falling madly in love with Fawzia, I had an array of other girls who attracted my attention and interest. The first of whom was a Chinese girl called Linda. I had always considered Fawzia my first love, but I wonder now if it was really Linda who captured my heart for the very first time. I was probably around eight or nine years old when she appeared in my line of sight. What a beauty she was too. I tried to pay scant attention to her, by choosing to spend as much time with the boys as I could, but it was very difficult not to keep being drawn back to her. We were in the same class and sat close to each other.

She was very pretty, and I could not help but keep looking at her. At break time she would join us and elected to join my team for a game of 'Police and Thieves', which was one of our favourites at the time. For some unknown reason I was always one of the team captains beit for this game, 'Rounders', 'Dog and the Bone', or anything else we played in the school courtyard. Linda was always in my team. The rest of the children treated us as a 'couple' as we always seemed to be together. I could swear there were times when we played that she would hug me for a little longer than was absolutely necessary.

We grew close and I am almost certain we did once actually kiss. Our relationship largely involved holding hands and any kiss would have been nothing more than the pressing together of lips. I do remember 'blushing', when we did. My face felt as though it was fire and had it not been for my skin tone, turned a bright red.

I suppose I was infatuated with Linda, as when she changed school and moved to St. Andrews, I persuaded my parents to move me from St. Georges, where I was, arguing at the time that an Anglican church school was better suited to our religious standing than the Catholicism that St. G's represented. I doubt that my parents accepted that point of view, but gave in to my insistence and moved me, despite the fact that St. G's was merely a stone's throw from where we lived.

Linda and I grew apart almost immediately after we moved school. I think now that our separation was intended. She seemed very distant. I missed my friends at my old school and my parents were pleased when I elected to return to St. G's. Was Linda one of my great loves, or at least my first? Probably, but feelings for her have not really stood the test of time, as have those for Fawzia.

After Linda, my attention turned to Maria Theresa. She was one of Filipino twins at St. G's. Both girls were truly beautiful and definitely the talk of the school when they joined. Her sister Maria Christina was sweet and lovely too, but protocols would obviously not allow me to date both of them simultaneously. I am not really sure how I ended up with MT rather than MC, as I was keen on both, but I think it was more their exercise of choice than mine.

MT and I dated, if you could call it that, for a seemingly long while. It was more play dates, if you will. Being in the final years at primary school we considered ourselves more mature, but we still only met at parties or at each other's houses to play. We did get to hold hands for the first time at one of MT's parties. I remember making a special effort to dress up. I still relied on my parents to buy clothes, but I know that I was beginning to be a little more aware of what I wanted to dress in. My brother was several sizes bigger than me at the time, so I did avoid hand-me-downs from him.

The party comprised the usual round of musical chairs, pass the parcel, and other games, but whatever the game, we made sure we were seated next to each other. We danced together, of course. On one occasion she grabbed my hand, and we ran off into the garden. If anything happened between us at that party, I honestly have no clear recollection. I do remember though being truly happy and rather besotted with her.

It helped that I was one of the more popular boys at primary school and in my class. I was bright and generally always came top of the class, but I was also very much the centre of the fun crowd. The one usually called upon to be the game's team captain, etc. I also joined the Boy Scouts at MT's instigation. What is it with girls and their love for boys in uniform? I did enjoy it, though. I can still remember how to make a boiled egg without water and tie a reef knot. I think I looked rather dashing in my uniform and made it a point to ensure it was well starched and pressed, when we went out on scouting activities.

Like Linda before her, MT was the only girl I had eyes for, despite some popularity I had amongst others. I quite liked the fact that we spent time together, even attending Catholic mass to ingratiate myself with her parents. I remember us being one of the more popular and 'serious' couples at school. But all that changed at the start of secondary school.

It is rather sad that no one at primary school advises you that popularity at primary school creates no credibility at senior school where new entrants are regarded as just one level above pond scum. It really is like starting all over. MT joined an all-girls school, and I ended up going to school in India for a spell.

Although my eldest sister Isabel loved it, neither Rachel nor I enjoyed school there. Rachel could not bear it for long and headed back home to Brunei and from there directly to school in England where Carole and John had already been sent for their schooling. I stuck it out for a couple more terms to finish Form One, before returning to Brunei also. Although in India only for a short while, I do have some fond memories, particularly of the girls. Indian girls are some of the prettiest in the world, in my view. I vowed I would marry one if ever any opportunity arose.

I joined SOAS college on my return to Brunei. The headmaster considered me quite bright and had me skip a year to join the Form Three class. Thankfully I was not considered pond scum and welcomed warmly by my classmates. It did help that my sisters had been at school there before me and my brother also for a period before he left for England. Most importantly, the fact that my father was one of the teachers there and held in very high regard. Knowing how strict he was, I just prayed that he was not going to be one of my teachers.

Joining senior school meant that for the first time in my life I had to wear long trousers as part of my uniform. I had practically lived in shorts all my life until that point, as even Form One boys in India were only required to wear shorts. My brother's old uniform could not serve the purpose as I had grown tall, and my parents had to invest in new trousers, ensuring a long hem as they found I was getting taller by the term. All in all, joining senior school was rather a new, but strangely exciting experience.

I took to my life at senior school quite well. Unlike the English educational system, the system in Brunei required students to pass final exams each year before being promoted to the next class. Those who failed stayed on to repeat the year until they passed. This meant that there were some students who were older than the average expected for that grade. I got on well with the older students, as they took to my sense of humour, and I soon regained some of the popularity I enjoyed at primary school.

All counted for nought when I met Fawzia.

I became a babbling lunatic unable to construct a meaningful sentence or conduct myself with any decorum with her. I do not know what it is about her that not just caught my eye but had me totally mesmerised. Beautiful skin, the colour of lightly browned wholemeal toast. Dark eyes that seemed to glitter every time she smiled, and lips of such a heavenly shape that intimated offer of passionate kisses.

Her slim figure showed gentle hints of the shape of the woman to come. Although a Muslim, she did not wear the long skirts and hijab that some of the other girls did and displayed her long slim legs in more or less all their glory. But the attraction to her was not entirely superficial. She was kind, generous, charming, very bright and wonderfully amusing too. I was always attracted to girls who could amuse me. She could and was beautiful with it. I was totally captivated. My heart was hers to keep.

She may have thought of me as an uncoordinated imbecile as I always appeared clumsy and incapable of stringing many coherent sentences together for effective conversation, when we were together. But I made her smile, and therefore won a coveted spot in her company at most break times.

I gained in confidence the more time we spent together. We sometimes just conversed for hours. I also had an ally in her friend Susan, who ensured Fawzia and I were together most times. I had met Susan before, as my parents were friends with hers. We also became quite good friends, if she had a soft spot for me, she never said anything as I poured my heart out to her about my love for Fawzia.

This was the first time I had employed a girl as my confidante. In all of my previous affairs of the heart, I relied on the sound advice of my male friends especially Ronnie & Roger, twin boys from a Eurasian family. The two boys and I had become inseparable soon after meeting. We spent considerable time in each other's houses and in all manner of activities which included fishing (for catfish especially, as these appeared easier to catch); scrambling in the mud in our bikes; playing private detectives to solve some of the local 'mysteries' we learnt about through the school grapevine; cycling to the beach sixteen miles away; and discussing girls.

We were fascinated by adolescence and would discuss sex without having the slightest notion of the subject and would take to reporting regularly to each other on progress with respect to the number of pubic hairs we had sprouted.

I learnt from my mother after I left for England that they constantly asked about me. They were such good chums - I wish I had stayed in touch. Unfortunately, they were no longer in Brunei when I went back to visit my parents some years later. As with anything significant in my life at that time, I told the twins about Fawzia.

They were naturally supportive, and we discussed the best means of courting her, but I still felt that I needed a girl's perspective as this was no longer a primary schoolboy crush, but a prospective 'mature' relationship.

Susan was enlisted as my *aide-de-camp* for this purpose. I am grateful to her for arranging the many rendezvous' that I ended up enjoying with Fawzia. She even suggested that I should express my feelings for her in writing.

It seemed a little pointless sending letters to her as we were in the same class, so Susan suggested that I send the first note in a textbook. I asked to borrow Fawzia's Physics textbook, and 'accidentally' left a note in the book declaring my love for her. She wrote back. It was not quite the 'I love you madly' return of message, but encouraging in the suggestion that she was very surprised but extremely flattered, etc.

This exchange of messages continued for a while as did our wish to sit together in the science classes. I could sense from the way we would sometimes have shoulders pressed against each other or our feet touching, that she liked me too. She was evidently extremely shy and also from a strict family, so it would have been very difficult for us to be any more overt. Moreover, she was a Muslim, in a country where the outward and physical display of affection would have been very seriously frowned upon.

I decided to take up acting to spend my extra-curricular time also with Fawzia. I was selected to play the part of Sergius Saranoff in Shaw's "Arms and the Man". Part of the reason for electing to play this part, was that I would have a chance to legitimately hold Fawzia in my arms and kiss her. Fawzia played Raina so beautifully opposite me.

I literally followed Fawzia's every move. She floated across the stage with the grace of a Bolshoi ballerina. I felt reluctant to do anything that involved taking my eyes off her.

I cannot remember the name of the girl who played Louka, but I could sense that she had a crush on me and took the on-stage flirtations during practice and final performance seriously. I was focused on playing the character, but she fell for my performance, believing it to be real. It was a pity, as although she was quite pretty, I had eyes only for my beautiful Fawzia.

I was now convinced that Fawzia had feelings for me, because she took my flirtations with Louka to be real (probably as a result of my acting skills) and made me feel a little jealous in playing the part of falling for Bluntschli (my adversary in love for Raina), or the 'Chocolate Cream Soldier' as he was referred to in this play, rather too convincingly.

Whatever the dynamics, I certainly impressed the drama teacher, who was moved to comment that my performance was both convincing and imperious, and subsequently chose me for a part in Macbeth. My acting career was short lived thereafter, but I have to tell you more of that another time.

I don't know what would have come of our relationship had I stayed in Brunei, but I left for school in England, shortly afterwards and lost touch. I could never tell anyone about how I felt for her other than the few friends who had been sworn to secrecy.

In reality, I would have had to convert to Islam in order to have any chance of securing a long-term relationship with her. I ask myself if that was something that could realistically have been enacted, but at the time it was a love that was never consummated, so where it would have headed to will never be known. Besides, we were only very innocent thirteen-year-olds then.

I did think of her from time to time and wondered what would have happened if we could have continued our love throughout the teen years and been together in adulthood also. Would we have married young and become parents early? What sort of woman did she develop into? Did she preserve that incredible beauty she possessed? For now, those questions will remain unanswered.

Until we next speak or correspond again, my love as always.

David

Letter 14 – French Fascination & University Comradeships

September 2019

Dear Geoff,

I tell myself that it is pointless being in love with someone who does not feel the same way.

There is nothing worse than unrequited love, surely? Why is it, therefore, so difficult to rid myself of feelings for H? As indicated to you before on several occasions, I feel so connected to her, emotionally, intellectually and spiritually. In fact, so much so, that exercise of sheer will-power is proving grossly insufficient at the moment. Giving up smoking was easier, in hindsight. I have definitely been in love before, certainly infatuated many more times, and in lust probably with several million. But being truly in love with someone who does not similarly carry a torch for me, probably never.

I have written to you previously about my childhood loves and the innumerable cases when I crash heedlessly in love with one pretty girl or another. I thought it would be an appropriate time, now to speak about my other loves also, and offer some order of chronology so that you may charter my development in this area. You may decide, after learning of this, that my emotional maturity has not progressed much from me as an eight-year-old, when I first discovered that girls were far more interesting than butterflies or fish. I shall start with my fascination with a delightful French girl called Paulette, who was definitely my first love in adulthood.

Paulette was truly a dream come true. I had turned 20 and was well into my second year at university but had not met anyone so incredibly beautiful in all of that time, and certainly not one who had such a correspondingly beautiful soul. I was introduced to her by my sister Carole, who had a Saturday job in a store called Fiorucci.

When I met Paulette for the first time, I honestly thought that I had suddenly contracted some dreaded disease, as I had become so dumbstruck in her presence, unable to form words or perform actions other than open my mouth from time to time like a stranded goldfish gasping for air. I may have uttered an inane phrase or two in very poor French when my brain eventually began operating (sub-optimally), but this would have done little to impress her. It did, however, elicit a smile. The sort one would imagine kindly bestowed on a fond but intellectually disabled relative, but enough to give me an inkling of her charming personality.

Paulette epitomised generally what I found physically attractive in women. Do I fall for blondes? Yes! She was petite in stature, with wavy shoulder length hair and eyes of the brightest blue imaginable. Small but divinely shaped would probably best describe the most beautifully contoured figure I had ever laid eyes on. I would soon discover how even more sublime her figure was when we became lovers, but at the time of meeting it was still to be imagined. I sensed that there was more to her patently obvious vivacity.

I followed Carole out of the store, still goggle-eyed with visions of this wondrous beauty, reluctantly, but grateful that we seemed to have secured an arrangement of sorts to meet with Paulette again. I played no part in the negotiations but had been providentially included in the invitations for drinks with them.

Carole may have unintentionally come to my aid as wingman, but I was eternally grateful to her for this introduction. It was now up to me to string a few coherent sentences together to prove to Paulette on the next occasion, that I was actually capable of speech, and impressing her with a barrage of charm and wit.

We were to meet them at a pub in South Kensington.

I headed there with Carole, chatting animatedly, in the hope that I could keep up the patter, to avoid being dumbfounded again in the presence of Paulette. We waved cheerfully to the others who had arrived before us.

I scanned the faces excitedly to make sure Paulette was there, as it would otherwise have been a less fulfilling evening for me.

If it is at all possible, she looked even more beautiful.

I could feel my throat begin to constrict. I was in the presence of a goddess. I had to be content with sitting within sighting distance of this enchantress, to avoid disrupting those already in their pews. I made polite conversation with others, looking toward her from time to time to see her lovely face, and was gratified to be rewarded with a smile every time our eyes met. The conversation turned to music, and this was my cue to take the floor, which I did without too much persuasion.

This was my subject. I made sure that the drinks were sufficiently far away from my hands as I held forth, being prone to gesticulating wildly the more excitable my conversation. I was safe. No drinks were spilt in the midst of my oratory. Paulette looked at me spellbound.

By this time our eyes were locked together, and it would have mattered not had the others denied me an audience, as her attention was all I sought. I felt sure that she must have assumed me an idiot child or one with a speech impediment of sorts previously but was now fascinated to hear me express knowledge of what seemed her favourite subject also and delivered remarkably fluently too.

The night went well, and she was happy to take my arm for the short walk to the tube station. I held her hands, as I leant forward to kiss her cheeks. She insisted that I repeated the process but applying three kisses instead, as was the practice in France. I was more than happy to oblige. Her skin was of gentle softness. Her perfume had an exhilarating scent. We arranged to see each other again a few days later.

The day arrived. I brushed my teeth, taking care to ensure my breath was minty fresh, and trimmed my moustache too. Yes, the previously faint smattering of teen fluff was now a reasonably robust growth of facial hair forming a thick black line on my upper lip. With a hideous protrusion as my nose was, it would seem imprudent to underline it so strongly, but I felt that the moustache provided me with a degree of gravitas, and I remained unbending on this, despite suggestions from siblings that it looked positively hideous.

I assumed it was to be an evening comprising just Paulette and I at a chosen rendezvous, so I was rather taken aback, and a trifle disappointed to see her friend and flatmate there too. She was also called Paulette. She was not an intergalactic robot, but I shall refer to the second Paulette as P2, hereon in to avoid confusion with my beloved.

Paulette explained that her friend P2 had encountered some misfortune with a boyfriend and needed consolation and companionship. Much as I wanted to be alone with Paulette, I was happy to extend a little gallantry to provide the required succour to P2. We had our dinner of burgers and fries, (which along with pizzas formed a staple diet for us as students on an evening out) and did our best to cheer P2. Paulette's English was not, strangely enough, as good as P2's and she was happy for me to spend the time conversing more actively with P2. I sensed that Paulette liked me, as I could feel her play footsie under the table with me and smile broadly each time I looked across at her. I could swear her eyes sparkled.

She took my arm as before, when I walked them back to their flat. P2 went in ahead, whilst we remained on the doorstep. I held her hands again to enact our kisses, but this time she offered me her lips. The first kiss was a perfunctory coming together of lips, as it was rather unexpected. She looked directly at me inviting another. Her lips were soft and welcoming. They were sweeter and softer than I had imagined they would be. I enjoyed breathing in the scent of her perfumed skin, whilst the play of tongues continued, neither of us wanting the kiss to end.

When we finally came up for air, I was convinced that I had kissed an angel. It must be three times, I told her. She smiled and pulled me to her. Our lips locked as though they were meant to be glued together, and our bodies also folded into each other's in a correspondingly warm embrace. It was sheer ecstasy. If people thought me unhinged as I skipped down the road afterwards, I had not care. The word 'happy' may have been apt, but not even vaguely sufficient to express my feelings that evening. Not only had I secured the affections of the most beautiful woman in the world but had kissed her too. Three times!

I could not believe my luck, as it appeared that Paulette liked me rather a lot and we had the basis to develop a good and lasting relationship. We would meet at various times when we were both free. She loved waltzing around the shops with me, choosing clothes for herself and determining what best suited me. Although her English was limited, we would speak incessantly and for hours seeming to understand each other comprehensively. There were times when we held hands and words were never needed, as it seemed that our souls spoke for us instead.

We upheld similar principles and shared similar values when it came to family closeness, profound friendships, cultural wealth, and even a shared love of music, which allowed us to create a partnership beyond the obvious physical attraction. I had never been with anyone I found more engaging or alluring. I found her company intoxicating, and all I wanted to do was spend every waking moment with her.

One evening at dinner, where we held hands throughout, choosing to eat using our free hand, she told me that she had to return to France for some time. I was disappointed and tried my best to persuade her to stay, but she was insistent. The walk home was sombre, as I was dreading the parting. We kissed at the doorstep as usual, but this time she told me that she 'wanted' me. That could mean only one thing! I was not sure I believed my ears.

I loved the way she would greet me. Her *"bonjour Davide"*, never failed to make my heart melt. This *"I want you Davide…"* request in the same seductive tones, made my heart, not melt, but beat at a fearsome rate and leap around performing cartwheels in my chest instead. I think it was the sexiest invitation to bed ever uttered. To me, anyway!

I needed no further persuasion. She wound her arms and legs around me as I carried her inside. She warned me to be quiet as she shared a room with P2. We undressed each other hurriedly. She had me unclothed even before I had unhooked her bra, deftly I thought. I made a mental note to practice this art more thoroughly. Our kisses were long and passionate. Every inch of her skin was as smooth and silken to my exploratory touch and kiss.

We tried to be as quiet as possible, but the bed creaked violently. Amidst much shushing, I whispered that we should adjourn to the bathroom to continue. She refused to be defeated and suggested that we move the mattress onto the floor instead. We did, causing much giggling and more shushing. If P2 had heard us, she gave the impression of deep and comatosed sleep. We resumed our love-making on the now mattressed floor. The feeling of being with her and inside her was a feeling beyond euphoria or bliss.

I could not at that age profess to possessing too much prior experience, as my entire history up to that point usually entailed a lot of fumbling around with genitalia and sometimes anticlimactic sensation, but with her it was different and very special. Every nerve was sensitised to experience a heavenly pleasure. Every moment was to be savoured. Our bodies fit seamlessly together, and moved in harmony with every touch, caress and stroke, working to the rhythm of our heartbeat, paced to an eventual crescendo. To call it an orgasm would do it a great disservice. It was an exhilarating flow of breathless pleasure through mind and body. We held each other for a long time afterward, our kisses interminable.

She was gone for a while. She wrote to me telling me that she missed me and that she would be back. I told her that I would wait an eternity for her return, if required to. When she eventually returned, she explained that she had originally gone back to break up with her boyfriend there, as she had not expected to meet and fall in love with me.

Whilst she was there, many family matters had also required attending to. She told me that she found it difficult to communicate all of this in a letter or a telephone call conducted in English. It was entirely understandable, and I promised to learn French to facilitate our communication, under her tutorship. I was completely enraptured, and blissfully in love with her.

I wonder what fate may have held in store for me, and if my college years would have been as memorable had I not met Paulette. In my first year at college, I encountered several girls at parties, but none with whom I made an emotional or lasting connection. My friend Munir, or Sach as he was more affectionately known as then, seemed to trip quite happily from one delightful passionate conquest to another. He was a handsome fellow and appeared capable of merely smiling at a girl to cause her to fall willingly into his arms. He then met a stunningly attractive girl called Priti. They dated for a long while.

Sach and I formed a close friendship almost immediately after meeting at shared lectures in the Engineering Faculty. Although there were many people I was meeting for the first time, I was drawn closer to some instinctively. I had become accustomed to many close relationships at school but those were resulting from being thrown together into 'forced' circumstances and strong bonds created from many shared youthful experiences. The University environment was different.

There was nothing that required us to develop strong friendships, but I did with those I was drawn to, Sach and a few others especially. Having hit it off almost instantly and deciding that we could take our relationship to the next level, we ended up sharing a flat together with my sister Carole, in our second year of college.

He was exceedingly companionable, compliant and tidy. The only complaint that would have arisen was that he could not cook to save his life. Rice. That was the limit of his culinary skills, and the sum total of his experience in this regard. He offered to make Dahl once, claiming it was his mother's recipe. If only his poor mother had known that the recipe she toiled over and caused many to travel miles to visit and taste, would suffer merciless in her son's hands. It served as the tipping point for Carole and I, who subsequently took turns to cook, whilst Sach fastidiously did the clearing and washing up afterwards. *Sans* cooking, he was the almost perfect flatmate!

I was soon in my final year at university and had moved into student halls. The accommodation, called Goldsmith House, was wonderfully located in centre of the West End. The Halls could not have been more providentially sited, as far as impressing others was concerned, as it overlooked Oxford Street with a discrete entrance just off the main thoroughfare on North Audley Street.

Shingai had the best view from his window, as his room was diagonally opposite Selfridges, and these were the very windows we often leant out of hoping to attract the attention of the many pretty girls that walked past, particularly on sunny summer's day. We once played "Check Out the Groove" by Bobby Thurston at the loudest volume we could generate from the sound system in his room to enhance this prospect, with Shingai opting to place the speakers on the sill outside to garner maximum impact.

We did not enjoy much success from this endeavour, apart from the odd wave and smile, not necessarily from the prettiest, but it was great fun trying. Given the proximity, we found ourselves often haunting the floors of

Selfridges, where Shingai kindly introduced me to coconut cake, procured from the food halls at that great store. There was no turning back. There were many times when I was prepared to forego a proper lunch to indulge entirely on this delicacy, and this cake remains a great favourite to this day.

Shingai, or Shing as I chose to address him subsequently, I met through a common friend called Eddie. I was introduced to this tall somewhat lanky Zimbabwean with a broad engaging smile and infectious laugh, on the understanding that we shared a common interest in funky music. On meeting him, I realised that we shared much more than a taste in music, and we began constructing the basis of a firm friendship.

I don't know what it was that caused bonds to form with some and not others. I suppose that I had the benefit of developing an inherent ability from my parents and siblings which equipped me with a sense to filter out relationships based on meaningful friendships from those of superficial acquaintanceships. Whatever the reason, I knew that only some of the numerous people I encountered in my years at college, would become part of a group of lasting friendships.

My knowledge in the area of music was easily surpassed by his. He bought me an album at only the second time of meeting me. An incredibly generous gift, in light of what they cost relative to the student's weekly budget.

It was unlikely that the determiners of educational grants ever took into consideration the need for music in a student's life, and therefore only catered for some basic allowance for food and shelter. A few textbooks too, I suppose. There was no provision for music, treating girlfriends to dinner, clothes, art and other basic requirements, which required a supplemental source of income.

You can imagine my gratitude and appreciation, therefore for this heroic gesture. Our conversations naturally progressed to other important aspects in life, such as music, girls, food, and culture and what a great part they played in determining our access to happiness. We spent many a long afternoon at the coffee shop in the CCB building, where we met up regularly with several other friends also, from the spread of UCL's vast array of faculties.

As a result of our firm friendship, he is only a small handful of friends who address me as "Dave", for I usually made it abundantly clear my preference to be called "David". Or if you really wanted me to turn to putty, "Davide", as was Paulette's favoured call. Shing was very much the gentleman, and suitably the best man at my wedding many years later.

It was rather wonderful that we would spend our last year together, in a trio with Sach at Goldsmith's. We became indivisible, and participated in most things together, except sleep and bathe of course. Study was conducted separately also. This we did in shifts, given our varying body clocks. I did the night shift and awoke Shingai around four, who in turn woke Sach at six, by which time I would have hit the hay.

Dancing we did, until dawn, and this was where Shing was in his element, and occupied space in a league entirely of his own. Whilst we swayed and bopped energetically to the best of our ability, we were no match for his athletic agility on the dance floor. He was able to move his tall frame languidly and effortlessly to the beat of the music in a mesmerising manner, which would leave most wanting to just stand and watch in reverence.

Cooking was sadly shared only between Shing and I, as Sach stuck assiduously to his repertoire of one – rice, which by now could probably have sought worldwide acclaim for its amazing consistency. Shing produced a dish of rather delicious spicy chicken wings, which I felt could have rivalled Colonel Sanders' recipe had it been patented and replicated on mass.

Our rotation of diet, therefore comprised, spaghetti Bolognese, spicy wings, tuna fish rice, wings, Chinese stir fry, and wings again! Notwithstanding the limited menu, we had enormous fun just sharing time in the kitchen preparing and sharing a meal together. It might have been our upbringing, but we loved our food and believed that whatever was eaten had to be prepared with love, care and attention. The results spoke for themselves, and to be fair, even Sach's sole contribution of rice was prepared with his greatest ministration.

We had a developed an inexplicable kinship founded on a firm adherence to values, and subsequently cemented on with layers of shared experiences, interests, etc. We had the most wonderful time together at Goldsmith's, I shall remember it fondly particularly for the love, laughter and wonderfully deep friendships it forged within its walls.

I remember vividly the first time Paulette come to stay with me there. I was called to reception to meet her, but she had already started walking down the corridor to my room. It might have been entirely for my benefit, but she looked so eye-catchingly sensual in her walk. I embraced her warmly and picked her up and kicked the door open to *ma chambre* to carry her in over the threshold. She loved the romantic gesture. She treated me in turn to lovemaking I could have only previously dreamt of. She turned out to be the most energetic lover I had the joy to experience.

Her embraces defined passion, and her kisses heaven-sent joy. It makes me smile whenever I think of the times I held her in my arms and enjoyed the blissful taste of her lips, and the sensual feel of her silken skin against mine. These were sensations, I had thought existed only in mushy novels, but they turned out to be so very true and realisable with her.

I loved the way she spoke, laughed, walked, danced, touched and held me, the loving glint in her eyes, her kisses, her thoughts, her values, her smiles, the way she dressed and undressed, the way she fed me off her plate, her unassumed sensuality, her generosity, her everything. Most of all, the way she would say my name softly, especially when we made love. I may have possibly fallen in love with her several times over.

After a few months of blissful romance, she left for France, this time permanently and I was left completely and wretchedly heartbroken. We wrote to each other, and spoke every now and then on the phone, but did not rekindle our love until more than a year later, when I met her again in Paris.

I did actually write (or more precisely type on an old-fashioned typewriter) a story about my love for her, but it is now nowhere to be found. It is a pity as I felt that I had written it rather well and it certainly helped me better understand what it was that caused me to fall so deeply in love with her. I am now applying the same logic of putting pen to paper to determine the basis of my feelings for H.

Paulette was blonde and blue-eyed, unlike H, but they appear to share many common traits, beyond both being French - in their outstanding beauty, stature, poise, tinkling laugh, fashion sense, family and other values, and even their gestures. The only pity is that H does not reciprocate my feelings as Paulette did.

I hope that my skipping back and forth over my college years has not caused confusion. However, for clarity, let me begin with my first experience at college. University life was so different to that of school. I was responsible for managing my own time and method of learning, which was a task in itself. No regular mealtimes existed either. I wanted so badly to excel, so I did work hard in my first year there, wishing to prove to myself that I could do better after achieving dismal results in my 'A' level exams. I had done rather well in the mock exams at school but had obviously assumed that being clever would see me through the actual exams. I should have applied myself to acquiring a more thorough grasp of the subjects and also practicing past papers. I did neither, and only just scraped through with the required grades to satisfy the intake requirements at UCL.

I did very well in my first-year coursework and exams, and was well placed to attain a First Class Degree, according to my tutor. If I could, I would blame being in love for my failure to keep up my grades in the second year. But it really was unforgivable in hindsight, I was more determined to party rather than study and managed to only just get by. Propitiously, I managed to keep a relationship going well, and still draw sufficiently pleasing grades to qualify for a good Upper Second-Class Honours degree.

It is interesting that both my daughters have chosen to attend my alma mater. It may have been partly due to my waxing considerably lyrically about my wonderful carefree time there. We did work hard, but also played hard, as was the highly recommended advice provided to Jack.

The only pity has been that their days have not been carefree as mine were, primarily because I have struggled to meet their tuition fee payments. In making the comparison between their university experiences and mine, it irks me considerably that, despite our inalienable rights as British citizens, my daughters were categorised as foreign students for the purposes of their tertiary education and were required to pay an exorbitantly high fee as a result. Does that even make sense? That one is granted citizenship with the full protection afforded by Her Majesty's government, and yet regarded as a foreigner when undertaking University study on home soil.

One hears of draconian and punitive financial measures being applied to citizens of countries, but one tends to associate that with psychopathic behaviours of authoritarian regimes, and surely not the rationally derived and debated regulations of elected democratic governments of the industrialised nations. Does one lay blame for such short-sighted policy on the doorsteps of government departments or the universities themselves? My poor children obviously suffered. Anyway, this is a matter for much active cogitation and future discussion. For now, let me continue the recount of my days at college.

I was glad to have chosen a London college, as I enjoyed the vast cosmopolitan mix of students from every far-flung corner of the earth. It was quite a change from boarding school which was made up primarily of English pupils.

I had no problem integrating at school, and made some amazingly good friends there, but it was even nicer to be able to meet people from so many other countries, all of whom had an interesting story of heritage to weave into the rich pattern of friendships we managed to create.

It was quite interesting to see the student body in my faculty and year break into three distinct clusters – one of Englishmen, one of the Chinese fraternity and one of the rest of the world! Our group was by far the largest and easily the most interesting to be with. It was not that the other groups were more studious than we were, it is just that we enjoyed working together in partnerships. We laughed as much as we buried our heads earnestly together into books to understand complex equations. I think that we were cultural richer for our integration.

As a family we appeared to have assembled a very cosmopolitan group of friends anyway. Perhaps as a result of most of us attending London University. Rachel had finished at UCL by this time, whilst Carole was in the midst of her course at Chelsea College and I had just started, also at UCL. We had assembled a wonderful international mix of friends, besides the many English, we had Sri Lankans, Goans, Poles, Italians, French, Chinese, Malaysian, Iranian, Zimbabwean, Armenian, Mauritian, West African, Jamaican, Indian, Pakistani, Kuwaiti and others.

When I first arrived, Rachel, Carole and John were sharing a house in Hendon with friends. With the commencement of their university years that household arrangement unbundled for logistical reasons, and I found myself staying with Rachel and Carole separately at various times in various locations. We moved an awful lot. I had become accustomed to ensuring that my belongings did not exceed a comfortable fit into a single suitcase. But in my first year at college, Rachel, Carole and I serendipitously found a delightful flat in Chelsea to share.

The landlord of this flat in Tedworth Square was a retired army officer and wonderful gentleman, (they just do not make them like this anymore), who believed that a word was as good as a bond. He trusted us as completely as we did him. He took an immediate liking to all of us and could barely offer or do enough to make our stay there exceedingly welcome.

The flat was huge and arranged on several levels. The girls shared a large bedroom at the very top. I was on the level just below and a further flight down led to an enormous sitting room and a separate kitchen with a generously proportioned dining area. The large family bathroom, which the girls occupied seemingly forever, was sited at the very last level.

Our eclectic group of friends were frequent visitors to our flat, where we ended up hosting several parties, many of which were totally impromptu. We danced, we drank (to limited extent), and listened to music without a break. Friends would turn up with piles of records and our house became a well-regarded party destination.

I think that some people assumed we were exceeding rich, living in a fabulous flat and exhibiting good taste.

This impression seems to have followed us throughout our lives. I am still not sure why. Can't one exercise good taste without having oodles of cash? We were all well-educated, well-travelled, well-dressed, well-read and well-spoken, but other than Rachel, we were all relatively poor, in a monetary sense, anyway.

This image of apparent largesse, amongst our immediate neighbours, was exacerbated further by some friends of friends turning up to our parties in Ferraris and Lamborghinis. One such regular attendee was a chap called Bolaji. He was exceedingly tall – standing well over six feet in his socks and had to duck his head under our doorway for entry. He became a regular haunt at our parties and once turned up to tell us that he had been approached to play a part in a movie. We refused to believe that it was anything serious, suggesting to him that it was probably a prank, or a seedy lure into the sex industry, and teased him endlessly. Little did we know until he actually landed the part as the creature in the film Alien!

Sometimes the 'after party' continued with games of bridge until well into the following morning. We would get peckish most of the time and I introduced my friends to the pleasures of peanut butter and jam on toast. A lot of thought went into the preparation – from the firmness of the toast to the correct layering of the ingredients. First a gentle layer of butter, followed by a more generous application of peanut butter and then relatively frugal spread of jam. They loved the way I prepared this, and soon became wholehearted converts to this simple but delicious recipe. This peanut butter speciality, thereafter, became our staple diet during those long nights. I must qualify this culinary preparation a little to add that it was best enjoyed if the peanut butter were the 'crunchy' rather than the 'smooth' variety.

Although primarily students on limited budgets, we ate well. I remember being at the receiving end of several wonderful meals as both my sisters had become very accomplished cooks. Whether culinary skills were passed from mother to daughter via DNA or other means, I could not be sure. What I was grateful for was their ability to cook with whatever was available and produce aromatic meals that we shared at the table with much enjoyment.

Food always seemed to taste much better when prepared collectively and shared at the dining table. I was the chief bottle washer. I did not mind in the least, as being treated to one scrumptious meal after another was ample reward. Dinner was the mainstay of meals, as I rarely had more than coffee with a bowl of cereal for breakfast and would often forego lunch.

I was still carrying the lean hungry look from my school days, and this became a good frame from which to build a new wardrobe. My fashion consciousness had begun in earnest.

I was fashion-conscious before, if you could call the desire to wear enormously flared trousers, loudly patterned and wide-lapelled shirts and the tallest platform shoes that I could barely walk in, being fashionable. Straight-leg trousers were now in vogue, as were flat shoes and neutrally coloured shirts with modest collars. I gleefully embraced the new fashion, and gladly exchanged my entire wardrobe for the new look. My feet of course welcomed the arrival of shoes that provided me with closer contact to *terra firma*. I even regained some poise and balance in my walk.

I may have mentioned to you at some point my evolving taste in music with each passing year, partly through sibling influence and the parties I attended with them. If I have failed to adequately inform you of these wonderful phases, remind me to do so at some point. In the meantime, I shall limit myself to the phase that was relevant to my life at university.

I was already progressing out of a love for rock (but retaining love for some of the classics), and into funk and soul music. This was enhanced further by friends I met when staying with Carole in a bedsit in Canfield Gardens, just prior to starting at university.

I was happy to be led astray by the more audacious and enterprising in that group and ventured with them into nightclubs called the Purple Pussycat & Cage D'Or, where my love for the music in those darkened and loud-volumed spaces became firmly established. Thanks to these wonderful people at Canfield, I had grown somewhat keen on smoking marijuana too.

This had to be accompanied, according to Paul who swore by its credentials, with the partaking of a Hungarian wine called 'Bulls Blood'. We would sit on the floor, as there were never chairs, drinking this 'good value plonk guaranteed to put hairs on your chest', whilst regaling each other of various stories, which always resulted in much joviality and laughter, and sometimes followed by carefree dancing at the clubs later.

I wonder why politicians deny smoking marijuana in their youth. It really is an integral part of growing up and should be included as a vital extra-curricular activity or recommended holiday homework, for university students at any rate – with due caution, of course. Suggesting that they may have smoked a joint without inhaling would be akin to suggesting that they had sex without physical contact. Was there not an issue over how much 'contact' constituted the very definition of sex in Clinton's rather impoverished defence?

Smoking without inhaling is therefore to be recommended only when smoking cigars, unless one wished to choke unnecessarily, but not inhaling when smoking dope is, as I suggested earlier, choosing to only think about sex when presented the opportunity to have it! To deliberately opt to forfeit the pleasure in this instance is beyond bizarre, but politicians are a mystifying and incomprehensible breed at the best of times anyway, in my opinion. Having met Paulette, I knew that it was not just thinking about her but being with her and enjoying every inch of her divine being to the fullest was what provided ultimate and heavenly joy. In fact, the only thing that could possibly cause coital interruption when with her, was a bomb being set off in the throes of orgasm. And would you believe that this almost happened?

Paulette and I were once awoken by a bomb blast. We were not in the midst of sex, thankfully, but sound asleep when a bomb exploded a few blocks from our student hall on Oxford Street. We were actually awoken by some frenetic activity in the corridor. No, there were no screams of panic to be heard, but just much semi-animated conversation unusual for that time of day.

University students never panic, unless they run short of revision time. There is not much that would persuade us to wake up before the appointed hour. Not even the smell of a full English breakfast, could lure us from coveted sleep. Students valued their time in bed. Every subsequent activity upon arising (preferably at mid-morning) was timed to perfection, from dressing, inhaling breakfast and legging it down to the tube station, to the arrival at the lecture room just in time to take a seat (preferably next to a friend), before the lecturer opened his notes and uttered his opening line.

So, we awoke rather bleary-eyed to make our enquiry on the reason for all the kerfuffle in the corridor. Paulette had slipped into my shirt and came to join me at the door. Hair tousled and not a hint of make-up, she still managed to look so marvellously sexy, and I could not help but be rather proud of being selected as the *cestui que trust* or grateful beneficiary of her affections.

We gathered what news we could and returned to bed. Fortunately, no one was killed in that incident. But, had anything happened to us that evening, I would have been grateful to have been happily ensconced in Paulette's warm and loving embrace.

Was I on the subject of music? How on earth did I digress so badly? So, to continue, my musical fate was now sealed with the advent of disco music, thanks in part to the mania caused by "Saturday Night Fever". Not only did I venture to parties and clubs but began to collect records and build an enviable collection of dance music. I went so far in my enthusiasm and love for this, as to create the Funk Society at college.

We never really grew our membership beyond my immediate group of friends, but I never lost faith. As self-elected President of the Club, I made it my task to enlist as many members as I could. We had a great logo too. Our first disco to launch the Club was productively and sufficiently well attended, however we failed to capitalise effectively on this initial interest. I should have perhaps, as a form of legacy asked my daughters to create a revival in this interest during their time at UCL.

It was a sad day for me when we finished our final exams, and had for all intents and purposes, graduated. I loved my time at university. Those were easily the best years of my life.

I probably did not think so at the time as I was desperately keen to emulate those with established careers and acquire all the attributes of a seemingly comfortable life. I wish sometimes that I could be taken back in time to those magical carefree years.

We all bade our tearful farewells to Goldsmith House too. So many memories of friendships, romance, study, laughter and music were created there. It was nice to know that some friendships proved more resilient and enduring, and still exist to this day.

As is mine with yours, despite the wear and tear of many years that have passed since we first met.

I shall leave you now to reflect on the moment of our first meeting.

Love,

David

Letter 15 – French Re-Connection

September 2019

Dear Geoff,

I was very glad that you were interested to learn more of Paulette, as there was indeed more to tell as far as she was concerned. The story had not ended with one heartbreak. There was more to come. She was after all my first love and I could not leave you uncertain of either of our futures together, particularly if there was further disclosure to be made on our relationship.

I met Paulette again in Paris a year or so after she returned to Bordeaux. I was visiting my sister Rachel, who had a wonderful job at the OECD, and an equally wonderful apartment in the *sixteenth arrondissment*. I was working in Nigeria at the time and involved in a relationship with a lovely girl called Madeleine. If I have not yet mentioned her to you, I must. She too was one of my great loves, and of whom I hold very fond memories.

I elected to fetch Paulette from the station, and I could feel my heart leap with great joy when I saw her alight from the train. She possibly looked even more beautiful than I had remembered. It felt wonderful to hold her in an affectionate embrace again. The flowers got crushed in our enthusiastic greeting, but it only caused laughter and further embrace.

Any prior apprehension I may have harboured evaporated in that instant. Our animated conversation continued on our journey home. Rachel and Paulette seemed to get on like a house on fire, especially as they jabbered away in French offering me only an occasional translation if they felt me worthy of inclusion. Even little Anthony, who was about three at the time, but spoke better French than I did, seemed to take to her instantly. It is generally a good sign when a girlfriend manages to win the hearts of family members too, so I was happy to watch the snug and agreeable conversation develop amongst them.

At Rachel's suggestion we went to a Korean restaurant specialising in their barbeque form of meal. The food was delicious. Paulette's English had not improved noticeably since we parted previously, and neither had my French, but we managed to understand each other, as well as we had done before. Probably better in some respects, as we had both gained a little maturity also. She told me that she was still living with her mother and helping her when she could at the hair salon. She told me that her mother often enquired about me. I was pleased, but probably not too surprised, as I was the only one who called often asking for Paulette in a form of patois French that only I could comprehend.

I am sure that it was only as a result of Paulette having told her that I was an Engineering student, that I managed to garner her respect, as she would otherwise have taken me for a halfwit with a speech impediment. I told Paulette that I had bizarrely and unexpectedly ended up in Nigeria after college and described my life there in some gruesome detail. As far as our love lives were concerned, she appeared to have returned to her boyfriend of old, and I told her that I had met Madeleine.

We went onto a jazz club later. The maître d' remembered me from previous visits and guided us to one of the better tables. This gesture seemed to have impressed Paulette, especially after an enjoyable meal together earlier, where I appeared to have chosen wisely, and selected a suitable accompanying wine also. At one point in the evening, I leant over to speak into her ear over the sound of the music. She leant forward too, but offered her lips instead, and kissed me ardently. Can you imagine how differently history would have unfolded had the Romans offered similarly to Anthony's request, in the time of Cleopatra?

I looked at her. It was not accidental. Her ever-alluring smile appeared in her eyes too. There was definitely a flow of magical current as our lips had touched. It awoke an unspoken and unquenchable desire within us. More kisses followed. It was difficult from that point onward to appreciate anything outside of the enchanted bubble we had created around us. The attentive maître d' responded to my call for the bill with great alacrity, either noting our display of passion, or desiring our table for others who were there to appreciate the music and not just each other.

We hailed a cab urging him to speed us home. Little was said, as we sat together hands wrapped in each other's, wanting desperately to be in a tight and loving embrace, and let our bodies do the talking. Our first lovemaking was frantic, and rightfully so, as we were almost destined to be together and our previous parting was painful. We needed it to be heartfelt but urgent. Our subsequent lovemaking was more gentle and subdued, but equally passionate.

It was difficult saying goodbye. Much as I knew that I had a relationship with Madeleine to return to, I could not help but feel my heart being wrenched asunder. She cried, and I did too. I realise it sounds rather corny and best left to tear-wrenching scenes in movies, but I ran along the platform until she disappeared from view. I returned to the flat feeling empty. Rachel did her best to offer consolation, as we made our way through a bottle of wine or two. I could smell Paulette's Chanel perfume, on the shirt that she had borrowed to sleep in, and I buried my face in it for the pitiful sleep I experienced that night. I clung onto the shirt for dear life and vowed I would never wash it. I wanted something tangible to remember her by, always.

As I had promised to do, I began implementing my desire to improve my spoken French. On my return to Nigeria, I employed a houseboy (I would have preferred the term 'butler', but that was the preferred address), from Chad who spoke French and no English whatsoever. I had also purchased a Linguaphone course to practice my French.

I was doing well, working on the course's verbal exercises diligently most evenings, and in mutilated conversation with my newly engaged Chadian accomplice in the mornings. My mastery of the language did improve considerably, except that, according to the fluent speakers, I now spoke with a strange west African induced accent. My French may have improved, but I never saw Paulette again.

I am sometimes amazed at the unclouded clarity and wisdom imparted by the youngest of minds. An example of this was when I recounted this tale to another friend recently, her daughter of sixteen, Sofia, who learnt of it, offered me a very insightful and appropriate phrase from the 16th century French writer Madeleine de Scudéry, which she felt best captured my heartfelt loss of Paulette: *"L'amour fait les plus grandes douceurs et les plus sensibles infortunes de la vie."*, which I understand translates to *"Love creates life's sweetest pleasures and its most sensitive misfortunes."* I could not have agreed more.

I had toyed with the idea of dropping in to see Paulette in Bordeaux when I planned a trip to France with friends from college, several years later. Seven years to be precise. My friends and I actually started with the intention of visiting the Loire Valley and nothing more. We congregated at Robin's house and set off with great enthusiasm and fanfare in Nadeem's company car, which at the time seemed judiciously selected for this trip - a Citroen.

Nadeem was the very first person I met at university. We were the first to arrive dutifully at the reception area of the Engineering faculty building seeking our introduction and orientation into the Civil Engineering programme. He was genuinely warm and effusive in his greeting, and I soon realised that he had a great sense of humour too. I loved people who could make me laugh, so it was very difficult not to be drawn to such a fellow. It may have been because we spent a lot of time laughing together, but we appeared to entice others to us also, and we eventually became a large group of internationally minded students.

As I think I may have already mentioned to you in an earlier letter, we were a fun group, but with a reasonably good focus on our studies too. Nadeem's parents were originally from Pakistan, and unlike my parents who always seemed a little rootless, had settled in London. His educational background could not have been more different to mine – his was a cosmopolitan but challenging educational environment, whilst mine was a sheltered and primarily educationally focussed one. But despite this, and the fact that he was also considerably brighter than me, we developed a friendship based on a robust underlying kinship. I will always think of the first meeting rather fondly, as we have managed to keep up the

friendship over the years, despite the very different pathways in life we have chosen to follow since graduation.

I met Robin, or Rubik as he preferred to be known
through another close friend, Basit only in the following
year. Robin was the only Armenian, I ever met, and probably is still the only one I know personally, as they appear
to be thin on the ground, in my circles at any rate. Robert
Kardashian, whose family appear to be vogue (I am not
entirely sure why, personally), was also Armenian I understand, but I never met him.

Robin was one of those who appeared to be quite well
networked to the lab technicians and those in the senior
years, and was therefore a great 'go-to' person when it
came to obtaining notes, concrete test results, etc. I remember he was a very keen volleyball player, and although I often threatened to join in on one of his games, I
never made it all the time I was at university with him. I
was, without doubt, very busy consuming endless cups of
coffee at one of the University cafés, eating coconut cake,
playing bridge or partying. And the course work would
have kept me occupied too.

We probably became friends as a result of playing several games of bridge together from dusk to dawn. Besides
becoming friends, I used to regard him also as a walking
encyclopaedia of sorts, for he seemed to possess a profound knowledge of a variety of things. We did not have
access to the Internet in those days, so he became my
equivalent of Google. He may have acquired this vast
spread knowledge by breaking into libraries in the dead
of night, but I never asked.

For some equally unknown reason, Robin also appeared to be the only one who truly understood how to
programme computers using Fortran. If I had only known

214

then how technology would impact upon all of our lives, I may have paid more attention at this class.

We arrived in Blois. We roamed the town, which was beautifully bathed in the summer sunshine. The trees were green. The flowers everywhere of vivid colour. The birds chirped. The bees buzzed. It was beautifully picturesque and felt almost like stepping into a Monet or Lorrain landscape masterpiece. We visited the Château Royal de Blois, drinking in the marvel of architecture, the ornate splendour of the interiors and the meticulously maintained grounds. We were so enraptured, by the idyllic setting, that we decided to tour the entirety of France.

We obtained a map of France from the friendly hotel receptionist and set about planning our tour – a journey to cover the whole country in the remaining six days. The words 'crazy' or 'impossible' did not exist in our vocabulary at that time. It was a challenge we took on with unfettered relish. For the purpose of equitable distribution of responsibilities, we were to take turns driving, with the person riding a shotgun acting as a navigator in the absence of a GPS, which sadly only existed as a germ of an idea at that time.

In order to make the most of the scenery, we agreed unanimously to journey to each of our next stops after dusk, so that we had time during the day to admire the beauty of our chosen spot. Our next stop, after Blois was via Orleans, Auxerre, and onward to Geneva via Beaune. To while away the time and avoid monotony, we played a game of spotting petrol stations. The idea being that whoever saw it first would claim the point. But, as with bridge or anything we played together, this game became progressively more competitive. Did it matter for example, if the petrol station was closed, or that it was not in the direction of travel? All very valid debate, and amid all the shouted contest, the driver was eventually called on to be the final arbiter.

We stopped on the French side of Geneva before crossing the border into Switzerland to enjoy the city in its entirety. If Blois had been captivating, Geneva was the next to steal our hearts. Although strictly not conforming to our tour of France, we believed this minor deviation from our itinerary was forgivable. We forsook lunch to tour the city leisurely, pounding its cobbled streets to admire a city that seemed to effortlessly blend modern architecture with buildings from many centuries past including the stunning St. Pierre's Cathedral. Although we were all Engineering students, we were appreciative of the marvels of various architectural designs, both contemporary and historic.

We captured ourselves in photographs whilst marvelling at the engineering feat of the Jet d'eau and stopped also to admire an amazing Henry Moore sculpture at the Musée d'art et d'histoire. So enamoured were we by this sculpture, that the photograph we had taken of the three of us draped around it now occupies pride of place on the profile of our WhatsApp group.

Our meanderings eventually brought us to a quaint square in the midst of Geneva's old town where we enjoyed a much-needed break at one of the many charming cafés in a square, overlooked by numerous windows adorned with wooden shutters on equally charming period buildings. Feeling reinvigorated by the splendid coffee and pastry, we headed toward the next destination - the delightful town of Nice.

To quote Nadeem verbatim, "on the way south, through Grenoble, we took the mountain route, 'Route Napoleon"!! The narrowest most tortuous road ever to go from Geneva to the south (of France)." It very much

216

proved to be the case, as I was the driver on that particular leg of the journey, and recall with frightening clarity the numerous hairpin bends, and around one such bend nearly getting us all killed whilst attempting to overtake a slow-moving truck. Mercifully we arrived in Nice, mind and body intact, save for that fleeting but traumatic part of the drive. We treated ourselves to a MacDonald's meal before retiring to bed, nerves adequately recuperated, but bodies completely fatigued.

We enjoyed a good leisurely breakfast the next morning, seated outside one of the many sidewalk cafés that lined the main thoroughfares of Nice. We should really have treated ourselves to better food in our tour, but time was never on our side. We were happy to be more concerned with, and satiated by, drinking in the beauty of what we beheld. As we raced from one city to the next, we usually arrived at the next hotel, with only time for a shower before bed. We usually swallowed with great haste, the proffered breakfast along with copious amounts of coffee, and after bagging an extra croissant or two, sauntered out to delight in the surroundings. Lunch or dinner for that matter, never appeared to be a necessity.

Booking the hotel in advance was no easy task, as I had to explain each time that we were three grown men, at least in the physical sense (the emotional maturity was yet to be determined), happy to share a room but with a preference for separate beds.

I had to ensure they understood that we were not a family travelling with a child, as I was concerned that we would find a double bed and cot on our arrival, particularly as I would not have put it past Robin and Nadeem to assume maturity over me, or insist on playing hig-hag-hog, which I always invariably lost. All this careful planning was left to me to arrange with my token French,

217

generously interspersed with heaps of English words, alongside many *"s'il vous plait's"* and *"merci beaucoup's"*, which mercifully was well understood as we were welcomed with warmth at every stop.

Having made it to the southern coast relatively unjaded, we felt duty bound to take in the sights of Monaco also. We could understand the reason for all the international hype – it was delightful. And despite choosing not to sup at the myriad of restaurants boasting uninterrupted coastal views nor whittle away our limited budget at the casinos, we gained an appreciation of the attraction to the city-state. We ambled around soaking in the vibrant and celebrity enriched ambience.

A pit stop at Cannes was also deemed a must. We strolled along the beach front with our ice-creams absorbed in the charm of the sea, sparkling with glitters of reflected sunshine. The waves gently caressed the shoreline, which bristled with a myriad of bathers of varying shapes and sizes. Most lay idly basking in the warmth of a beautiful day, but it was difficult to avoid admiring the numerous delectably winsome women who chose to parade around instead, mostly topless. We did our best to keep our eyes rooted to the ice-cream or the distant horizon, when not affixed to the camera to avoid staring. We drove on to St. Tropez, very slowly, windows wound down to venerate the unfolding prepossessing scenery, and breathe in the gloriously babelicious air.

If we thought that Monaco, exuded an air of ostentation and abundance of affluence, St. Tropez appeared to be even more heavily scented in wealth and glamour. Men and women beautifully clad in casual designer wear and subtle but obviously expensive jewellery existed in throngs. We strolled through the narrow streets lined with an array of wonderful shops onto the harbour, where it proved difficult not to admire the beauty of the many yachts and of people who generally occupied them.

Unfortunately, we had not parked in a very clever spot, and found the car clamped on our return. The police were not interested in my little French but were keen to interrogate Nadeem further as vehicle owner. It was rather unfair to leave him there alone, but Robin and I were drawn to a small crowd of people playing boules in a nearby square. We joined in, much to their amusement. I appeared to have some affinity for this game and have loved to play it ever since. By the time we freed the car, the sun had almost signalled its final departure for the day. Nadeem and I felt strongly that we could not possibly leave the southern coast of France without having swum in the sea. Despite many calls, Robin refused to join us in the water, so we got him to be our photographer instead.

This was a truly amazing trip. Bearing in mind, the manner in which we were bound in perpetual company – locked together in a car or sharing a bedroom in the evening and all the meal stops in between, we completed the journey without any major mishap. Even close families may have argued, but we did not, we merely had a competitive debate. I think we only managed this because of all the laughter along the way, stemming from a shared sense of humour and the strong friendship created from our time together at university, which has proven to be enduring.

There was a limit to how much a photograph could capture, and we hoped that our experiences would endure in our hearts and minds instead. It may sound a rather barmy undertaking by some, but even with the benefit of hindsight I would do exactly the same, and not change a single aspect of this journey.

As we drove through France the thought of visiting Paulette, became a more fervent wish. But we had run out of time, and instead of heading west, we had to take the shortest route north, stopping only in Lyon (how coincidental to my future aspiration), and Paris (the city of my dreams) on the way home. A quick stop at Dijon was thankfully and unanimously agreed, as I could not have left this part of the world without arming myself with one of my favourite mustards from the very town that carried its name.

It was a pity that we did not have much time in Paris, as I would love to have shown my friends the view of the city from a resident's perspective, as I had experienced with my sister, Rachel. But it was not the right time of year to enjoy Paris at its best, given that most Parisians would have been vacationing on the south coast, where we had just been, and the city would now just be bursting with tourists. Robin appeared to have had an interesting exchange with some ladies in the lift at the hotel we were staying at, or so he claimed, as Nadeem and I never really got to trace and establish their actual existence. As to who these supposedly delightful women were, will remain a mystery. I guess what happens in Paris, will stay in Paris. At least for now.

I sometimes wonder what would have happened if I had followed my heart and pursued Paulette to Bordeaux and proposed marriage. Should I look her up now, or are old flames best left to burn away quietly in the corner of one's heart? I felt that even after a few years of being apart, the magic would somehow reappear, as it did when we met again in Paris.

There are some kisses which remain forever fixed in my mind, and those with Paulette I can recall vividly. For when we kissed, it was as though all the previous years and other relationships bore no significance or intervention in our profound feelings for each other. She taught me how to love unconditionally, and to be loved similarly in return. Does such love ever die?

We can but ponder. I realise that I have taken much of your time already, and it may be best to end here, lest I end up re-creating another epic letter as I had penned to you previously.

Much love,

David

Letter 16 – Danish Delight & a Taste of Africa

October 2019

Dear Geoff,

Have you sometimes looked back on a relationship from your youth and considered what could have happened if you had acted differently?

I wonder at times, what could have occurred in my life had I allowed my love for Madeleine to follow its natural course rather than cut it painfully short, as I had rather foolishly done.

Moving to Nigeria was quite a major decision, but one I felt I had to take. I put together my worldly possessions for shipment to me there. It really did not amount to much.

Having just graduated, and not really accumulated much in the course of my career at University, a survey of these worldly goods reflected; a wardrobe of clothes, which could easily fit into no more than a couple of small suitcases; a table lamp given to me by a friend called Vicky; a swivel chair I had been offered in my time at the Conservative Party Headquarters, when they were doing a clear out; a couple of posters of Debbie Harry and Marilyn Monroe, both of whom I worshipped; a stereo system; and three boxes of LPs.

I was so attached to the chair and spent many a happy hour spinning around in it or zipping back and forth on it within the confines of my tiny closet of a room in Goldsmith House and was sad to leave it behind. The lamp was to be held in my sister's custody until my return, so it was really my music and clothes that called for shipping.

Why Nigeria, I hear you ask, and quite rightly so. It would not strike one as being a destination of first choice for anyone in their right mind. It was due to an understanding of my wish to travel the world in pursuit of my career that I had conveyed in my interview for a job as a Graduate Trainee in a firm consulting Engineers in Surrey. One of the senior Partners felt that I was just the person to fill a vacancy that had arisen in their offices in the town of Jos.

I should have perhaps enquired into the whereabouts or health of the previous incumbent. Had his life been blighted by the Tsetse fly, or had he been caught in the crossfire of yet another coup, or just decided that he had finally arrived at wit's end and headed for an exit as rapidly as possible? I was never told.

But, after spending three years there, I could well understand that my predecessor had felt a better calling existed elsewhere. If it had not been for some wonderful people I met there, including the lovely Madeleine, I would have found life there, past a certain point, unbearable too.

Before I tell you about how and when I met Madeleine, I must first tell you about my experience on arrival at this land that time seems to have forgotten. My first arrival in Nigeria was definitely a life exposure worth relating. Actually, on reflection even before one arrives, one gets a flavour of what lays in store. We (as in some family members and I) had arrived at the departing airport and stood in line to check in as expected. However, there seemed little respect for an orderly system of queue and fellow travellers felt inclined to head toward the check-in counter at will.

My sister would not stand for it and firmly re-established our position as next to be attended to, especially as my mother, despite being wheelchair bound was keen to bid me farewell at the airport too. The gentleman at the counter was engaged in a heated debate with the air attendant on what exactly constituted hand luggage. He was insistent that a fridge, still in its packaging was what he hoped to carry into the seating area of the aircraft, despite its size. To our great amusement, he picked it up at one stage to demonstrate his ability to lift it without hydraulic assistance. The matter was finally resolved only when he was escorted to one side and told politely but firmly by a group of determined looking air personnel that even if he had purchased an additional seat, he would not be allowed his fridge in the cabin with him. We laughed, thinking this a once off occurrence, little knowing that it was merely a taster of what I would experience in my air travel within, and back and forth from the country.

On arrival, I was greeted with the same melee at the immigration counter, where signs urging people not to spit on the walls were displayed prominently. Why anyone would choose to spit on the wall, baffled me. Thankfully, I encountered no major salivary problems other than being asked why my passport was lacking a page. It was soon obvious to him that I truly had no understanding of what he meant, and he stamped my passport in a show of disgust and motioned for me to move on.

On enquiry to friends later, I discovered that this was the means by which they sought a bribe. A single note, preferably of more than a dollar's worth was to be inserted as the 'missing page' and handed back for consideration and approval.

I had less success with the customs officials who offered to release my suitcases without inspection if I had a gift for them. I indicated that I had none, and promptly had most of the contents upended in their frustration. What a welcome to Africa, I thought, unaware of what further surreal encounters lay ahead.

A driver had been sent to meet me. We were driving from the international airport in Kano, where I had landed and now headed to Jos, where I was to be based. The noise and traffic were not substantially different to those I had experienced in India, and in some cases less chaotic. I was happy not to be navigating through the crowded streets on my own and luxuriated in the comfort of being chauffeured instead.

It was during our journey out of the city that I realised that a tarmac surface was not to be taken for granted. Whilst there were patches within the city where some road edging would have been desirable, I never expected large sections of road where tarred surface did not appear in any shape or form once we were on the 'highway'.

Although this was disconcerting enough, it was the dead body lying in the middle of the road that we had to skilfully avoid without running over that caused considerable queasiness.

I was not sure I could be of assistance, as I found it difficult to deal with corpses, and once even resigned my post as a night guard at a hospital when I was asked to help move a cadaver to the morgue in the absence of the night porter.

But I felt we should do something. If the body still had some life in it, we could at the least have my driver apply CPR. The decent thing I felt was that we should stop and at the minimum move the body to the side of the road. My driver told me that the worst thing we could do was

226

stop, as it would be assumed that we had caused the loss of life and be held accountable in vigilante justice. In other words, they would have placed a tyre over us and proceeded to set us both alight. 'Necklacing', I understand is the term. I would have been deemed guilty even though I had been merely a passenger, a young and innocent one at that.

On arrival in Jos I asked my boss, Alastair about this violent act of purported 'justice', and was told that the driver had done the right thing by not stopping. In fact, he cautioned me to drive immediately away from any scene of an accident should it ever happen again and report it to a senior police officer after the event. It did actually happen to me during my time there, and I must admit to being so very frightened, and was the first time I truly understood the meaning of the term 'legs trembling with fear'. I am happy to say that on that occasion, the erring cyclist suffered injury only to his pride.

I met the delightful Madeleine, after a few months of settling in, which I considered myself as having accomplished rather well, given a dire lack of friends or family to act as a support structure. In pursuit of entertainment, I had joined the Social Club, one of the many clubs, expatriates were entitled to as an employment perk. Given how bleak the general environment often was, these memberships were a considerable blessing. I had taken to playing bridge and snooker as often as I could. My competence at bridge was more laudable that the poor attempts to strike the white ball with some degree of accuracy on the snooker table. The other aspect the club boasted and hosted was Ceilidh dancing.

I was at the bar with a friend hoping to be advised of a free slot for snooker, when I caught sight of this absolutely heavenly looking girl. There was a definite shortage of available girls of my age. I was considerably younger than most of the expatriates there, and either played bridge with a trio of elderly persons or snooker with some of the relatively younger.

The only other option was to chat with the older pupils at the nearby International School. One of the boys called Greg, soon became a friend. He was of drinking age and would therefore join me for a beer at the bar. Greg had introduced me to a rather delightful blonde named Pam, who was his classmate at the International School, shortly after we had become acquainted, and whom I flirted with briefly until my heart was captured by Madeleine.

I watched the Ceilidh dancing with some amusement as I watched the folk with varying degrees of competence follow the instructions of the dance tutors issued in their musical Scottish accents. I was still into my disco and jazz music at the time but found the bagpiped music for Ceilidh dancing equally entertaining.

I pumped Greg for more information on Madeleine, who was dancing at the time with a broad smile on her face. He told me that she was one of two daughters of a man called Olaf, who ran the Danish brewery in Jos at the time. One of whom was at university. Perfect for me, I felt, as we would have much more in common as fellow University attendees rather than exchanges with those still at school.

It was only after commencing university that I began to better comprehend the gulf in the thinking and confidence that existed amongst students in these vastly different scholastic environments, and it provided some explanation for a few of the failed attempts experienced when trying desperately to woo grad students in Canterbury whilst still at school.

She came over to the bar with her friend, Niki, who Greg seemed to know also. Niki was this wonderfully bubbly girl who, also soon became a good friend and confidante. I am delighted to tell you that, although we have not seen each other in a long while, Niki remains a close friend to this day.

They both appeared flushed from their exertions on the dance floor. Niki made the necessary introductions.

I was so taken by Madeleine, that I could barely offer a murmured hello in response to her greeting and fetching smile. An auburn blonde with a slightly freckled face, straight nose, and lips of the most beautiful shape almost perpetually curled into a smile. Her eyes danced and sparkled with hints of curiosity and amusement, as she held out her hand. I could feel the same charge of current I experienced when first meeting Paulette. This coupled with the goldfish routine, left me in little doubt that I had once again been struck by Cupid's arrow.

The girls insisted that we join them in the dancing. There were no protestations from my corner. Despite never having danced the 'Strip the Willow' before, I was happy to give in. Madeleine led me confidently to the dance floor. I could not help but be captivated by her charm, enthusiasm and endless smiles. It was wonderful having her arms entwined with mine as the dancing occasioned. Her mesmerising aura had me falling in love with her ten times over. The dance ended, but not my excitement. I thirsted for more, as did she. We danced the night away.

Burns Night was some time away yet, but the preparations had begun, and we were happy to have been a part of it that evening. I wanted to see Madeleine again and I got the distinct impression that she liked me too.

I had something you could vaguely describe as a social life pre-Madeleine, but it primarily revolved around bridge or the social club. I always had invitations to Alastair's house for barbeques but having stayed at his house for a couple of months whilst I waited to be given a place of my own, I was quite keen to cultivate friends of my own and create a separation between work and play.

I was thrilled to have a house I could call my own. It was rather Spartan by way of furniture or furnishings, but Alastair's wife did her best to make it appear as homely as she could. The houseboy they installed with me served me well, except on the food front. I should not really refer to him as 'houseboy' as he must have been an octogenarian or a septuagenarian at the least.

He was a wonderful chap who was kind enough to attend to my needs, fastidious as I was about cleanliness, and always look well-presented in his starched white or khaki uniform. He struggled however, with preparing anything more than sausages and mash or an English breakfast. I called him my butler thereafter, a title I felt more befitting his age and import.

Whilst I appreciated his perfectly prepared eggs, I longed for some variation in diet and sought refuge in the Social Club for their Sunday lunch, or at a Lebanese restaurant some miles away. I had frequented the Lebanese so often that I got to know the owners quite well and they would often invite me to their home or keep me entertained until late at their restaurant chatting and consuming much more alcohol than I should for the long drive home.

They felt so concerned about my lack of female companionship that they once bundled some poor sot into the back seat of my jeep, having paid her to entertain me for the night. Despite being scared witless from finding her only on my return home, and a little worse for wear from having consumed a few too many scotches with my Lebanese buddies, I managed to quite adroitly decline the woman's persistent advances. As it was too late to organise a taxi and feeling that leaving her to sleep in the car may be a little unkind, I got her to occupy one of the spare rooms.

My father would have been appreciative of my actions, as the sole advice he offered me before I left for school in England on the subject of 'the birds and bees' was that I should avoid members of the oldest profession at all costs. There was no talk about love, the female anatomy, or indeed what to expect from one's first kiss. Nothing. *Rien du tout*. Just avoid the ladies of the night were the words that rang in my ears as I left his study.

My butler thankfully dealt superbly with the unwanted guest the next morning and awoke me at the appropriate later hour with some strong coffee and a welcome full English breakfast.

I met up with Madeleine again at the club amongst a group of others. I caught her eye every now and then and could feel my heart melt when rewarded with a smile. I managed to monopolise her attention for a short while and she suggested we take a walk in the grounds of the club. I love women who show initiative. It rather makes up for my ineptitude in dating protocols. We talked and realised how much we had in common, except in the field of shyness. I was amazed at her incredibly confident demeanour and lauded her straightforwardness.

She laughed when I described the events that befell me on arrival in Nigeria, and how I was tempted to take the first flight back. She told me that she was glad that I had stayed so that we could meet. She said that whilst looking directly at me, with eyes alight and an enchanting smile playing across her lips. If there ever was a clear invitation to kiss, that was it.

I was so tempted to take her in my arms and kiss her then but resisted for some unknown reason and merely smiled weakly in return. I eventually plucked up sufficient courage to ask her to tea at my house. I thought that dinner may be a little presumptuous or premature given the recency of our meeting. She accepted and I arranged to meet her at the club, which was only a short drive from me, and take her home. Greg was also there and chose to follow us.

I decided not to be impolite and welcomed him in to join us.

We were taking photographs and Madeleine elected to have the first one with me. I put my arms around her waist in jocular fashion, but she pressed against me encouragingly, smiling cheekily. I kissed her cheek, taking in the alluring scent of her perfume. I longed to kiss her passionately. I sensed that I soon would.

After a while of Greg's company Madeleine made it clear that she preferred to be alone with me, and he left. I made a mental note to ask him afterwards why he wished to join us, as it was very clear that three was truly a crowd in that instance. Madeleine and I sat on the edge of the terrace to enjoy the sunset. I placed my hand on hers and she rested her head on my shoulders. I told her that I thought she was outstandingly beautiful. She turned to look at me. This time the invitation for a kiss did not go unattended.

I was aware that Madeleine was only around for the holiday, so I hoped that I would see her as often as possible. She invited me back to her house to meet her family. I met her sister. It was only then that I realised that she was the younger of Olaf's daughters and had not quite finished school. Before you hurl accusation at me of cradle snatching, I was only twenty-one then and she was eighteen. I was a little older, yes, but not menacingly so.

I must admit to being a little surprised at the time as she displayed all the confidence of what I assumed to be a university student. Anyway, it mattered not what anybody thought, as we were both very obviously keen on each other, and nothing and nobody could alter the course of this budding relationship. I never got around to asking Greg about why he had been insistent on joining us for tea on the previous occasion, but it dawned on me later that he had been keen on her also and did not anticipate her opting for the 'older man'.

Burns Night arrived. I did not possess a dinner jacket then but dressed as best I could in jacket and tie. Madeleine looked spectacular.

To be honest, I would have thought she looked beautiful even if she tipped up in a bin liner, as I was by now completely besotted. We danced, drank, ate, and drank and danced even more. I was now a complete convert to Ceilidh dancing. Madeleine had to return to Copenhagen shortly after, but we promised in between several kisses to see each other on her return during the summer holidays. We would spend two further Burns night evenings together.

We loved the dance practices and were inseparable partners for most of the time. If she did get asked to dance by anyone else, she would always look over to me and smile. Imagine the sheer exuberance of knowing that your lover may dance with others but only had eyes for you. Her father had now accepted me as her boyfriend and invited me to their Christmas lunches.

233

These lunches were a wonderful Danish tradition but should actually be accompanied with a health warning for the uninitiated, given the amount of Schnapps one feels obliged to consume in the multitude of toasts made. My first one to Madeleine and her family was remembered as rather slurred and very inebriated, but humorous, and therefore forgiven.

Madeleine's parents were divorced, and much as we hoped to see each other sooner, she had to spend alternate holidays with each of her parents and therefore her coming Easter break had to be spent with her mother in Denmark. I told her that I would be happy to wait for her to return during summer holidays. It would be an extended break for her, and we could spend a lot of time together. Had modern day technology been available we could have at least spent time communicating on WhatsApp or other mediums, but we had to make do with the occasional letter.

The postal service in Nigeria was so bad that despite letters being marked 'airmail', they took as long to deliver as it would for a blind man with a limp to have carried it on his person the entire distance between Jos and Copenhagen. Time seems to fly past when you are older, but when you are young and in love, waiting even a day feels like an eternity.

Madeleine was thrilled to see me again. She told me that after meeting me she broke up with the boy that she had been dating at school. First Paulette with her boyfriend, now Madeleine. Was this the beginning of some trend?

I felt a little guilty snatching a girl from under the nose of another man but thrilled at the same time that they would choose me over the incumbent. We spent a considerable amount of time together, some with friends like

Niki, who had us around for several parties at her house, or out at picnics.

Madeleine and I had now become lovers and passionately so. I could see that it was a trifle difficult for her father to accept, and now being father of two daughters myself I can understand exactly how difficult. He did notice however that this was no mere holiday romance, and that we were truly happy together. It was a blissful time whether we were holding hands and talking, driving together as a couple on a picnic, watching sunsets on terrace steps, or making passionate love in their summer house. After Paulette returned to France, I never thought I could meet anyone to fulfil me so completely until I met Madeleine. I was truly very happy.

I travelled extensively around Nigeria on various projects but tended to be back in Jos to see Madeleine during her holiday trips out. I no longer had the house to myself, as I now had to share it with another Engineer sent out from England.

He was the Engineer I worked with briefly in the office in Surrey. He was as much exciting company as a wet sock, and mostly moped around looking as dour as a stale snapper left neglected on fishmonger's display. He was not the most engaging social companion with others either. Madeleine thought so too, as she would spend the night at my place occasionally.

We opted to be completely alone in the summer house at her father's residence for continued privacy. Much to my disappointment, I was then posted to Yola, which was more than 500 kilometres away. It was a promotion of sorts but took me away from easy access to Madeleine.

My established circle of friends and bridge partners in Jos were sad to see me leave but were kind enough to offer me a home at any time I chose to visit. One lovely

235

couple I knew gave me a fairly full-grown pup to keep me company. I love dogs, anyway, and took to this very agreeable mutt instantly.

I called him Bingo after one of our pets in Brunei. I believe I had mentioned our menagerie to you before. It was the one that comprised at various times six dogs, a cat, monkey, duck, hen, and a rooster. Bingo was an absolute charmer, following me around everywhere. He was a quick learner and a great companion.

He made it clear that he wished for my constant company and would join me at the office every day sitting quietly at my feet whilst I worked. I took him on short trips out, and he would just require my opening the car door for him to jump in and happily occupy the floor of the passenger seat. He would gladly retrieve the ball I used to practice bowling against the front door of the office, if ever bored at lunchtime. He was well looked after by my houseboy or the next-door neighbours, whilst I was away at the weekends to meet Madeleine.

It was during one of my trips away that Bingo passed away. He had apparently mistakenly assumed the sound of my car and run out onto the main road to greet me. He was run over.

I buried him in the garden on my return. I hate losing pets, especially devoted ones like Bingo.

Madeleine's father had been rather adamant that she could not come and live with me in Yola. Again, understandably so, I could therefore only see her at weekends during her holiday visits to Nigeria. It was better than not seeing her at all. I only wished there had been some means of avoiding the long-distance drives to see her, but I was lucky to have befriended the manager of a decent hotel at one of the towns along the route and he and his wife would offer me plenty of food and a bed for the night, to help break up the monotony of the very long drive.

It was during one of these marathon journeys that I had a somewhat 'ghostly' encounter. It was late evening. I was on my way back to my home at the sugar estate, just outside Yola, when on one particular stretch of road, I saw a wheel bouncing along the road menacingly toward me. I just kept my hand on the wheel and ducked.

Nothing hit me, so I assumed that the wheel had just bounced over the car, but there was no vehicle ahead of me. I was both shaken and mystified. As soon as I got back, I threw my bag inside the house to unpack later and headed straight for the bar.

I ordered a large scotch for myself and one for a drinking buddy seated at the bar with me. He commented on the fact that I could barely hold the drink steadily as my hands were shaking badly. I told him about the inexplicably troubling experience. He nodded sagely and told me that I had indeed had a lucky escape. It was a stretch of road that had witnessed many an accident, and it was assumed to be haunted. We drove out the next morning to see what I had narrowly avoided. There was a steep ravine to one side and a cliff face on the other. Had I not kept the wheel straight, I would have met a rather ugly fate. I thanked the God I believed in at the time. It would have been an untimely end to a beautiful and blossoming love.

My relationship with Madeleine grew stronger, despite this seemingly endless trek back and forth, or perhaps as a result of this. I decided to quit my job, although I had become indispensable to the project and had cultivated a good relationship directly with the Minister of Industries at the time. He tried to persuade me to stay, but I would only do so on condition that I was paid substantially more and offered paid holidays to Denmark.

Needless to say, that my asking price appeared too high, and I set about packing my things to leave. Madeleine wanted me to route my trip back via Copenhagen so that we could spend time together there. My little crate comprised very little more than I had brought out with me, primarily a few carvings and curios I had purchased at the local market. I had become so absorbed in my work in Nigeria that I gave little thought to what I would do on my return to England. All I wanted at that point was to carve out a future of some sort that would involve a continuing relationship with Madeleine.

Madeleine met me at the airport in Copenhagen, and I began waving excitedly at her, whilst in the queue to clear customs. I am not sure what prompted it, but I was suddenly pulled to one side and asked to enter a little room where I was sat at a table and asked politely a series of questions primarily about my port of embarkation; what plans I had for my stay in Denmark; and the contents of my luggage.

No matter the number of trips I make, nor the airline, I always feel a tad nervous when walking past customs checkpoints. It is strange, as I have never flouted any regulation, at least not deliberately and was probably the most agreeable when it came to compliance, but my nerves seem to act independently of sanity and move into overdrive as soon as my eyes catch sight of a sign saying "Customs".

There were cases of Nigerians smuggling cash out by wrapping wads of it in foil and stuffing them into the carcasses of cooked chickens, but I had not employed any such ploy. I had toyed with the idea of packing some weed into my luggage but was now glad I had not.

They had me strip down to my underwear and inspected my clothing thoroughly. Nothing to show for their efforts, they took one further look at my passport and then indicated that I could leave. There was never any hostility or threat, as they were exceeding polite throughout this exercise. Heaving a huge sigh of relief, as I had visions of another 'Midnight Express' styled experience, but with less squalid conditions than Turkish prisons, I collected my belongings and the remnants of dignity and made my way, less excitedly to the exit doors.

Madeleine greeted me with such enthusiasm and love that my experience with the customs officials appeared no more than a minor inconvenience. I put it down to the possibility of my point of embarkation coinciding with my slightly hippy-like appearance (as I was sporting long hair and a beard at this time) which may have drawn some attention. And the animated waving would certainly not have helped.

I was just grateful not to have the sometimes-reported probing of the rectum applied on my person. Just the thought of such a violation makes me shudder, especially now when I associate it with my recent hospital visits. For future arrivals, I showed a muted response to any excitement from those sent to greet us, at least until I had cleared the customs area.

Madeleine, however, was incensed when I told her of my experience, and I had to hold onto her quite firmly as she was all set to march back into the building to remonstrate with the officials in question. She was still young but showed considerable empathy and strong insistence toward standing up against any perceived injustice perpetrated against her loved one.

We could barely keep our hands off each other on arrival at her father's apartment. I motioned for some restraint in our amorous endeavours, so that I could take a shower to wash away the accumulated grime from the journey, both real and imagined.

She refused to wait. She joined me instead and introduced me to the joys of making love in the shower. We did not bother to dress and spent the whole time in bed not caring much to even eat, for fear of forsaking any time spent in each other's loving embrace.

It was such a remarkably blissful feeling to be in love and be loved equally strongly and reciprocally. My attention was devoted entirely to Madeleine, and I am not sure I even felt a twinge of guilt for the time I spent with Paulette in Paris the previous year. I was in love with both of them. I sometimes believe that I still am. Does love ever die or fade away? I think not. It may alter its form occasionally but rarely leaves the compartment it occupies in one's heart. I felt I could see Paulette again and recapture the feelings for her and enjoy intimacy without jeopardising the love I felt for Madeleine.

As soon as we felt suitably inclined to leave the apartment, she introduced me to her friends and one of the best pizzas I have ever tasted in a restaurant called 'Doctor Peppers'. We were a large number of people and the perfectly cooked, thin crusted pizzas arrived in sufficiently large a size to feed the several hungry mouths. It was such a perfect evening. Everyone spoke English for my benefit, and made me feel so welcome.

Madeleine was so ardent and zestful in her display of affection toward me that her friends, though not knowing me well at the time, were happy to extend their goodwill to me without question.

Olaf arrived a week or so later and was understandably reluctant for me to continue staying there with Madeleine.

She was adamant that I spent more time with her and even arranged for her friend of hers to offer me room in his apartment so that she could stay with me. We also stayed together at her mother's house for about a week.

I had nothing pressing awaiting me, so I was happy to remain in Copenhagen with her and enjoy the delights of the city seen through her eyes. I could not have asked for a more charming or attentive companion, as we toured the city taking in sights - the little mermaid sculpture, Tivoli gardens, national museum, and the national gallery, amongst others.

Even the most mundane of bus or train journeys, and supermarket shopping were made delightful excursions in her company. She had a great sense of fun. Shopping for lingerie was not just erotic but highly amusing. Her laughter was infectious, and I cannot recall a single moment with her when we were not happy, despite sometimes being in a pensive state over where we could stay together or in discussing the future of our relationship.

Although it was obvious that we made a loving couple, it became progressively more difficult for us to lead the nomadic existence of retiring from one place to another, and I felt it best to journey on to England. The intention was that once I was settled back in England, she could come over to visit during her breaks from university, much as she did on visits to Nigeria during the school holidays.

We bade each other a sad but fond farewell. We drew comfort from this painful parting through promises to see one another again as soon as we could. Those promises made between as many kisses as we could practically exchange before releasing each other from a tight embrace.

Settling in did not go quite as planned, as employment opportunities were difficult to obtain in the Engineering field. With the benefit of hindsight, I should have opted for a change in career at that point. I was only twenty-four and young enough to switch to an alternative profession, which valued my Engineering skills, together with analytical and management skills that I had acquired whilst abroad. Stubbornly I resorted to a pursuit of a limited career as an Engineer. One of my great regrets as indicated to you many times. *Je regrette beaucoup de choses. Cela par exemple.*

To make ends meet I took up some part-time work at the St. Laurent shop on Bond Street for a short time. It was hard work being on my feet for almost all day, but very enjoyable. I loved being in clothes retailing and harked back to my time at university when I had a Saturday job at a Men's fashion store. This store involved more *haute couture* fashion however, which was a nice experience for me from the sales side. My claim to fame at this time was to have sold a suit to Charles Saatchi. I believe I convinced him to buy some shirts too.

I was also at that time living in a tiny bedsit in Hammersmith, having undergone a rather messy affair with a rather attractive Spanish blonde called Maria, which disrupted the flat share arrangement I had with my sister, Carole.

Madeleine and I had been infrequently corresponding during this time, but she clearly still held strong feelings for me, and wrote to say that she wanted to see me. I was still rather rudderless in part-time employment and not in the best of hospitable circumstances. Much as I tried to dissuade her, she was insistent. I was delighted to see her, though. She was every bit as beautiful as I had remembered her being. The weekend, however, was a lot more difficult to endure.

My bedsit was barely home for one, let alone two. Some friends kindly offered us a room in their flat for this period. It barely provided for the much-required privacy we needed. It was difficult to see how we could maintain thoughts of a future together with my seemingly endless vagrancy. I longed for the stability of a home that I had in Nigeria, and would have put up with even longer drives, than those I had undertaken, to be with her.

She cried.

I cried with her but could provide no reassurance. It was heart-breaking to see as she was always the person I associated with endless smiles and beautiful laughter.

It was a dreadful ending to a truly wonderful relationship. I knew that when I saw her off at the airport, she left with her heart broken. Mine was too. I truly wish I could have done something to provide hope, but I was in a confused state myself and had little stability in my life to create the foundations we badly needed to sustain a future together. I knew that I had hurt her, but with no malicious intent. I am not a bad person, as you know, but I sometimes undertake the most disastrous course of action supposedly in the other person's best interest. Here was a case in point. Should I have allowed our love a chance to offer a solution, rather than pre-empt matters? In hindsight, yes. Solutions to problems can be relatively easily found, but true love not so. I may have considered myself valiantly selfless at the time but in acting unilaterally I had offered no time or space for consideration of her thoughts and feelings.

I believe I still hold a deep love for her. Even though she was younger than me, I think that she was the more emotionally mature in our relationship. I have often wondered if I should look her up to beg forgiveness for breaking her beautiful heart, but even with the availability of current day technology, I am not sure where to begin.

Your thoughts, please sir.

My fond farewell to you in the meantime.

David

Letter 17 – Swiss Sweetheart & a Lost Love?

November 2019

Dear Geoff,

As I mentioned in my last letter to you *'Je ne regrette rien'* would definitely not apply to me, for I have regrets aplenty. And none more so than in course of action taken in ending a potentially wonderful relationship with a very beautiful (both within and without), girl called, Ravinia.

If I could turn the clock back, I would definitely have acted differently. If there was something called fate, and I had taken a wrong turn by having a relationship with Ravinia, before re-treading the path to getting married and having the children that I did, then so be it. But I should have, at the least, allowed my relationship with her to develop further before ending it painfully prematurely and rather injudiciously.

I met Ravinia through Dieter. In fact, I met two of my previous lovers through him too. Something about German women, I think. I had seriously contemplated moving to Germany at one stage. The women there seemed to find me enchanting. At least four of all my lovers have been German.

I am sure I have mentioned this wonderful fellow to you before. Not only did Dieter introduce me to Robert, as a source of Shunga and general erotica, but appeared to have an abundance of attractive women friends from Germany. All of whom so far had taken a liking to me.

Ravinia wasn't from Germany, but by God was she lovely!

I used to help at the Singapura almost daily. John and Maureen were living in Fulham and kindly offered me their spare bedroom in exchange for my assistance at the restaurant. It was a great escape from the ghastly bedsit that had been my accommodation prior to this invitation. On the days that I did not help at the restaurant and was not out socialising I played reserve babysitter for my niece Francesca.

This arrangement came about after my relationship with a half-French, half-Spanish girl called Maria went hopelessly awry. I shall tell you of that sad affair on another occasion, suffice to say for now, that there is something about good-looking girls with French accents and names like Maria that creates a fatal cocktail of draws for me.

The way we met should have provided sufficient suggestion that the relationship was headed nowhere. It was good for as long as it lasted, as she was a wonderfully passionate lover, but it was not the most emotionally gratifying relationship. Thankfully, the ending of this affair was rewarded with some progress on the career front. I use the word 'progress' cautiously, as I have many regrets in the pursuit of work in this field.

I had secured a job with an Engineering firm outside of London. It was a tiring day, as I had to commute to the town of Reading each day. I absolutely hated both the job and the commute but had to undertake this to make a living and further my career.

After all the seniority and lifestyle, I had enjoyed in Nigeria, this was a huge career downscaling and reset, but the professional engineering body would not have it otherwise. They felt that my Engineering experience in Nigeria was more of management ilk, and that I had to develop an understanding of the very basic practical experience in the field. I wonder if my fellow Chartered Engineers in England feel the erosion of professional regard, as I do. I sense we are rapidly becoming part of society's forsaken.

The days of Brunel appear to have long been forgotten and the term 'Engineer' seems to apply equally to the person ensuring the structural integrity of some of the world's tallest buildings and the chap who fixes your faulty cooker. This is not the case in many other countries where Chartered Engineers are held in high regard. Whatever the reasons for the degradation of the status of Engineers in England, I felt obliged, to gain my Chartered status in the field, so I reluctantly applied myself to the tasks that would count towards the fulfilment of requirements for my professional exams.

What a waste of time in a dead-end career, in hindsight. I would have fared better economically had I attended night school to acquire plumbing skills, or better still opted to do an MBA much earlier in my life. I should have sought a much better career path at an earlier point in my life.

But had I done either of those things, I would never have met you. I suppose I could say I did quite enjoy my days in Jealott's Hill overseeing building works and executing my project management skills a little more than those in the Reading office doing nothing more than sitting at a drawing board or going out to construction sites occasionally to just measure topography. Anyway, I am very happy that we met.

It was the first occasion that I felt I could have a friendship with a contractor which would not affect the transparency of the professional relationship that needed to exist between us, given my role as the client representative. I am thankful to know that such arrangements can actually work well, and I am sincerely grateful to you for allowing us to prove that it can. Our friendship must be somewhat robust to have lasted for the thirty-six-odd years we have known each other; wouldn't you say?

Forgive me for deviating somewhat from my story of the lovely Ravinia. It was one of the evenings waiting tables in the Singapura, when Dieter and his girlfriend Zelda walked in. Dieter with yet another beautiful lady companion in tow. I directed them to their table conscious of the fact that I began to notice the classic symptoms of being thunderstruck. I had not been quite as captivated by the previous of his companions that I ended up having a relationship with, as I did with Ravinia. There was something beyond just the sexual allure.

Gisela, who was the first of Dieter's friends with whom I ended up having a brief, but frantically passionate relationship, was a very attractive blonde with a superb figure. I was very attracted to her but would have to admit that the enticement was primarily a sexual one.

It would be fair to say that although I flirted outrageously with her, it was Gisela who in fact seduced me. I had taken her and Dieter to one of my favourite wine bars called Julie's Bar at the top of Portland Road in Notting Hill. It was an exceptionally beautiful and warm summer's day, which as you know is an absolute joy in England when it occurs. It was made all the more wonderful by seeing Gisela in a white linen dress which left little to the imagination as to what lay underneath.

As we were having drinks, I could feel her foot rub against mine and trail a path further up my leg. I took it to be accidental at first, until I felt her naked foot continue to caress my unclothed legs, noticeable as I was sporting shorts on that gloriously sunny day. She smiled when I looked at her. She moved closer toward me. I felt encouraged enough to place a hand on her thigh. She promptly inched her dress up and placed my hand back on her now bare thigh, all the while engaged in a serious three-way conversation. I could barely concentrate. How is it that women seem more able than men to undertake several tasks simultaneously, without compromising attention to any?

I struggled to focus on maintaining a civil conversation with Dieter and nurse a drink on the table, whilst attempting to keep him oblivious to the progress of matters pleasingly taking place immediately below our tabletop. I tried heroically to just manage two matters simultaneously. One was to keep talking without moaning with pleasure, and the other was to dutifully take up the heaven-sent offer to caress the silken skin of Gisela's thigh. How she kept a straight face as I traced my fingers over her skin, I will not know. My face, on the other hand must have been contorted in all sorts of pleasurable expressions as I did my best to feign total innocence to Dieter.

If he had noticed the lustful pleasure reflecting in my face from the arousal of stroking the upper part of Gisela's dainty leg, he was gentleman enough not to say so. By happy chance, I had plied her sufficiently well with scintillating conversation and tender caress to engineer (no pun intended) an invitation to enjoy other parts of her lovely body later. It was a night of heightened passion.

But the wait was almost intolerable, as Dieter was almost glued to our company for all the time and we were forced to sneak in kisses in his short absences, when all we both wanted was to tear each other's clothes off at the soonest opportunity. I felt a little guilty seducing his friend, but as I had indicated earlier, I felt this overture had been more obviously prompted by the feminine component of the relationship. She turned out to fulfil all the promises indicated in her caress and was a truly exceptional lover. It was the first time in my life that I had been so effectively and marvellously seduced, and it was an enlivening experience. It was just a pity that she remained in London only for a short while. Had it been the days of better mobile telephone communication, I would definitely have stayed in closer touch. I did see her again a year or so later, but she was then in a committed and long-standing relationship.

Ravinia was wildly different. She was incredibly attractive and sensual too without any shadow of doubt, but in a very different way. She was outstandingly beautiful. Her sensuality apparent, but decidedly more subtle. She wore her dark hair combed back into a ponytail. Her creamy skin bearing not even the smallest of imperfections. Her face bore a straight and delicately small nose, which accentuated her high cheekbones and drew one's eye alluringly to her sweet cherry red lips.

She was beautifully dressed also, suitably defining her slim and petite frame, offering subtle hints of the swell of her suggestively perfect breasts and her shapely legs. I was utterly smitten. She reminded me of a beautiful lady I had been in love with since time immemorial – Audrey Hepburn, who, as you will have heard from me many times, I believe to be truly the most beautiful woman in the world by any measure.

There were many screen and pop idols to whom one could so readily attach one's affections to, but there was only one with whom it appeared to be consistent no matter what stage of my life. I had grown up enjoying the enchantment of so many beautiful and sensual women from Brigitte Bardot and Marilyn Monroe to Sophia

Loren and Lauren Bacall to Raquel Welch and Debbie Harry as well as my current favourites of Gal Gadot, Kylie Minogue, Paz Vega, Claire Forlani and Jessica Alba, but none caused a more enduring appeal than Audrey H.

I fell madly in love with Audrey H when I first saw her in "Roman Holiday".

Her angelic countenance and charm struck a chord and affixed an indelible imprint in my young mind. I do realise that half the population of the world was in love with her also, but there was an appeal of hers that ran very deep and took up permanent residence in my heart and head. She grew more appealing with each year that passed. I loved the elegance and beauty she carried and displayed with such humility throughout her life. Could I ever find such grace and comeliness within my social sphere? I certainly hoped so, and I was possibly looking directly at her.

In everything from the large eyes to dark hair framing an angelic face, and a sylph like figure clothed beautifully, Ravinia almost replicated my beloved screen idol to a tee.

I loved beautiful women, but even more the ones who knew how to dress well. Ravinia had a wonderful sense of dress and looked amazingly well-presented even when she was casually dressed in jeans and a cotton shirt. This was my *haute couture* period and therefore a time in my life when I was a great admirer of well-dressed and groomed members of the opposite sex too. One hoped that her heart was equally sublime.

I seem to go through periods of fashion consciousness. After my brief relationship with Maria ended, I took to retail as a form of therapy. I discovered a wonderful clothes shop on Kensington Church Street, the name of which escapes me, and as it has long since closed down, and I have no means of tracing it.

It is such a pity, as I think they had a wonderful formula for men's clothing. They rarely had more than a single piece by any designer. I call it my *haute couture* days, as the shop stocked items that were rarely seen in your average men's retail outlet and carried clothes by a mix of well and lesser-known designers, all enticingly displayed and staffed by impeccably dressed individuals. It was there that I cultivated a taste for Katharine Hamnett, Issey Miyake, Galliano, Paul Smith, Jasper Conran, Gaultier, Donna Karan, Casely-Haford, Bobo, Yamamoto, Boateng and others. I got to know the staff well and appreciated the fact that they were attentive without pressuring in their sales. It was not the cheapest of shops, but I learnt to value quality over quantity and would often save up to buy specific items of clothing, some of which I have kept to this day.

It was the period in my life when I was more of a trend-setter than a blind follower of fashion. I was still very slim – relatively broad-shouldered but shaped to a 28-inch waist. The staff thought that I had the perfect figure for many of their choice of clothes – everything from high-waisted cashmere trousers and long-tailed silk shirts to Japanese army-styled jodhpurs with short, fitted jackets. If I had considered myself even vaguely pulchritudinous, I may have been tempted to apply for a role in fashion modelling.

I loved fashionable clothes. As it was, I just chose and wore clothes that pleased me, which I was gratified to note attracted considerable attention, and some favourable comments. My long hair worn in a ponytail for most of the time assisted in making the requisite fashion statement. It was a strange period in my life too, as I had to dress very conservatively at work. Engineers would not normally comprehend *couture* even if even the term had been tattooed on their foreheads. I abided by this poor dress code by wearing very rudimentary suits to blend in.

I could barely contain my excitement to get home and change into something more fashionable, and reflective of what I felt within me. I think that some of the customers at the restaurant may have considered my dress sense a little quirky, but I enjoyed the attention, nevertheless. It may have been my choice of attire, (and I would like to think a little charm that helped my cause too) but I was happy to have obtained dates with several lovely women during this time. Ravinia, thankfully, being one of them.

Poor Dieter. He could sense from my demeanour that I was very attracted to Ravinia and almost appeared resigned to the fact that I would make a play for yet another of his friends. Zelda seemed less concerned, but she was neither witness nor privy to information on the Gisela affair and was welcoming of my particular attention at their table.

Even when surveilling the room to note others in the restaurant requiring attention, my eyes would invariably be drawn back to Ravinia. I had seen many attractive women, London after all was a fashion capital and played host to an incredible array of beautiful women, but Ravinia seemed to hold such added inexplicable appeal. Was it because she had so many of the physical attributes of my screen idol, or because she appeared more accessible by virtue of my having been introduced to her? But then why? Just because she happened to be a friend of a friend was no guarantee that she would grant me the attention or affection I sought. My roaming eyes that evening were continually drawn back to her. If she noticed me looking, she would smile engagingly. Her lips shaping beautifully into the most enchanting and bewitching smile. Just as Audrey's smile engaged a million hearts, Ravinia's had claimed mine.

The Latin's refer to it as being struck by the thunderbolt of love. The French call it *'coup de foudre'*, which sounds to me more appropriately romantic. I knew that she was the girl I wanted to have a pluck at my heartstrings. I just hoped to make a good enough impression that evening to ensure a future opportunity to see her. That was the difficult part.

I was sometimes a little clumsy, but even more so when emotionally hampered by a *coup de foudre* instance, as my sense of balance, and the art of verbal articulation seem to desert me almost completely.

Things that required little concentration to execute, such as carrying a single tray of food, or pouring wine without spillage absorbed enormous amounts of my concentration. I fared reasonably well that evening, I am happy to report, despite being somewhat stymied by the inveiglement of Ravinia's charm and beauty.

I obtained Ravinia's details and accumulated sufficient courage to ask her out on a date. I took her to one of my favourite places - The Joseph coffee shop on Sloane Street for our first date. I loved talking to her. I loved the sound of every word she uttered. A Swiss national of Italian origin, she spoke English with a charming blend of Italian and French accents. We appeared to have much to talk about, and discussed interests, values and aspirations we had in common at great length. The afternoon coffee extended into an early evening of drinks. We would have gone on to dinner together had it not been for a prior engagement she had. We agreed to meet again. I was overjoyed. The gentle brush of her lips against mine as we parted gave me a sense of future expectations.

I believe I may have mentioned the three-date rule to you previously? In essence, the purpose was to determine how interested a girl was in progressing toward an intimate relationship by the third date. My average, for your interest, hovered around the two-dates mark. If one had not kissed a girl by the third date, according to my school time oracle, Camel, there was little point in pursuing matters. The best thing to do in that situation was to 'move on', in order to preserve one's dignity. Sound advice.

First-date kisses, as you will have learnt from my previous sermon on the subject were generally best avoided. Having said that, I did recently meet someone who I ended up kissing passionately on our very first date. She was a very attractive and petite auburn-haired lady, and we appeared very well suited as we chatted first over coffee, thence to wine, and then onto long kisses. Unfortunately, this was another relationship headed to the friend zone due to a lack of follow-up enthusiasm.

I had no problem dispensing with any rule with Ravinia. I loved her company and would have happily extended the 'three strikes, and you're out' dictum to a fourth, fifth or umpteenth time. I was convinced that she would be well worth the prize. She was. I didn't have to wait long, as I kissed her at the start of our second date.

I had arranged to meet her at her flat, before going out to lunch together. I bought a single long-stemmed rose on my way. She smiled in her inimitably charming way when she saw me. The smile broadened when I handed her the rose. I leant forward to kiss her cheeks in greeting. She kissed me on the lips instead. I was caught a little off guard but wanted to be sure that it was intended. It was. I kissed her on her doorstep several more times, before we eventually set off to lunch. I had assumed when I first saw her that her kisses would be divine. And they were.

Our date involved lots of hand holding as we chatted. We went on several dates after that. She worked at Asprey during the day, so we really only had some weekends or weekday nights when I was not busy at the Singapura to spend together. And spend together we did. Joyously and amorously. I took her to all my other favourite haunts. The fifth-floor coffee shop at Harvey Nichols, the cheap and cheerful Stick & Bowl Chinese restaurant, the Cumberland Hotel for a New Orleans jazz brunch, the 606 club for smoky but fun-filled impromptu jazz sessions, or the Monkberry's nightclub, where I had become a member and regular visitor.

When I joined Monkberry's in the eighties it was run by an Irish couple who had become good friends, and I loved going there sometimes on a date or other times with a large group of friends, but always with the intention to dance the night away to great music. Ravinia loved to dance. I loved holding her close to me when the music of a softer melody played, as her body seemed to melt into mine as we moved gently together.

Ravinia quite liked the 606 too. The club was run by a diminutive but charming man called Steve, who loved the Singapura and was very happy to reciprocate the welcome at his venue. There was very little room to dance, but she loved the music and enjoyed sitting close to me, letting me hold her hands all the while. And what perfect hands she had to hold.

She was also a great enthusiast for fashion. I took her to all my favourite shops including Joseph, Comme des Garcons, Margaret Howell, Katharine Hamnett, and Issey Miyake most of which were located on Brompton

Road and not far from my usual haunts for a glass of wine or coffee.

Whether it was window shopping for jewellery or clothes, dining out or just conversing, I delighted in her company. I loved her taste in everything from clothes to furnishings, and fragrances to art. She looked more beautiful each time we met.

I loved looking into her mesmerizingly beautiful eyes, which were either inquisitorial or inviting. Inquisitorial when we were in conversation and when she wanted to know more about me; inviting, when she wished to be kissed, which, thankfully, was very often.

There were times when she would just stop as we were walking along the street and turn toward me to exact a kiss. I was more than delighted to provide these of course, as there are very few women, I can honestly say, that had lips as sweet or wonderfully soft as Ravinia's.

She was the most wonderful companion and beautiful partner. We kissed on many an occasion, but I could never seem to lure her to bed, and I was not sure why. At least not until later.

I suppose that we could have limited our intimacy to the exchange of many kisses, as I could not have asked for anything more pleasant to apply my lips against. I loved the fragrance of her skin, which I could not help but breathe in when I held her close to me. She wore a perfume by Van Cleef, if I remember correctly. I adored the smell of her hair too. I was so taken by this woman, but very surprised that despite our obvious attraction for each other she did not appear too enthusiastic about progressing our relationship more intimately. I exercised patience, but soon needed either an explanation or fulfilment. She provided one.

It was her last night before returning to Geneva. We had just come back from dinner at a Thai restaurant. One of many that appeared to become very fashionable in Fulham and other adjacent areas. I drove her home.

It was not the nicest of my vehicular ownerships. It was a pale blue Vauxhall Opel. It had nothing going for it, neither its awful colour, engine performance nor interior.

I am such a dreadful snob when it comes to selection of cars. I realise that I should be grateful to have even owned a car at that time, but I was of the view that in some instances it was preferable to pound the streets in one's footwear than be seen in a vehicle so ghastly that it begs the question as to how it ever passed the stage of design and subsequent manufacture. Even after buying the car, I often opted to use public transport in lieu of this car. As you can imagine, it was not long before it was sold, rather given away, as I received nothing in return for its disposal.

She invited me in for coffee and a nightcap. I could never refuse such offers as I loved her kisses. It was more than kisses that evening. She was being particularly forthright and yielding that evening and I was certain that we would make love. She allowed me further advances than she had on previous occasions, and I undressed her to reveal a figure even more beautiful than I had imagined. I was also stripped off my clothes, and there was only one way this evening was headed – heavenly pleasure. She stopped me mid-stride, or whatever the 'mid-'expression would be when one is about to apply one's best lovemaking moves. I assumed it was for me to wear a condom. I had gotten so carried away that I had not even considered this most basic of precautions. But it was not

for a precautionary measure. She wanted to tell me something.

I was happy to pause knowing that I would make the
long-awaited passionate love to her before she left. She
proceeded to tell me that she had not intended to stay
longer in London than the few months she spent then.
That was the case at least, until she met me. She told me
that she had not expected to fall in love either. She
wanted a future with me, and that she was waiting for
such a special occasion to lose her virginity. She told me
that she was so happy that it was with me.

I leapt out of bed like a scalded cat.

This was the second time in my life I was presented
with a virgin encounter. The first time was after a disco
night at university. I was not sure what induced me to
invite this girl back to my room, but I did. I assumed it
was just another occasion when I would regret my actions
only the following day. We had similarly undressed and
were about to perform the ritual, when she advised me of
her virginal state. I had jumped out of bed so quickly that
I crashed into the adjacent desk with some degree of
force. I have no rational explanation for this reaction. A
visit to the psychiatrist's couch may yield answers. But I
am unable to provide one to you at the moment.

Thinking back on that occasion though, one reason
was blindingly obvious. I was not attracted to this girl in
any way and would have chosen not to see her ever again,
after that evening. It was intended purely for a single
night's pleasure.

Perhaps another scratch on the headboard but definitely nothing serious or prolonged. So, it was understandable. She may have wished to continue a relationship with the man with whom she had her first sexual experience with, but I held no corresponding desire for such

continuity under any circumstances, other than one involving a gun pointed at my head, so it was only reasonable for me to be the gentleman and plead out. I did. I spent the night uncomfortably in the armchair next to the bed, nursing a bruised elbow. The sad thing about it was that this girl kindly offered a rethink the next morning, and I was possibly even less inclined.

Anyway, I have no idea why I would repeat this leaping-out-of-bed performance with Ravinia. She was gorgeous. I had seen her in the cold light of day and loved every inch of her. Having seen her naked, she was even more alluringly desirable than ever. Her skin was so gloriously unblemished, fragrantly perfumed and of the silkiest texture. I wanted her. I wanted to kiss every inch of her and make love to her all night and every night that followed. And yet I was now sitting on the chair by the bed with my head in my hands.

The only explanation I have in hindsight is that I was petrified of commitment. I knew that I had caused her to feel strongly for me. I had constantly plagued her with my wish to make love to her. I had not realised that she was just waiting for the right time. The time that she felt so in love with me also that she was prepared to give up something she treasured.

I felt desire, but guilt at the same time. Had I been so intent to bed her that I applied undue pressure on her? Was I in love with her as much as I had indicated? Did I consider her too precious to de-flower? Did I have to marry her if I slept with her? Could I not commit to a future with her? I had no answer. I told her that I was not sufficiently in love with her, and that it would be very unfair on her to give up her virginity to me. I left, thinking that I had done the right thing.

I was so stupid, Geoff. An absolute and utter dope. I only realised much later how much in love with her I really was. It was not lust. It was not a passing infatuation. She was the perfect person for me. I know that to think someone completes you would suggest that one is devoid of something, but Ravinia filled me with the utmost happiness and completed me in every aspect. I could not have asked for a better partner in my life, at that point.

There were some girlfriends I was not too keen to introduce to my family, but Ravinia was a girl my parents would have adored and hastened me to marry at the earliest juncture. They would have been right, but I was still in my twenties, and imagined myself due for more beautiful women and more sexual encounters to come. What an absolute arse I was! I had the most beautiful woman in the world, and she loved me in return. I had forsaken her love for an inexplicable and inexcusable reason I have yet to fathom.

She came to see me the next morning before she left for Geneva. She told me that she really liked me still and hoped that we could stay in touch. The realisation of being truly in love with her had yet to crystallise, and I was noncommittal. I hated myself later for not taking her into my arms and telling her that I was not sure of the future but that I wanted her to be a part of it.

I did not know you well enough to consult you on this matter. Did I even know you then? But I remember a friend of the family, Tony, who had met her, telling me that I was a fool to let her go. He might have been a tad impartial at the time, being Italian and not wanting hurt to befall a compatriot, but I now agree with him entirely. She was definitely the woman of my dreams, and the best thing to have happened to me at that time.

Do you perhaps understand my regret better now? If I could turn the clock back, not only would I have made love to her that evening, but I would have been inclined to marry her. She was everything I had always prayed for and more.

After giving up a beautiful soul that Madeleine was, and exchanging her for unfulfilling sexual partnerships with others, I should have known better than to wish for the proverbial birds in the bush. Did I carry such a deep-seated fear to commit to a relationship? I know not the answer, but Margaret was right in suggesting that there are times when we should put pen to paper to gain a better understanding of ourselves. Having done so, by way of this letter to you I realise now that I lost a great love.

I had sometimes recounted that tale of Ravinia to depict myself as a hero and gentleman for not taking her virginity and allowing her to find love elsewhere. But I think now that I was neither hero nor gentleman. Not by a long shot. If anything, a base and cowardly fool. I had dismissed something offered with such love and tenderness with sheer and unreserved callousness. Whilst not meant maliciously, it was uncaring and thoughtless, nevertheless.

I sincerely hope that Ravinia found a truer and better love than I. What of me? I deserve no pity. I should have been stood up against a wall and shot, preferably at close range. I had something so wonderful, in front of me, a gift of sweet and tender love, and I chose to disregard it. My only prayer now is that I will better appreciate such love offered to me in the future.

If I broke her heart, it is only right that mine should be battered and splintered into a million disintegrations, in return. I hope that you will not only understand my regret and forgive my past actions but advise me timeously and sternly on the next occasion when I have obtained such a pure and beautiful love in my grasp - one that I should not so foolishly relinquish.

Is this one of the reasons, my heart refuses to give up on my love for H? I wish I knew. Perhaps you could enlighten me with your thoughts on the matter.

As always, I shall await your reply with great anticipation.

Love,

David

Letter 18 – Holland's Heartbreaker

December 2019

Dear Geoff,

I just realised that I have written to you about some of my past loves but failed to tell you about Luisa. But do I need to? I think we were already firm friends when I met Luisa, and it is very likely that I have divulged much about her to you already. For the sake of being comprehensive in my recollections of past loves, excluding specifically my ex, let me remind you of my romance with her.

Having broken Ravinia's heart so brutally, it perhaps serves me right that my next love would break mine. A year or so had passed when I met Luisa at a Bridge Club in Sloane Square and was irresistibly attracted to her. She was considerably older than me, which I was not fully aware of at the time, as I could only feel an ineluctable draw to this tall stunning blonde.

I was not completely devoid of relationships after Ravinia.

I had a brief affair with a girl called Laura who I met at the Singapura. She used to frequent the restaurant with a large group of friends from a nearby Marketing Agency.

Pretty with dark hair in a short bob, and a nice slim but curvaceous figure supported by a great pair of legs. It was not a *coup de foudre* by any means but a strong lodestone, nevertheless.

As she was now a regular there, I made a point of striking up a conversation with her whenever an opportunity presented itself, which was rare as they mainly arrived as a group. I decided to court the opinion on how best I may attract Laura's interest from Charles, who was the only one of the group with whom I was best acquainted. Whatever, magic wand Charles waved worked, as the next time I saw her she seemed particularly happy to see me. We spent a lot more time together, and I felt comfortable enough to extend an invitation for her to join me at a party I was attending at the weekend.

It was not due to start until late, as most good parties do. There is nothing worse than attending a party starting at eight or so in the evening and being politely ushered to the door at midnight. The best ones are those where one feels comfortable enough to consider the possibility of staying on for breakfast also. This was one such party. In anticipation of a late night, Laura had agreed to attend the party after I had helped at the Singapura through its busy early evening period. She stopped by the restaurant to pick me up, as I was now without a car.

I had ditched the ghastly pale blue Opel not long after Ravinia parted. Getting rid of this hideous means of transport was easy and a huge relief, but losing Ravinia was naturally quite the opposite and remains one of the more heart-rending periods in my life.

I opted for public transport to service my needs until such time as available funds would stretch to purchase another automobile.

I had neither intention nor the means to acquire a Ferrari, Aston Martin or Lamborghini, or Porsche, which incidentally are my favourite brands of cars, and was happy to purchase anything vehicular that had some appealing trait. For example, a car that I purchased together with Carole some years earlier absolutely hit the mark. It was a Triumph convertible which we acquired from one of her friends for a princely sum of £250. It may have been old, and in need of considerable attention to redeem it to its glory days, but it was an absolutely charming roadster. At least, it was until Carole drove it with the handbrake on for several miles and the only direction this piece of vehicular charm was headed, given the cost of repair, was sadly to its metallic grave.

Laura waited patiently until I was free to go. We would arrive around ten thirty. Not a bad time to arrive at a party. Laura drove. And extremely well too. Fast but very assuredly.

I hate to sound sexist, but there are some women drivers who have had me clutching the seat in absolute terror when they drive fast. Most drive with too much restraint, sticking maddeningly well under any speed limit and fastidiously to the motorway middle lane. This was the first time we had been alone, and the conversation was polite but not overly flirtatious. I had little means of anticipating how the evening would unfold.

It was a good party; we chatted, drank and danced. Laura appeared to be enjoying herself. At one point I sat down at the windowsill to rest. She came over to join me. I motioned for her to sit on my lap, and she gladly obliged. I placed my arms around her. The first display of affection. She turned to face me, and I kissed her. She responded enthusiastically. Our kisses grew more passionate. I suggested that we should leave. It didn't take much persuasion. If she had driven with speed to the party, she drove with even greater haste on the way back to her house. My hand in hers and rested on her thigh appeared to be no disruption to her ability to manoeuvre the vehicle with great ease.

It was almost a reliving of a scene from a movie when two people are so intent on getting each other into bed as quickly as possible, but almost deliberately delay the actual process of undressing by seeking the exchange of many passionate kisses on the way.

It started from the moment we got through the front door. Passionately but clumsily knocking over mail on the ledge, banging into plants, struggling in over-eagerness to turn the key in the lock to her flat, almost tripping over front door mats, etc. until we finally got to her bedroom. Had there been a cat, it would have been accidentally trodden on, as our attention was intensely focused just on each other. What started as a very sedate and polite conversation on the way to a party ended in passionate embraces which continued well into the night and the following morning.

I loved waking up the next morning in the comfort of her bed and the warmth of her embrace.

Laura was a lovely girl. I enjoyed her company and I believe that did enjoy mine. We enjoyed our lunches and coffees, but she was not the keenest of companions on shopping trips, but untiringly patient when with me. She did enjoy our visits to galleries and exhibitions more. We still had much in common, beyond the physical attraction.

I still have no idea why we stopped seeing each other, but we did after a while. I wonder if she felt that I was just drifting through life without any purpose or wish to commit. I was not clear myself as to what my ambitions and romantic inclinations were. I was just a hopeless romantic in need of an anchoring relationship with the woman of my dreams.

But I continued to drift, and I am not really sure to what end. I do not even know if I ever gave serious thought to settling down with anyone and working toward creating a steady and firm relationship involving marriage and children. I had by this time obtained Chartered status as Engineer, with still no love for the profession, but no clear idea as to what I wanted to progress to next, emotionally or otherwise.

I got the sense that Laura wanted more. I believe she was seeking someone with greater drive and purpose in life which I sorely lacked then. I can now relate to her desire to find someone to settle down with, and not just have fun. She started going out with an older man, but she was obviously not happy. She missed me, and I missed her. She used to come to the Singapura, but her new boyfriend could sense that we were still fond of each other and made it a point of being very abrupt with me. I then never saw her again. Charles, her colleague told me that she had contracted cancer and passed away. What a tragic end to a beautiful life. She was only twenty-six.

I had lost another very good friend at a young age too.

Toddy was in his early thirties. Although I had known him for a short while, he had become a good friend, and provided such incredible support when the relationship with Maria took a bad turn, and I was in between jobs. We discovered we had mutual friends and socialised quite often too. Shortly after Toddy's death, a good friend of our family lost his father also through cancer. I remember this giant of a man being reduced to a frail and helpless individual, who I once had to carry into bed. Little did I know then, that this awful and absolutely ghastly deadly disease would one day haunt my life more directly.

Anyway, back to brighter subjects. After Laura, I had a brief fling with another of Dieter's lady friends from Germany. By this time, Dieter had largely given up any hope of protecting his friends from my amorous advances. I was just amazed at how many beautiful women formed his entourage. Silke was a stunning blond with all the attributes of an Aryan goddess, and I was rather proud of myself to have won her affection. As with Gisela, she was only over for a short period, our romance was restricted to a weekend.

She did invite me to visit and stay with her in Dusseldorf, but I fell ill and by the time I got around to visiting her, she was no longer available.

I had at this time moved into the house I bought with Rachel. I was also the proud owner of a BMW. It was a navy blue 520i, which was past the four-year-old mark but had been extremely well cared for and appeared almost brand new. In terms of performance, this beauty of a car still had a lot of life in her. Although it did not possess the lure or charm of the Triumph convertible, I spent many a joyous day flying down the motorway in this wonderful high-performance carriage. It was on one of my daily commutes that I accidentally ran over a pigeon and paid a very high price.

I felt ill, but continued to limp into work, thinking it was nothing more than a bad cold. I had started working in Jeallot's Hill, and it was less of a burdensome commute than to Reading. I believe that we would have met by this time. The cold persisted. Coughing and fever ensued, and I was told by the doctor to take some time off to rest. My condition grew worse. I was admitted to the hospital with pneumonia. I abhor injections, but they insisted on taking blood for tests on a twice-daily basis.

I coughed and spluttered with no end. The only relief was provided by my father's daily visits carrying my mother's delicious chicken soup. My parents were retired and staying us with us at the time and like any good Indian parents ensured the provision of homemade chicken soup as the panacea for all ills. My mother is a wonderful cook, so I was grateful for anything she sent as an alternative to the tasteless hospital fare. My father's company although at times a little impatient, was always welcome.

The doctors probed me with some highly personal questions, which only made sense when put into context. They had assumed it was Aids, as they thought it highly unusual for a young man to have contracted a serious illness at the height of a hot summer. I was horrified, especially as I had several instances of unprotected sex. Thankfully, as it turned out, it was a rare virus that was transmitted by birds, would you believe?

This was at a time before H1N1 and all that nonsense that prevailed with the so-called Asian flu. That blasted pigeon I ran over, could have caused a major pandemic, I would have gained the notoriety of 'Typhoid Mary' and caused the first human-to-human transmission of pigeon flu – as 'Fowl-flu Dave' perhaps. Although the 'Dave' bit would have added insult to injury to me, it would have been necessary to convey the required dread. The only other difference that would have then existed with the iniquitous Mary was that she was mainly a carrier of the disease, whilst I had succumbed to mine. On the matter of names for plague carriers, 'Kung-flu Dave' may not have been precisely relevant but has a nicer ring to it, don't you think? I must confess, though, that my martial arts skills are very limited – any chopping I do is almost entirely food related and kicking tends to be largely accidental when attempting to cross my legs under the table.

Sorry, I stray once again – back to my hospitalisation. When interrogated further on how the whole thing had come about, one of the doctors suggested that the virus from the said bird would have made its way into the air conditioning system of the car and caused me to breathe it in by the truckload, or more appropriately in this instance, by the chestful. I have, since then as you can well imagine always literally steered (pun intended) well clear of pigeons.

I headed off to Dusseldorf after I had recovered thinking I would pick up where I had left off with the gorgeous Silke. My dreams would crumble, as she had met someone else in the meantime. Not in the least bit surprising, as she was outstandingly attractive, and such beautiful women do not stay available for long on the singles market. The lesson learnt – don't ever keep a beautiful woman waiting. If she invites you, take the next available flight out to her. I tried to make the most of my trip to Germany, regardless of this disappointment. Dieter and his friends were a marvellous company, and truly charming and very hospitable hosts.

Dieter felt apologetic for Silke although he had no cause to, as she and I were the architects of the relationship's demise on that occasion. He looked after me like a big brother, nevertheless. I was taken out to several lunches and dinners during my time there.

I even got to drive one of his friend's Porsche at high speed on a stretch of the Autobahn.

I had driven fast in my beamer but had always been fearful of taking her beyond a hundred miles an hour too often, in case I was stopped and penalised by the ever-vigilant traffic police. It was wonderful to put the pedal to the floor and feel the sheer exhilaration of speed without fear of the consequences of arrest and incarceration.

I was not sure whether I had partaken of too many slices of all the delicious hams and cheeses or indulged in too many apple strudels, but I found it hard to fit into many of the trousers I had packed. It was not until I got home and went shopping that I noticed I had put on a lot of weight.

A combination of abandoning smoking following my hospitalisation and packing in large portions of my mother's cooking had resulted in me ballooning from my slight 28-inch waist measure to a 32-incher. Thankfully, most of the weight had spread about relatively evenly but a little more noticeably resident around the middle. It was time to enlist at a gym. I joined Holmes Place on Fulham Road and took to exercising regularly.

The filling out of my frame was long overdue. I accepted my new weight and shape and began to dress more conservatively. This was indeed a new phase. I had, like my daughter Holly become very particular about dress at an early age. Actually, I think she did a lot earlier than I can remember in my case, as she was clear about what she wanted to wear as soon as she was out of the nappy era. Other than an occasional fashion blip, Holly has maintained a good fashion sense throughout her life.

I on the other hand had undergone various phases. My school days were reminiscent mainly of flared trousers and bright shirts and wide-lapelled jackets. In the latter part of schooling and the University days a generally trendy sense including investment into a pair of leather trousers and a pair of white shoes à la Saturday Night Fever, at the insistence of then girlfriend. Then followed a period of Parisian influence despite the stint in Nigeria, given my visits to Rachel in Paris. On my return to England, and shopping with Vicky, a lovely friend from University, I began to get into high fashion mode.

It is a real pity I never at the time considered a relationship with Vicky, as she was lovely. But I do not even know if she would have been inclined to take our very strong friendship into one of being lovers. We got on incredibly well, and shared a bed a few times too; but would a relationship as sexual partners as well as friends been on the cards?

It is easy to reconsider in hindsight, but I wonder if we both had too good a friendship for it to be tested or complicated with a sexual liaison. Don't know, is the short answer. Vicky continued to be a great shopping companion and a wonderfully close friend in between my girlfriends. Being a fashion devotee herself, she helped further my interest in fashionable clothes. Following my new body shape, I had entered my yuppie dress phase.

I did still flirt with fashion though and popped into the Joseph store or Browns in South Molton Street to browse through their slightly quirky or attention-grabbing items of men's clothing. By this time, I had tried to avoid anything too 'outrageous', and steered toward something generally conservative, but with a hint of playfulness.

A design on the back of the shirt, an unusual sleeve or pocket detail. I think that is why I came to love Paul Smith's designs more. I feel that his clothes reflect a very English style of fashion, but with an unerringly attractive twist in the detail. It is clothing that I could wear even at my age without feeling out of kilter with my generation. The Paul Smith shop in Notting Hill has now become my favourite destination for apparel. Anyway, to take you back to my yuppie era, it was during one of these browsing endeavours in Browns that I met Molly, the fashion student and model.

Tall with light blonde hair worn short and large bright blue eyes, I was attracted to, but not necessarily thunderstruck by Molly. She seemed to take a liking to me, and I was happy to be entertained by her attention and patient offer of all manner of clothing to try on. My self-deprecating remarks appealed to her sense of humour too. I decided to be bold and asked her to coffee. We met at a café in St. Christopher's Place, which served the most delicious New York cheesecake. We hit it off, sharing cheesecake and making each other laugh with stories of our lives. I loved her faint Irish accent, which added a delight to listening to her talk. And talk she did, no matter the subject, she had lots to say. We dated for a while. She was very natural in her appearance, which I love incidentally (as I am not a huge fan of heavy make-up) but was not clear why exactly she modelled. That would strike me profoundly in great revelation later.

I had popped around to take her to dinner. She had just stepped out of the shower and begged for a few minutes to get dressed. She did offer me a kiss which was an adequate reward for being patient. I would have been even more so, had she let me strip her off her towel and make love to her. That I was told would come later. As I mentioned earlier, she was generally plainly but well dressed and wore little or no make-up, but she must have felt a need to really push the boat out that evening, as I had suggested dinner followed by dancing. She dressed so glamorously that the sight of her was breath-taking!

She walked into the sitting room, and the transformation from towel to dress was fabulously remarkable. It was a metamorphosis of sorts, but not from ugly pupa to beautiful butterfly, but from one of simple beauty to dazzling, glamorous wonder. She told me that she spent very little on clothes, more on fetching accessories, and loved putting things together on a small budget. The dress was something she had bought as simple black number and altered herself. Whatever she did, it worked beautifully.

She highlighted her facial features to bring out a magical and impactful transformation. Her eyes looked like even larger pools of sparkling bright blue; her lips of cherry red promised fiery kisses, and even her ears with her hair dressed back behind them warranted comment for the way they beautifully displayed her earrings. She just laughed when I eventually got my mouth working again and told her that she was truly stunning.

I could barely take my eyes off her all evening, and when we went dancing later, it looked as though many other men could not either. Making love to her that evening felt like a night spent with one of the most ravishing and beguiling women in the world.

Although our affair was brief, she left an indelible impression in my mind and my life, as I have always since preferred women who possess an inherent ability to dress well without necessarily spending a fortune on clothes and also being able to enhance their femininity with a subtle but effective application of very little make-up.

Molly helped in my wish to be fashionably conservative or conservatively fashionable, whichever phrase more correctly defines that style of fashion with my slightly fuller figure. I still had to sift through and make a major adjustment to my wardrobe. The shirts I had purchased were all baggy, so I was fine with those as they were still in vogue, unsurprisingly as I was usually a season or two ahead of the average man, but all the trousers were no longer of practical use, and I ended up giving many of them to my sister Rachel.

I was very happy to see the back of some of the suits and replaced them with a better quality of wear purchased at Joseph, Hackett, Harrods or Harvey Nichols. Thanks to Rory, who was a regular at the restaurant and like Dieter had become a close friend, I also acquired tweed and dinner jackets and some great pairs of brogues at a fair price from Hackett. Other than for the time at work, I lived in Levi's jeans and white shirts for the most part.

With new wardrobe in place, and at the recommendation of a new friend, I took up bridge.

To say I joined a bridge club would have been a trifle exaggerative. It would be more accurate to describe the process as following a friend to a bridge class, and accidentally being co-opted into some form of participation. The enlistment took place at the London School of Bridge on Kings Road in Chelsea, a short hop across the road from Peter Jones in Sloane Square which was also one of my favourite departmental stores. David, a newly acquired friend, had joined the beginner's class, and I had agreed to meet him at the bar for a drink. I was told at the bar that I could join him in his class in one of the rooms on the floor below. It was a room with a scattering of tables and a mix of people all talking animatedly and in various states of play. I ended up joining one of the tables and looking across to see one particular lady, who stood out above the rest.

A blonde with striking features and looking dressed more suitably for an evening's dinner at the Savoy rather than to play bridge. She was very hard to miss.

I paid attention to my game, not having played since University, I had to rack my brains to remember half the conventions and subtleties of bidding. Playing was never the difficulty. As children we learnt very quickly from my parents the tactics and strategies to win. How to snatch defeat from the jaws of victory was a strategy we learnt from my mother, who was a very sharp card player, but who would deliberately play to lose a hand if she felt sorry for the opposition. This approach would constantly infuriate my father whom she partnered, but she never changed.

My memory for the game held up well, thankfully. I actually loved playing bridge and played lots of it at university, where it was regarded with some respect. At school the super bright and nerdy played chess. Bridge was for those of slightly lesser intellect. But we were the more socially engaging, and a fun bunch of people to play with, some of whom I taught the game of three-nought-four. I am so happy that my daughters have now adopted this game as their own and seem to have inherited the family instinct for cards.

Nicola Gardiner, as she was then (she is now Nicola Smith MBE), thought that I had a good feel for cards and suggested that I help with the beginners, rather than play as one. I was terribly honoured. I had risen in favour from being just another participant to a role as a tutor. I felt a considerable amount of attention now focused on me, including that from Luisa.

After a few hands of bridge and post-mortem discussions at which she seemed to hang on my every word, I was invited around for lunch at her place. We chatted and she seemed a very enjoyable companion outside of the bridge environment. I just had a hard time focusing on the conversation as she was clad in a bikini and transparent sarong of sorts.

Nothing happened at this first date. I never expected anything to. I found her very attractive, but assumed from her luxury flat, her dress, jewellery, art, etc., that she was way out of my league. All that changed on the second date.

She invited me over for dinner. We were having a glass of wine and discussing music. She loved opera, as did I.

I would not profess much knowledge of names of particular arias but had developed a keen appreciation primarily through my father's incessant instruction to acquire some European culture with repeated loud renditions of works from Puccini, Verdi and others.

I was sat on the floor by her feet as she lay on the *chaise longue*. I tilted my head back to say something to her. She leant forward and held my face as she kissed me. Wow! It was amazing. Firstly, I had never been kissed in that position before, and it truly was a wonderful first experience. Secondly, and more importantly, it was so nice to have a woman show the initiative. I was still unable to read a situation well enough to know when a woman desires to be kissed.

As indicated to you previously, I work on the principle of 3 dates, unless it is one of those alcohol-infused college discos or school dances, where the aim is to apply one's lips to those of a member of the opposite sex as soon as practicable. As you will know from my correspondence to you on the subject of kisses, my previous experiences would suggest that unless one had the benefit of the clear light of day, misjudgements do take place and regrets sometimes arise. I had grown accustomed to preferring to err on the safe side.

There was, of course, no cause for concern with Luisa.

I found her incredibly attractive and visions of her in her bikini provided constant reminders of what delights one could behold under her clothing. As the kissing grew more intense, so did the discomfort of having my neck tilted back at an awkward angle. I was able to adjust my position without losing the passion of the moment and we ended up with me on the *chaise longue* and her delightfully unfastening my clothing.

She was an incredible practitioner in the art of seduction. What surprised me was how expertly she had me unclothed without my having even removed a stitch from her. She let me remedy that, and thankfully the skills of unhooking a bra with a single hand did not desert me at this juncture. We both approached dinner half-heartedly and half-naked after passionate lovemaking. It did not take much to resume our endeavours, which we both seemed intent on continuing well into the night.

The generally held belief, amongst young men at least, about older women being great lovers, proved to be true. There was not a single delight I was not introduced to. One sometimes merely had to lie back and think of England. There was no place in the house that remained sacred or sacrosanct, as lovemaking took place on the dining table, kitchen counter, breakfast bar, bath, shower, hallway floor, balcony and even the stairs. I must have led a very sheltered life up until that point, as I had assumed that the bed was the ultimate destination for such intimate activity, unless occasion deemed otherwise. Not so. The bed was primarily to sleep in, after exhaustive effort everywhere else.

Our life together was not just one of making love, although one would not have been averse to that. We played an enormous amount of bridge too. I was now her personal tutor and adviser. If we happened to be a group of five, I would opt to sit next to her and guide her game. I could see that some of her friends were envious of her young tutor and beau. I had always just assumed myself just another bridge player, but after the pat on the head from Nicola at the bridge club, I was regarded as the beginner's bridge guru. I enjoyed bathing in the unexpected limelight. Although, I loved playing cards, I sometimes just wished to be in her company.

Luisa worked for a major airline on their long-haul routes, so she was often away. I looked forward to her return for us to spend time getting to know each other better. We did to some extent, but her love for bridge and her eagerness to learn and play seemed to sometimes overtake the need for us to enjoy time as a couple. I was happy to give in to this eagerness, as she was always attentive and loving afterwards and demonstrated an insatiable appetite for sex. She was more than willing to please; so, who was I to complain?

She was also very thoughtful and generous. She organised a surprise 30th birthday party for me. It was the one birthday I had been dreading. As with Rachel Green's reaction in the series Friends, turning 30 was the most unwanted birthday celebration.

What exactly is it about this age that concerned me? Was it because I looked back and saw no great achievement in my life? Was it because I was fearful of the fact that the days of irresponsibility and fun were no longer there to be enjoyed? Whatever the cause, I was clearly not looking forward to this celebration.

Luisa was very sweet. She had arranged for a few friends to come over to help me commemorate the occasion. We played bridge, of course. In bed, later that evening she made me feel very special indeed. She always did. No matter how late the evening, she was always wanting to please me. Although that particular evening went well, the tipping point of turning thirty had been reached, and the nagging fear of getting older never left me.

It was a tipping point also as far as world affairs were concerned. This was the year of the tearing down of the Iron Curtain that had cruelly divided people and nations for many years. Luisa and I were avid viewers of the scenes around the Berlin wall, which had been one the major symbols of this divide, but which was now being justifiably and irretrievably torn down by several eager hands. We discussed this matter and that of the Cold War, which in turn led to a discussion of cosmopolitan relationships, which in turn led to a lot of passionate love-making. If, by now, you felt that our relationship was constituted of bridge, sex, conversation and more sex, you would be totally and absolutely correct.

On reflection, there was much to enjoy in my twenties. Besides meeting many wonderful women with whom to romance in this era, I had accumulated many new friends, whilst maintaining friendships with many from university. Although my career seemed directionless, I enjoyed myself enormously on the social front.

Kedgeree and champagne picnics at Henley, leisurely days of tennis spectacle at Wimbledon, clothes shopping with charming and attractive lady companions, numerous dinner parties and summer balls.

I loved these black-tie events and once actually was part of the organising committee, with some very good friends for the Jazzmin Ball raising funds for a charity. There is something about the ambience at a Ball that makes the event an almost magical evening. The women collectively look enchanting, and the men at their most debonair. I always felt most at home in a dinner jacket anyway, so any Ball was a delight to attend. Turning thirty was somehow a goodbye to this era.

Did I really get to know Luisa as a person? I thought I did, but I was never really sure. I did constantly crave her company. I thought of her often and our embraces were full of longing and passion. What had commenced as a sexual adventure turned into an emotionally intense affair as I grew to love her. I only realised how much I did when our relationship finally came to an end.

I found her incredibly attractive. I loved gazing into her lovely eyes as we supped together, often holding hands. She always dressed elegantly and was a pleasure to accompany anywhere. She loved art as much as I did, and we loved exploring exhibitions and galleries together. She rather admired my collection of erotic art too.

The only aspect of our relationship that I found disconcerting was that she never felt comfortable in the company of my peer group, and we tended, as a result, to socialise more often with her friends, who were predominantly in their forties and fifties. I had to therefore catch up with my group of friends when she was away on her trips. I was happy with the arrangement, and completely heartbroken to find myself without her in my life. Many of my friends thought otherwise, and felt I was best out of that relationship.

I am sure you felt the brunt of the unburdening of my sorrow upon you. Did I weep continuously on your shoulder? I found it very difficult to come to terms with the fact that Luisa and I were no longer. I tried calling upon her friends for advice on what I should do. I desperately wanted to understand what had gone wrong. Was it just my ego taking a bruising for being ceremoniously dumped after a two- and half-year affair? I doubt it, as I have been ditched before and although I grieved a little, I soon bounced back like the proverbial phoenix from the ashes, fired up for the next romantic crusade.

It was not just for the sex either. I was sure. I met another older lady a few months later. I obviously had the Mrs Robinson syndrome well and truly established at that point. After the courting, she was more than happy for me to bed her. The night came. After a few glasses of wine, the kisses began and gathered momentum. It was at that point that I realised I was just looking for sexual relief. I had no intention to prolong this relationship any further than a night of sexual gratification. I could not face the avoidance and lies that would invariably follow the coital endeavour, and I decided I would end it there and then.

I told her that I was in love with someone else and that it would be wrong for me to entangle her in a web of emotions of my making. I was rather proud of myself for being the ultimate gentleman, but a part of me still considered my actions a trifle premature. I wondered if I should have at least completed the evening of lust, as she was already mostly undressed at this point and allowed myself the pleasure of rampant sex with an obviously willing partner, before conveying the bad news. A sort of, and almost literal, 'shoot first and ask questions later' approach.

I think that perhaps works with some like Gisela and Silke, etc who are those I was not opposed to seeing again, but others ...?

Forever the wish to conduct oneself in a gentlemanly manner, in my view. My *noblesse oblige*, when it comes to treatment of the fairer sex. So, if I do have many barren periods in my life, it is sometimes largely of my own doing. I would appreciate your sympathy, nevertheless.

And there you have it. Another love fallen by the wayside.

It took me a long time to get over Luisa.

I sometimes wonder how she is now. I would definitely like to meet her again and just understand what went wrong between us, so that I may leave the ghost of that relationship to rest. 'Closure', I believe, is the applicable term.

I fear that I have yet again taken up much of your time in a lengthy missive.

I trust, however, that you understand me better as a result.

Love,

David

Letter 19 – Solitary Christmas

January 2020

Dear Geoff,

   This is the first Christmas that I have spent completely alone!

   I was trying to remember if I ever spent the Christmas period so alone at any time in my past, and unless my memory fails me very badly, it appears that I have never ever done so in my life before. If I had not been with family, I was staying in the warm and welcoming home of friends.

   This is very much a first and hopefully, my dear friend, the very last of such a solitary Christmas.

   I miss my girls so very much. Ever since they came into my life as beautiful little babies, I have never felt as truly blessed as I am with them. This is especially so at Christmas time. I love Christmas. Ever since I was little, I felt that there was something truly magical about this time of year. Even now, when I should have grown weary and cynical, I cannot help but feel instead that Santa will indeed come to town!

   Whilst on the subject of Santa Claus, I must tell you of a trip my ex arranged for us to Lapland to see that wonderful man in person. The children were still young and enthralled at the prospect. Actually, so was I. It consisted only of a journey there and back in a day, but it was such a wonderful experience, that it seemed an eternity of joy. The excitement was palpable from the moment we arrived and were taken to what appeared to be a large hangar to hurriedly dress ourselves in the thermal suits ' provided. The rush for thermal suits could have erupted into a bun fight though, as some families comprised errant children and rude parents when it came to obtaining the appropriate sizes of garments. We did not allow this behaviour to mar our experience.

The snowmobile ride to 'Santa's Grotto' was an incredible joy in itself. It was hard, though attempting to multi-task. I have mentioned to you before the difficulty I face in attempting more than one task, or for that matter thought, at a time.

On this occasion, it involved holding onto a child on my lap on the bumpy ride, capturing this moment on film without dropping the camera, and keeping my now ungloved hands warm. All this whilst also simultaneously viewing the sky above us beautifully bathed with a litter of colour in the Northern Lights.

The girls were wonderfully patient despite their obvious excitement to see Santa. There was much to keep us occupied, whilst we awaited our turn. The tour operators made a splendid job of providing an overall enthralling experience, allowing families to enjoy the various other activities on offer including all manner of rides – a sleigh drawn by reindeers, sleds by huskies, and toboggans down mini slopes.

The food may have comprised nothing more than a searingly warmed sludge, but was very welcome, nevertheless. Anything hot was appreciated merely to fend off the biting cold. Several cups of hot chocolate were consumed. The only downside to this provision of warmth was the process of peeling layers off thermal wear to pee, which the girls and I seemed to want to do quite often.

The look of sheer adulation and joy on their faces when Chloe and Holly eventually met Santa was remarkably memorable. I believe that I was equally enthralled

and shook his hand with great fervour. I was even inclined to hug him and tell him that I never stopped believing in him or the magic of Christmas but thought that
it may appear a little too excessive an expression of joy
and chose to limit my enthusiasm to an effusive handshake. He was very sweet about posing for the obligatory
photograph with them.

Their presents were, of course not to be opened until
Christmas Day, but Chloe and Holly both registered even
more delight on their faces when taking receipt of gifts
directly from Santa. It was an infectious delight, which
we shared with them in our broad smiles. It was a short
but very memorable trip.

I am so happy that between my ex and I, we managed
to keep the children convinced of the existence of Santa
for many of their young years. I hate to say this, but I
honestly believe that one of the reasons for the dysfunc-
tional society we have these days is that people no longer
regard Christmas as the best time of year to extend goodwill to all men, to reach out and re-establish family link-
ages and generally be of good cheer.

If you remember, my mention to you of warm sunny
days of the English summer bringing about a general
sense of *joie de vivre* and good spiritedness. Well, that is
exactly what we need more of, even if it is created intan-
gibly by making children believe in the existence of Santa
Claus. Their fragile and all too easily lost childhood innocence in this regard is so important to preserve for as
long as possible.

Chloe was almost 12 when she discovered that Santa's
gifts were really those of her parents. The only shame was
that the revelation was made to her by the children of
friends we were staying with, rather than a gentle admission by us as parents that we would have preferred.

Holly's discovery of Santa's reality was far more brutal, as her poor young mind was very troubled by discovering one of her cards to Santa in the most unexpected of places. Her uncle had unthinkingly folded her card and used it to wedge a window open. The card had fallen, and so had her childhood dreams.

I am truly thankful for the many Christmases I had with them as young children. I remember staying up late on many nights in the lead up to Christmas to wrap their presents. And there were many. Their stocking gifts alone took enormous effort, as I had to make sure that I used a completely different wrapping paper to differentiate those from us as parents and friends to those from Santa.

However well prepared I thought I was, I invariably ended up wrapping presents well into the night. It involved trying to recall exactly where I had hidden the ones already wrapped, adding ribbons and bows to these wrapped gifts, and arranging them all around the tree in a manner that appeared as though Santa had been and delivered gifts for all in the family. I had to then set about filling everyone's stocking, including my own, which usually took me until three in the morning on Christmas Eve. Lights were only turned off and my head allowed to hit the pillow after I had left convincing evidence of Santa's visit with a half-consumed mince pie, and a poorly chewed carrot (for Rudolph).

It was worth the long night to witness the exuberance and uncontained excitement the girls displayed when they awoke (generally very early) to leap upon our bed with their stockings brimming with a multitude of gifts. Despite going to bed late the previous night, I was never tired for Christmas Day. I was probably just as excited as the children were, sitting at my feet enthusiastically unwrapping each stocking gift with an utter and unrestrained show of delight.

But it is not just Christmas Day that I enjoy. I love the whole lead up to the celebration of the day and all the days that followed too. I realise that for commercial reasons, Christmas for retailers sometimes commences as early as September, but I love it. If it were not for the fact that I love prolonging summers for as long as possible, I would be happy if they began even earlier. I will happily listen to Christmas songs being played repeatedly throughout the whole time, without ever getting bored. I could also consume a gazillion mince pies without tiring of their delicious taste.

Mince pies must be one of the most divinely ambrosial foods ever created by man. Having said "man" I would not be in the least bit surprised if the recipe had in fact come down from the heavens, perhaps in the form of another tablet, containing clear instructions for their creation on earth that Moses had in his possession but had chosen not to immediately disclose to others.

I could never, and still cannot, resist devouring as many of them as I possibly could over the Christmas period. As you can imagine, I have now become a little bit of a connoisseur as a result. Not all mince pies are wonderful, however. Avoid Mr Kipling's offering like the plague. He supposedly makes 'exceeding good cakes', but in my view falls dismally short when it comes to mince pies. 'Tesco's Finest' still reigns supreme, though Harrods, Marks & Spencer, Waitrose and Harvey Nichols have great offerings too. I recently had some from Fortnum and Masons which also tasted like little pieces of heaven.

Should we ever have the opportunity to partake of them together, please note that I like my mince pies warmed slightly and served with lashings of thick fresh cream.

One of the down sides of spending Christmas in Zimbabwe, besides the weather (being unbearably hot at this time), is the unavailability of a decent range of mince pies. They are edible, but for me, mince pies are not just to be consumed like any other food but are to be delicately savoured. Each bite or spoonful being allowed to reside on the palate for that moment longer before the onset of any digestive process. The same approach I have to caviar, I would say. In England I would make sure that we held a good stock of mince pies to last the entire season from the preparatory period to the season finale, or even beyond if at all possible.

The other edible must for the festive season is Christmas pudding. Anyone who leaves this item off their Christmas list must have their heads thoroughly examined. I am happy to do without turkey, but Christmas pudding is a pre-requisite to completing a good Christmas dinner. Preferably partaken of whilst watching a good movie and suitably inebriated. As with mince pies, there are several competing brands in this product, but I hope that you will be guided by my recommendation for the ones developed for Harrods, particularly the variety which boasts an abundance of brandy.

I appreciate that turkey forms an integral part of Christmas lunch and a multitude of other meals in many households, but I am not its biggest fan. I use the words multitude of meals appropriately, as there have been some Christmases, in my experience when the enormous turkey has provided sufficient leftovers to continue appearing in many subsequent meals – pizzas, pies, fried rice, and worst of all – curry! I feel that I have already, from these previous Christmases, consumed enough turkey to last me a lifetime.

In terms of food, I much preferred the Christmases, Rachel and I hosted when we shared a house in Fulham, where seafood tended to dominate the primary meal offerings. Between Rachel, Maureen, John, Carole and I, we prepared an absolutely delicious array of seafood. There was a feast of fish, prawns, crab, clams and mussels. I cannot claim to have actually cooked any of the aforementioned but was always on hand to provide help and certainly to lay out serving dishes and top up everyone's drinks. We would then sit together to enjoy the collectively and lovingly prepared food, ensuring no one was excluded from the table. When the kids were little, they would occupy the several welcoming laps of uncles and aunts.

Spending most of the days in varying degrees of intoxication, was the other joy of the Christmas period. I do not remember being completely incapacitated, but generally very merrily intoxicated. In case you were wondering if we ever flouted the law, I can assure you that none of us drove whilst in any state of inebriation.

Speaking of inebriation, one Christmas Eve was made especially memorable because I attended midnight mass a trifle intoxicated, but only because a good but incorrigible friend of the family, Tony insisted on taking a bottle of champagne to the service. He then proceeded to top-up my glass frequently. I am glad to advise you that neither of us drove that evening. Coherent and cheery without causing drunken offence, would be the category into which I would proudly place ourselves.

When it came to alcohol at Christmas time, Rachel and I would usually hold ourselves in check until midday and then commence with champagne, progressing onto white or red wines, subject to what meals were on offer and also very much as the mood took us. It was only when all of us felt suitably satiated, would we adjourn to the sitting room to open the rest of what had earlier in the day been a vast array of presents under the tree. Our tree always formed a centre of attention in the room.

What would Christmas be without a proper tree? It is the very essence of Christmas; don't you think? You can almost imagine the strain poor Joseph was put under on the Eve of Jesus' birth – not only would he have had to be by Mary's side aiding her intake of breath and assuring her that all would be well without any need for epidurals, but also having to rush out before the stores closed to find a suitable tree and decorate it before the wise men arrived.

Everything is centred around this integral item.

I have spent many Christmases with fake trees, especially the ones spent in Zimbabwe, but although they can look pretty, it is not quite the same. The comparison between Mr Kipling's mince pies and those of Tesco's Finest comes to mind. I remember even in Malaysia, Brunei or India, when my parents would go out of their way to secure a real fir tree or a suitably big branch thereof. Many they found looked anaemic and a little bare in hindsight, but more importantly, they were real.

Did I ever tell you that one of the first things that endeared me to my ex was her willingness to indulge me in the purchase of a really tall tree on the very first Christmas we spent together? We had just started dating then, and she gaily accompanied me to a place in Wandsworth, where I was told they had trees for sale at reasonable prices.

Once there, we chose an exceedingly imposing one with a bevy of branches. As I was at the time staying with my mother in a high-ceilinged but sparsely furnished flat in Chelsea, I felt sure that it could be accommodated with ease. Choosing and purchasing were the easy part. Getting it home proved to be a veritable mission. I was not prepared to pay the exorbitant delivery price, so we opted to take it on the bus instead. Despite the netting which contained its branches, manoeuvring this tall beast of a tree into the bus was not the easiest of undertakings, but we persevered, encouraged by the cheers of the driver and passengers collectively.

Unfortunately, we ended up going a little further out of the way than intended and had to walk for miles back home, each with one end of the tree in our slavish endeavour. We did stop for coffee *enroute* to keep our spirits up and our hands warm.

As soon as we cut away the netting that bound the branches, the tree opened up to reveal itself as a truly splendid specimen. It looked magnificent even without a single ornament decorating its branches. It was worth every single penny spent, and every ounce of sweat expended.

Last Christmas, the girls and I bought a rather wonderful tree too. The only problem was that it was a little taller and broader than we had anticipated. The broader was something we could deal with reasonably well – it just needed a few more baubles than we had purchased, and also an additional string of lights. The height was another matter. Thanks to a little saw obtained from the concierge downstairs, we valiantly applied ourselves to rectifying this issue. I sawed, whilst Holly acted as tree-turner and Chloe cleared up the debris. The joint effort paid off, and once again a magnificent Christmas tree rightly dominated the attention in our household.

This Christmas, I had a little fake tree to erect and decorate. I was not enthusiastic about doing anything initially, but I love Christmas with a passion, and I could not help but try and make the most of it, however solitary it was going to be.

I am sure you will agree with me that even the prettiest of trees, real or otherwise, can have its beauty marred by over decoration. The girls and I seem to share an opinion that each Christmas should be themed to a colour or pair of compatible colours, like red and gold for example. We would not add anything garish, like multi-coloured lights or tinsel. This Christmas I decorated the tree with only red baubles and bows and it looked so marvellous that it was worthy of a photograph to send to you.

The decorations around the house also needed to be prominently displayed, but sensibly subtle. So, with a few choice pieces distributed hither and thither, alongside some candles and tea lights, I felt I had created the desired effect at home this Christmas. At least it felt a little more like Christmas, albeit a lonely one.

The only problem I was left with now was one of the presents. The base of the tree was noticeably devoid of a spread of the beautifully wrapped gifts of previous Christmases.

I abhor wrapping irregularly shaped gifts. I am at my best with square and rectangular ones, sometimes extending to doing a grand job of cylindrical shapes too, but triangular and spherical shapes have me holding my hands up in surrender. Do you not suffer the same fate with these dastardly things? I often look for boxes to put these things in just to save myself the frustration.

I decided to approach the matter of a lack of presents in much the same way I had several years previously when I had little or no funds to expend. I had to make an outlay for some wrapping paper, horrifically priced here, but with no alternative, and with an attitude of 'as needs must', I set about wrapping up several items from the kitchen cupboards, focusing on the easy shapes - boxes of cereal, mince pies and even cans of various content, from beans to tuna fish. I soon ended up with a delightful spread of 'gifts' under the tree. Included within this array were presents for Dunmore and Sarudzai (for whom I assembled a large hamper of various items of food), the Dawson family (with whom I was to have Christmas lunch), and the dogs.

These clever little mutts had sniffed out their treats though and had begun to attack all the gifts with great gusto in order to find theirs. I had to now remove every single one on display until Christmas Eve. I was a little annoyed with these furry friends of mine for preventing me from having the gifts under the tree, but simultaneously impressed with their ingenuity to unwrap gifts slowly but effectively with their eager teeth and paws.

There was obviously a distinct lack of presents for myself, but in all honesty, I was really not too bothered, as I was quite happy to treat myself when I was once more adequately equipped with sufficient funds. I could happily forego for now. Besides, I told myself that I would rather be in receipt of gifts I would genuinely appreciate. It made no sense to gift for gift's sake.

Why do people think it is difficult to buy gifts for me? I am a man of very simple and very clear needs, as you know. I am exceeding happy to be gifted the usual socks, underwear, aftershave, skincare products, books, etc., but all I ask is that these items are purchased to my liking. I love jazzy socks and lightly patterned shirts, but they have to be 100% cotton and preferably from shops such as Paul Smith, Ralph Lauren, Margaret Howell, Thomas

Pink, Jack Wills, and those of similar ilk subject to budget.

Similarly, with underwear, except that you could include Hollister to that list. Books – preferably with action packed narrative, truly mystifying crime or classics, as anything too intellectually demanding has my eyes glazing over in the very first chapter.

I would like to think that I am reasonably well read and would not wish to come across as a complete peasant in the literary sense, but there are some books, including those appearing on bestseller lists and gaining other critical acclaim, which I struggle to read and on completion have left me rather unimpressed and deeply disappointed for having given them time. I suppose, it's just like one's appreciation of art – beauty in the eye of the beholder and so forth...?

What else? Ah, yes aftershaves. These should be a relatively easy purchase one would have thought. I make it abundantly clear my likes and dislikes in this regard, but somehow end up in receipt of fragrances which are a little too publicly popular for my liking. Skincare products – thankfully Carole never fails in this regard with a good supply of Clarins items.

If ever you feel inclined to treat me to something truly special, anything from Tiffany or Cartier would go down extremely well indeed!

I would like to think that I apply considerable thought when procuring presents for others. One of the joys of the long preparatory period available for Christmas shopping is having the time to research and obtain ideas for perfect presents for the various people one wants, or is obliged, to gift to. I hope that the thought applied is appreciated. I do not always get it right I am sure, but I do for most of the time, I feel. The best arrangement I think is to have one produce a gift wish list, as one does for a wedding, in order that the procurer is very clear about what will be well received.

There are many occasions, I have had to feign surprise and pleasure, which as you know is something I am not terribly good at. Many of these items have ended up in the gift box, which I rummage through now and again to find something suitable to pass onto someone else, who may be more appreciative. There must be many practitioners of this art I fear, as I have been at the receiving end of what they deem suitable to pass on to me.

Whilst my Christmas Eve here may have been spent in solitude, not so Christmas Day. Thankfully I was invited to join the Dawson family for Christmas lunch. Oddly enough once the news had spread that I was *toute soule* for Christmas, many other invitations arrived for Christmas lunch. I had already signed up to the Dawsons' for that day, so I politely declined the invitation in the hope that it would be extended for the following days during which I was totally free. But like London buses, they all came at once. I had made my choice, and that was it until the following year, I assume.

I loved lunch at the Dawsons. I am glad I had chosen their home for Christmas fare.

I had lost count of the number of times we had holidayed with them over the years. So many memorable trips to their holiday homes at Lake Kariba and the Eastern Highlands of Zimbabwe. I am sure I had mentioned to you a beach holiday we enjoyed in Mozambique with them also.

They were a marvellous couple, and I was very happy that the girls seemed similarly attached to their children – Jess and Nic. I have often considered them an extension of my family, and it was rather touching that they felt inclined to extend their hospitality to me on this occasion.

Lunch was delightful. We sat together around their large dining table. Sue and Simon had also invited some of their in-laws, as well as Sue's brother Peter, (or Touggs, as he preferred), and his little boy Rob. I was delighted to see Jess and Nic back from university. They had matured - no longer the pretty little girls I had first met, but now wonderfully grown women.

We had a jovial lunch with the party hats and corny jokes to accompany pleasant conversation and delicious food. I exercised restraint for fear of overfilling my stomach which, since my operation, has only experienced digestion of reasonable content, but was pleasantly replete, nevertheless.

We played several games of croquet. I must confess to losing most of them with my partner but blame the fact that the opposition seemed to enjoy a flow of lucky breaks and my game was a trifle impaired from consumption of a few too many glasses of sparkling wine. Jess recorded a part of the game, and a playback of the video suggested that I appeared to strike the ball well, despite slight intoxication. And I looked the part of an accomplished player. That, my friend, as you well know, is all that matters.

The days after that passed much too quickly and I failed to complete many of the intended tasks. Other than some minor tidying up of my wardrobe to select further items to sell and a few adjustments to furniture and furnishings, my days were spent either recovering from harsh workouts with Givemore, (you would have assumed he would have exercised more goodwill over this period, wouldn't you?), or watching TV. I watched "Elf", which is my favourite ever Christmas film several times over, before deciding that I should partake of some mind improving reading also, or at least extend my repertoire of visual engagement beyond the "Elf" DVD. I sought some entertainment offerings on Netflix, and subsequently watched several episodes of "The Crown" and "Flash". I can admit to the enjoyment of "The Crown" but must warn you that the other series was only mildly more engaging than watching grass grow.

I sometimes wonder what it is that makes one sit through shows that are so excruciatingly bad. Is it some underlying masochistic tendency to understand the limits of one's endurance for mental torture, or to see if what started off as bad could degenerate even further? It was a relief to get back to some sanity and regularity at the office when we opened again a few days ago.

The New Year was full of promise. I had been invited to two separate events and was quite excited to attend both. I joined Sue and Simon and some of their friends for supper and early celebrations before heading off to Shingai and Karen's for an all-nighter. This was one of the better New Year's Eve celebrations.

Those of the recent past have not really registered as terribly exciting and for now stored in the very dim recesses of my mind. The exciting parties of youth lamentably seemed no longer.

How wonderful those nights were when one ended up going straight from party onto breakfast the following morning sometimes forsaking sleep for more than forty-eight hours. I shall have to address this in the coming years.

This year's celebration was a reasonably good start, and hopefully sets the tone for the rest of the year. I got home at around five in the morning, to be greeted excitedly by the dogs.

It would have been nice to have also been in the arms of a loved one. I shall remain hopeful that this may prevail during the course of this year.

I trust you had a wonderful and restful period.

My love to you and your family,

David

Letter 20 – Musical Memories

February 2020

Dear Geoff,

I have just listened to a song by Tavares called "Heaven Must Be Missing An Angel".

This always leaves me itching to leave my seat, grab the nearest available partner, and head purposefully to the dance floor. It now makes me think of H and how descriptive it is of her.

I love dancing, anyway, and there is always some great classically soulful beat being struck that never fails to draw me toward the dance floor, like that of Michael Jackson's "Billy Jean" or James Brown's "Get Up Offa That Thing" and "Sex Machine", for example.

A more recent set of dance floor draws for me would be "Moves Like Mick Jagger" by Maroon Five, "Cake By The Ocean" by DNCE, "A Lonely Night" by the Weeknd and "This Girl" by Kungs & Cookin On 3 Burners.

I would never profess to be a great dancer, but I certainly like to give it a go when I am in the mood, and the song becomes too difficult to resist swinging a shoe or two, even if it's on my own.

Did you know that I once won a prize for dancing at the club I went to in my youth? It was all rather unexpected, as I was quite happy doing my own 'thing' with a group of friends, but the crowd began to clear around the girl I was dancing with, to the cheering encouragement of the DJ who obviously appreciated our dancing. I suppose it may have helped that I was with a partner who was dancing rather suggestively with me. We both won a bottle of champagne.

I did not get to sleep with the girl I was dancing with, which probably was not a bad thing as I had not gained a clear view of her face and may have regretted waking up to find myself in yet another awkward morning routine of polite exchange with no wish to continue further interaction. I was happy with the champagne.

As a student champagne was a real treat, as good sparkling white wines, especially from the 'New World' were not readily available then, and as students we were rarely in a position to stretch to more than some reasonably drinkable *vin de table*.

It is one of the reasons I loved being invited to a dinner party hosted by those in gainful employment, as I could indulge in my enjoyment of the finer wines, without feeling that I had to torture my palate with the equivalent of brake fluid that usually passed for an alcoholic beverage at student parties. The drink may have been poor, but the music was usually good.

I could live without most things, but I would be distraught if my life were to be led without music. I don't really know when it occurred to me that music was an integral part of my life, defining me in some ways, but more importantly serving to conjure up memories of events – happy or sad.

As you will recall from my earlier letters, as a child marbles, fishing, butterflies and food were sources of delight. Music did not feature. I progressed to chasing girls, whilst retaining an interest in fishing, but music was just part of the pleasure to be enjoyed dancing with them, (girls not fish), at parties.

All the pop songs were heralded. I was particularly good at the 'Twist' and made sure that I displayed this to good effect to impress a prospective girlfriend. I suppose I took music for granted. Both my parents loved music of all *genre*, from Nat King Cole to Elvis Presley, Louis Armstrong to Glenn Miller, and Mozart to Benjamin Britten and as a result the record player, radio or whatever other music medium, was never silent, dispensing music at all hours, other than the sacred hours set aside for news or a particular television favourite.

I developed a love for music I assume through having it constantly around me at home.

It was not portable at that time to my father's dismay, as he would have otherwise taken it everywhere with him had it been possible.

So, we enjoyed it for the most part at our home or at homes of others who shared our love of music. There were few such homes however, as most had the television as their mainstay of entertainment. We were somewhat a rarity in families who when indoors derived entertainment through playing games together as a family, rather than having reliance on the television. Music, of course, played continuously in the background.

It was not until I started at university that I began to truly appreciate that music was an important part of shaping who I had become and was now an aspect I could not live without. I invested in a stereo system with my very first student grant cheque.

The money was intended as an allowance for living costs, but music was more important to me than food or transport. I would soon forego lunch and happily walked miles if the sacrifice was made for a record that I had to have.

Music was so important to me that, wherever I moved to, the first thing I did was to set-up the stereo system so that I could listen to music whilst unpacking everything else.

I thought that of my children, it would be Chloe who inherited my love to be surrounded by music, because she responded so positively to music as a child. At home or in the car, she always asked for music, and even bounced up and down animatedly as a baby to MC Hammer's "U Can't Touch This" before she could even talk. But, strangely enough, it is Holly who has embraced this love of music more fervently.

Speaking of Chloe's early love for music, I recall a trip to India from Harare, which routed us through Mauritius. She was just over a year old, and we had gone for a walk on a promenade adjacent to the hotel in Port Louis. We stopped to watch a filming of a movie. Chloe obviously enjoyed the music and began bopping up and down in her rather enchanting and inimitable style. Someone on the film crew must have noticed this, as all of a sudden, the cameras slid on tracks toward us together with a huge collection of the film crew.

The cameras focused on Chloe, who was overwhelmed by the unexpected attention, stopped dancing and began crying instead. She was immediately picked up and comforted but had possibly missed a unique opportunity to become an overnight Bollywood sensation. The film leads adored her, and we later had the opportunity to have pictures of Chloe taken with the beautiful Indian actress Raveena Tandon and her co-star at the time, Govinda, I believe.

Holly was five, if I recall correctly, when we gave her a CD player and Michael Jackson's "History Album". That act, served as a tipping point in terms of music in her life. It was probably the best present we gave her. I had never seen such a young child become so absorbed in music. Not only did she develop a love for Michael Jackson's music but was capable of reciting the lyrics flawlessly.

There was no looking back for this child who was now keen to explore other genres of music too, rummaging actively through the collection of CDs, and sitting with me to choose new songs to download from iTunes to play on my iPod in our car journeys together. Holly continues to enjoy her love of music, and probably like me, cannot now possibly exist without it.

Music has also become a means by which I can reference or catalogue my life. Certain songs trigger memories of an event or person or sometimes just a poignant period in my life.

The most notable and immediately recognisable ones include those I shall recount to you in this letter, but not in any chronological order, so please bear with me as I skip back and forth through the various chapters in the musical story of my life.

I always think of my father when I hear the song "Living Years" by Mike and the Mechanics. I regret not telling him how much I loved him when sat by his bedside before he passed away. I never got to tell him how much I appreciated the sacrifices they both made as parents to ensure their children obtained a good education and a grounded start in life.

He had been ill for a few days, but we had every expectation that he would pull through. I think that he had just grown weary of being shunted from pillar to post and had no wish to live out any further days in a care home. I could empathise, as however comfortable these places were and no matter how attentive the care given by staff, they lacked the warmth of a loving home.

He took his last breath in April of 2006, on a Charing Cross hospital bed in London, surrounded by three of his five children. We were at his bedside, but we never got to say all the things we would have wanted him to know before he left, hence the memory of pain when I hear this song. Little did I know that I would soon be mourning the loss of a sibling also.

At Rachel's suggestion, we opted for Mozart's Flute Concerto for our wedding music, and what a delightful choice it was. I have such wonderful memories of that day in September 1996, when even the weather played a part, in making it a truly remarkable occasion. The only pity being that this particular memory is not one that I wish to rekindle too often for fear of re-living the considerable amount of unnecessary pain caused by irrevocable separation. I just choose, therefore, to focus only on the happier times of this particular union and the two wonderful gifts fortuitously resulting from it, by way of my children Chloe and Holly.

"Samba Pa Ti" by Santana, "Whiter Shade of Pale" by Procol Harum and "Me and Mrs. Jones" by Billy Paul, remind me of all my teen quests for dance floor kisses at many parties. They constituted a category of songs which when played, made it imperative to be on the dance floor with a girl of one's choice. There was a high degree of possibility that whichever girl accepted the dance, would at some point during the sombre songs proffer her lips to be kissed.

It was, therefore, imperative to position oneself to capitalise on this prospect, as failure would invariably involve standing in desperate solitude nursing a drink, alongside a shattered ego. A song called "Je T'aime… Moi Non Plus" by Jane Birkin and Serge Gainsbourg, was also held in high regard in this category, and a racing certainty for generating prolonged kisses.

In my university days, many a kiss was sought to a song by Rose Royce called "Wishing On a Star". It would be interesting to know what the popular songs are these days for the dance floor intimacy. I think that "Careless Whisper" by George Michael, was probably the last song I recall kissing anyone on the dance floor to. It may have been Maria.

But that was eons ago. Man has been to space and back many times since. Would it even be appropriate to do so now at our age? Or would there be buns hurled at our heads with calls to "get a room", and then unceremoniously hurled out of the premises with stark warnings to never return? I wonder.

Christmas songs – "Last Christmas", "Rocking Around the Christmas Tree", "Jingle Bell Rock", "Driving Home for Christmas", "Step into Christmas", "Santa Claus is Coming to Town", "It's Beginning To Look A Lot Like Christmas", "Rockin' Robin" and "White Christmas" are just a few of the songs, I play on an almost constant repeat over the Christmas period every year. As you already know, my very definition of the onset of the 'Christmas period' is rather vague, and currently could start at any time after the first week in September or whenever summer is declared officially over. I do hold myself in check for the sake of preserving sanity in others, and only begin playing Christmas songs during the last week in November.

There is something magical about this time of the year, and I cannot help but feel childlike again, honestly believing that Santa would put in an appearance, and make my wish come true. Christmas songs are vital to this fantasy.

Speaking of Christmas songs, the song "All I Want for Christmas is You" sung by Mariah Carey is particularly poignant for me, as it invokes thoughts of H's first ever Christmas message to me in December of 2017, and how it served to tip me over into falling madly in love with her, if I were previously only teetering on the edge.

I was standing in a queue at Waitrose at the time purchasing more mince pies and other Christmas essentials, when I heard the usual ping of an incoming message on my phone. I only had to exercise patience for ten minutes to get home to listen to it, but I somehow could not wait. I paid and hurried out of the supermarket and downloaded her message. I could feel my heart melt. It was so thoughtful of her, as I was feeling very much the same about her, and I subscribed fully to every single lyric in that song, and every emotion it stirred. Had she been with me, I would have held her tightly in my arms and kissed her until breathless.

"Mellow Mellow" by Lowrell is a song that never fails to evoke memories of my lovely Paulette and how passionately we made love in my student digs to this. This song is so particular to my relationship with her, that playing it to seduce anyone else would almost constitute a criminal act. Barry White's "Never Never Gonna Give You Up" had a great one-minute wordless introduction that must be the most sensual song ever made in my opinion, and gladly also shared in lovemaking with Paulette.

She loved dancing too, and many of the records of funk and jazz funk music I still have in my collection remind me of dancing together with her. I can almost visualise the way her body swayed sensually to the music, and it reminds me so much of how H dances too. If it were a song of gentle melody, our bodies would come together as two perfect pieces in a jigsaw puzzle. What is it with me and French women?

Speaking of French women, I believe I had mentioned meeting Paulette in Paris again. On that occasion, she had a particular love for Al Jarreau's album "This Time". We sat together on the floor chatting and exchanging kisses as we listened to this album over and over again. The more she played it the more passionate our kisses grew. If ever there was a memorable weekend of passion, that was undeniably it.

Whenever I hear Ray Charles & Betty Carter sing "Everytime We Say Goodbye" I cannot help but think of the wonderfully loving Madeleine. I always remember how sad we both felt, whenever she left after her holiday visit, despite knowing that we would see each other again a few months hence. I am convinced that Shakespeare must have suffered a similar fate, as never a truer word than "parting is such sweet sorrow…" has been spoken than those he penned for Juliet. On each occasion that I listen to the song, I could almost feel the warmth of her tears on my cheeks, as we kissed goodbye. The lyrics to "Tossing and Turning" by Windjammer, which Paulette and I danced too often, would also make me think of how I held a simultaneous love for Madeleine.

I have provided you a small excerpt from the song, with the seemingly appropriate lyrics.

"Tossing and turning, I wiggle in my sleep
That's all I do
Oooh, baby, to my surprise I realize
The problem was me and not you, baby
I was misled by the player in me
I didn't know I was falling in love
My only hope is that it's not too late for me

To continue the stories of love we've been writing 'cause
I still want your love,
do you want mine? ... "

Scottish dancing and bag-piped music never fails to remind me of Madeleine, too. I went to a Burns evening last month. It was extremely well organised and held at the British Ambassador's residence here in Harare. The men looked extremely smart in their DJs and the ladies resplendent in their evening wear. There was much ceremony on presentation of the haggis, and many a cheerful drink-laden toast made in its name.

It reminded me so much of the wonderful evenings of this celebration that I enjoyed with friends in Jos. The sparkle that I missed was being with the beautiful Madeleine, seeing her face flushed with excitement and exertion as we danced, but always bearing a radiant and dazzling smile. I wished I were holding her in my arms as we twirled and swirled to the rather joyful sounds of bagpipes, flutes and drums.

Whilst on the subject of dancing, I must tell you of a dance that my friend Camel and I used to practice and execute together to Status Quo's "Down Down", to impress girls at a disco. There was a particular rhythm or beat to this song, over any other that got us moving excitedly.

The 'dance', if I am allowed the generosity of the term, involved having one's hands on hips, preferably with thumbs tucked firmly into the waistband, leaning back and rocking one's shoulders either side for a count of two, and then leaning forward and bouncing a shoulder on one side for a count of two. This was repeated for the opposite shoulder, and thence continued alternating one side to the other. One's partner had to obviously move their shoulders in a complimentary direction to avoid a disastrous clash of heads. The art was to lean as far back as possible, without tipping over or losing a foothold, and applying oneself to keeping pace with the drumbeat in order to create the desired dramatic effect to hopefully win over the admiration of members of the opposite sex.

This peacocking movement was best undertaken without our jackets on so that we could more manfully display our lithe physique in energetic exertion. I can honestly say, that despite the possibility of it, in current day dance parlance, appearing like a savage ritual conducted by a pair of decidedly unhinged but otherwise supine teenagers, it worked well at the time, and girls appeared suitably impressed.

Camel and I managed to perfect this movement with further practice, and our brotherly bond grew even closer as a result. He was certainly one of my closest friends at school and although we ended up in different schools, we wrote to each other frequently. You do in fact in many ways remind me of him. He was able to prompt considerable and enduring mirth in almost all of our discussions, especially those involving encounters with members of the opposite sex.

There was a brief period in my mid-teens when Rock was the centre piece of my musical life. Deep Purple, Led Zeppelin, Pink Floyd, The Eagles, Chicago and The Who, were the bands I admired greatly, listening to the songs several times over. I do still occasionally play songs like "Time" or "Money" by Pink Floyd, "Smoke on the Water" and "My Woman from Tokyo" by Deep Purple, "Trampled Underfoot" and the wonderful "Stairway to Heaven" by Led Zeppelin. The Eagles music has also proved timeless for me. Other loves from this time

313

who have proved equally enduring include Fleetwod Mac, T-Rex, The Steve Miller Band ("Abracadabra" is still one of my delights), Eric Clapton, David Bowie ("Young Americans" "Space Oddity" and "Starman" my favourites), Elton John ("Daniel", "Yellow Brick Road" and "Candle in the Wind" of note), Cat Stevens, Queen, The Bee Gees and Bread.

This was the time in my life also when Lou Reed's song "A Walk on the Wild Side" seemed to have had some influence. I am not sure that I was too eagerly wrapped up in the profundity of the lyrics, but they provided an opening gambit that appeared to work with girls at parties or discos. "Hey sugar, let's take a walk on the wild side," had some very 'cool' appeal then. It will probably not go down terribly well if practiced on women today, and certainly at my age, as it may only serve to elicit incredulity or utter disdain.

Do you realise that I really do not possess any good chat up lines? Even the 'what's a pretty girl like you doing in a place like this?' or 'haven't I seen you somewhere before, your face looks so familiar?' must have exceeded their sell-by dates! I may have to become well-versed in other enticing soliloquies!

Anyway, back to the musical journey of my life.

Going to parties with older siblings meant that my tastes tended to generally align with theirs. Most of the good parties played soul music. James Brown, O'Jays, Harold Melvin & The Blue Notes, Marvin Gaye, Isley Brothers, Stevie Wonder, Temptations, George Benson, David Ruffin, Chi-Lites, The Four Tops, etc.

I began to develop a more sedate form of dance, beyond that of the teenage shoulder sway or head swing from side to side, whilst strumming a fictitious guitar. I felt that I had a generally good sense of rhythm, and danced acceptably, but not to the high standard set by those we watched on Soul Train, who seemed to move with such unrestrained athleticism and attractive cadency to the beat of the music.

The music from the movie "Saturday Night Fever", played a major part in my musical life too. I had been attending discos since the advent of puberty, but I only began to appreciate soul and funk when I frequented night clubs more seriously thanks to the crowd at Cranfield Gardens.

I'll remain forever grateful to them for introducing me to the pleasures of music and dancing in the easily accessible but dingy basement of Cage D'Or and the smoke-filled and forever crowded Purple Pussycat.

With the arrival of Saturday Night Fever, I sailed enthusiastically into the disco era of my life with all the energy I could muster. I listened and danced to any and every funky tune I could, adding also wherever possible to my growing collection of records. The Tramps, Tavares, Lou Rawls, Chaka Khan, Sister Sledge, Brothers Johnson, Funkadelic, to name a mere handful. I even turned my hand to a stint at dee-jaying.

Whilst still a fan of dancing, my tastes progressed from pure disco funk toward to Jazz Funk and the likes Grover Washington, Bob James, Earl Klugh, Hiroshi Fukumura, Gato Barbieri, Tom Browne and George Howard, amongst several others began to feature in my life, especially at concerts I attended.

A lot of this music was introduced to me by Shingai and another friend, Rob, who was the manager at Our Price Records, and who kindly let me buy LPs at a discount. As the shop was auspiciously located on my way back from college, it only made sense to stop off for an hour or so, to listen to what he considered were items of ideal music to invest in. We became very good friends, and he once invited me for drinks and introduced me to his girlfriend who danced for 'Pans People'.

I was delighted to meet her, as I remember being one of several testosterone-driven teens crowded around the television screen to watch these beautiful dancers leap around to selected hits on 'Top of the Pops'. The focus, as you can imagine was not on the choreography but on their supple and superbly shaped figures. His girlfriend, lived up to (and may have even exceeded), all my expectations of one such supple beauty. To meet such women, I should really have followed Rob's suggestion to become a DJ or followed a career in music or fashion rather than the uninspiring one in Engineering.

My current musical loves are for Drake, The Weeknd, Dua Lipa, Khalid, Jax Jones, Sam Smith, Charlie Puth, Nicki Minaj, Flo Rida, Sam Smith, Post Malone and a long list of many others, thanks to Holly's recommendations.

I compiled various playlists of music, by these artists to listen to whilst journeying on a crowded tube or bus.

If reading was not a viable option in that crowded setting, one had to resort to observing fellow passengers and contemplating the sorts of lives they led based on their apparel or shopping bags.

Crowded or not I often preferred to close my eyes and be elevated by the various lyrics and melodies on the playlist to pontificate matters on a more spiritual plane. These playlists were critical also to my visits to the gym. Either to keep out of the grip of a lasting *ennui* when undertaking the necessarily repetitive nature of running on the treadmill, or just being musically entertained when aiming to lift weights to the rhythmic beat of a song.

The Starboy album, which Chloe introduced me to, I have played several times over whilst I jogged, as they conjured up incessant thoughts of H. The songs on the album and H have become inextricably linked and have been ever since I first spoke to her, though I know not why. "When a Man Loves a Woman" by the great Percy Sledge is a constant reminder of how blinded I am with love for her coupled with an unwillingness to recognise the possible futility of this pursuit.

Harry Nilsson's "Without You", will always remind me of Fawzia. I played it constantly whenever I thought of her. I wondered if anything could realistically happen between us, had I not left for England, but I felt in my heart of hearts that the probability of anything developing, beyond the flirtatious friendship we shared, was rather remote. That thought, however, did not help ease the pain of not being able to see her again. The song allowed me to wallow in my teen misery.

"Crazy" by Gnarls Berkley was song the girls and I enjoyed downloading and listening to often. Other songs that we loved playing repeatedly on car journeys, especially on the long drives to our holidays in France, included "Long Train Running" by the Doobie Brothers, "Perhaps, Perhaps, Perhaps" by Doris Day (which was more reminiscent of my parents' era, but a joy for the girls), "Metal Guru" by T-Rex, "White Lines" by Grandmaster Flash (a great opportunity we took as parents to educate them in the dangers of drug taking – so thank you Grandmaster Flash!) and Pavarotti's greatest hits.

Tata Safari was a compilation album of contemporary Indian music, which the girls and I remember fondly to this day. We had no understanding of the words, but the melodies, both soothing and electrifying seemed to have struck a chord with us. One of the songs called "Punjab" was used at their primary school play, to introduce the three wise men, of whom Chloe played one, whilst Holly assisted wordlessly as one of the animals in the Bethlehem stable. Another song, "Spirit of Freedom", had a child's infectious laughter at the very end of the song, which I told them always reminded me of them as little babies gurgling with uncontained merriment.

Anything operatic reminds me of my father and also of Luisa. Although she preferred Placido Domingo to Pavarotti as a tenor, I delighted in listening to his performance on the various *arias* with her, nevertheless. Her favourite opera was Puccini's unfinished "Turandot", whilst I preferred the more joyful "La Traviata" or the amusing "Il barbiere di Siviglia", but we were both always mesmerised by either of our favourite tenors belting out "Nessun Dorma". Other than opera, Vivaldi's "Four Seasons", and a lot of traditional jazz, which we listened to constantly, Luisa particularly liked an album by Roy Orbison, which included the hit "Pretty Woman". I would regularly suggest that it was a reference to her, taking her hand in mine whilst I drove, and was always suitably rewarded in bed.

The songs that I remember playing over and over again from that album after we broke up were very appropriately "Cryin'" and "It's Over". In my contemplations of the relationship that I had with her, I cannot help but remain with a sense of displeasure at its unexpected end, and "You'll Never Find Another Love Like Mine" by Lou Rawls is a song that perhaps best summed up my residual chagrin.

Elvis Presley was a great love of both my parents and Jasmine too. No matter what song of his plays, I am always reminded of the kisses I shared with Jasmine on the terrace of her apartment one sultry evening in Brunei in that unforgettable summer of 1977.

As I mentioned to you before, neither of us could have, or did, profess love for each other in the all too brief relationship we had at the time, but our kisses probably communicated more of what remained unsaid by either, as they were some of the most remarkably tender in my life. The feel of her soft lips, and the gentle touch of her hands are certainly aspects that will remain firmly etched in my mind for a long time to come.

The Hallelujah chorus from Handel's Messiah never fails to move me, especially when played over the Christmas period, as it reminds me of my parents, my father in particular.

My mother would defer to any music he chose to play, but always listened in patient enjoyment, despite having musical loves of her own. She was definitely a fan of Nat King Cole, as I believe all of us in the family were. "Blue Gardenia", "L-O-V-E", "Nature Boy", "Stardust" and "When I Fall in Love" were their favourites, and enduring classics that I am happy to hear often.

What song would I associate with Ravinia, I hear you ask? I suppose that Cole's "Unforgettable" is what I would consider a song representative of my time with her. But was she more unforgettable than my other loves and affairs, or was it because of my failure to recognise the wonderful gift of her love being the more hauntingly significant imprint?

She enjoyed all the music I played for her and listened attentively as I spoke gushingly about the songs and artists in my now enviable collection of LPs. She enjoyed the music at the jazz lunches at the Singapura and Cumberland Hotel and loved dancing with me at Monkberry's on the more raucous evenings. I suppose the most memorable song should be Anita Baker's "Rapture", when I held her close, drinking in the soft smell of her perfume as we danced together, her head nestled on my shoulder, and our bodies united as though we were a single entity, softly swaying to the gentle melody.

An even more vivid recollection of those evenings was the tender look in her eyes, as I bade farewell and she would lean forward, her lips parting invitingly for a kiss. If I thought Jasmine's lips were soft and sweet, I think that Ravinia's were unforgettably delicious also. From the loss I felt afterwards, the most appropriate lyrics would be from the song "The Love I Lost" sung in an amazingly moving way by Harold Melvin and The Blue Notes – *"The love I lost, was a sweet love; the love I lost was complete love... The love I lost I will never, no, no never love again..."*

The only difference being that I did fall in love again.

Possibly as a result of thoughts of my parents, I associated Judy Garland's "Somewhere Over the Rainbow", and Louis Armstrong's "What a Wonderful World" with hope. They always provide me with a sense of calm even in the most dire of circumstances. As you can imagine, these songs have been played quite often recently.

A record of my musical journey through life would not be complete if I failed to include the many songs in French, Spanish, Italian and Portuguese, that I have enjoyed, and continue to.

The following are some of my absolute favourites: "Je Pense À Toi" (definitely), "Pardonne-Moi", "Belle", "La Fin D'un Amour", "La Mamma", "Et Si Tu N'exitais Pas", "La Boheme", "Ho Capito Che Ti amo", "Historia De Un Amor", "Sabor A Mi" (which I simply adore), "La Barca" (a must), "Abrazame", "Nathalie", "Hey", "Besame Mucho", "Verde Luna", "Solamente Una Vez",

"Acercate Más", "Quizas, Quizas Quizas", "Cuando Vuelva A Tu Lado", "La Llorona", "L'appuntamento" (an absolute favourite!), "Arrivederci Roma", "Che Vuole Questa Musica Stasera", "Momentos", "Con Te Partirò", "Canzoni Stonate", "Amore En Portofino", "Brucia La Terra" and " 'O Sole Mio". The last two songs conjuring up sweet memories of "The Godfather", (which is one of my favourite books and favoured film too incidentally), and ice-cream (was it the Cadbury's flake ad?), respectively. Delightful songs all, and sung beautifully by Burçin, Natalie Cole, Vanoni, Bocelli, Iglesias, Miguel, Aznavour amongst so many others.

I must direct your attention also to the YouTube video which accompanies the song "Cuando Vuelva A Tu Lado" sung wonderfully by Natalie Cole. It depicts the scene of a marriage proposal which is so wonderfully romantic, and one I would love to emulate when I do eventually find my dream love.

I have no real understanding of the lyrics, to any of the songs I mentioned, but being the ardent romantic, I just enjoy the sound of the lyrics and melodies harmonising to the beat of my heart.

I am reminded also of the time John and I went to see Astrid Gilberto in concert and watched her performance completely spellbound. I must say, she looked rather delightful too, and despite not understanding the lyrics for most of the time, she held our riveted attention for the entire evening.

I watched the "Sound of Music" the other day and could not help but be moved, particularly when the children sang "The Hills Are Alive". It was the touching scene of reconciliation with their father who had previously been a little remote in demonstration of his feelings for them. I tried watching the remainder of the film without tear-filled eyes, whilst I battled to determine what it was that triggered the sentiment.

As I have mentioned many times to you, I am very easily moved to tears and with the passing of years, this seems to worsen. I am beginning to think that the bags under my eyes are not a sign of fatigue or lost sleep, as much as they are pouches full of tears waiting to be shed.

I do recall seeing this film for the first time, with a big crowd of cousins whilst on holiday in India. It was one of those cinemas which played the film on repeat, and despite the fact that the film was already long, I remember staying to watch it with them, three times over, until we felt we had acquired sufficient mastery of the lyrics.

We may have been asked politely to leave, or did so of our own volition, but either way, we returned to my grandmother's house a short distance away singing the various songs from the movie.

I dearly loved my grandmother and visiting the large family, she had accumulated around her.

She was an amazing woman. She had married at a very young age (thirteen I believe) and had seven children. Very fair skinned, of gentle demeanour and fragile in physical stature, standing no more than five-feet-tall, she ruled the household with a disciplinarily firm and rigidly moral stance. But she was also very kind, generous, caring and compassionate with it. So, in her rather uniquely charming but stern way, (the phrase 'iron fist in velvet glove' comes to mind), she commanded considerable respect and deference from all her children, grandchildren and great grandchildren.

That was matriarchal rule at its benevolent best.

She seemed to have an especially soft spot for me. Possibly because I spoke Tamil very poorly and came across as the least bright button in her box of a multitude of grandchildren.

I have fond memories of sitting together with her on her bed and telling her all about the "Sound of Music" film, and even singing (rather poorly) some of the songs for her. I enjoyed talking to her anyway, regardless of my poor Tamil, and only wish now that I had interrogated her more thoroughly on her amazing past. I was terribly sad when she passed away. It truly signalled the end of an era.

Was it the thoughts of my grandmother that caused the joyful pain when watching the film again? I feel it had something to do with the name Maria also. I seem to be rather drawn to that name and know not why. I enjoyed watching the film, nevertheless. The songs were, and still are, very memorable.

I could carry on naming several more songs or artists who left strong impressions at various points in my life, but I would never get to finishing this letter.

I must leave you, however with one song that played repeatedly in my head after I had heard it for the first time and endured inordinately during my times of heartbreak and sorrow. The best rendition of the lyrics, (which coincidentally happens to sum up my life now), is by Ella Fitzgerald and the Ink Spots.

"Into each life some rain must fall
But too much is falling in mine
Into each heart some tears must fall
But some day the sun will shine ......"

On that rather appropriately hopeful note, I shall bid you a "so long and farewell...!"

Love,

David

Letter 21 – *La Vie En Rose Et Ma Sœur*

February 2020

Mon cher Geoff,

I realised only after I dashed off my last letter to you on my musical memories that I completely failed to mention Edith Piaf, whom I absolutely adore, as her music often also serves as a gentle reminder of other poignant moments in my life. Almost every song by Edith Piaf provokes recollections of my sister Rachel and the times we shared together. Listening to Piaf sing "Je Ne Regrette Rien" always brings me close to tears, as that is the song played at her funeral, after her life was cut so tragically short whilst still at a relatively young age. She was only fifty-three.

"La Vie En Rose", I could play several times over and never grow tired of, as it brings back truly wonderful memories of Paris and the times I visited Rachel there in the early 1980s. If you heard that song sung by Audrey Hepburn in the film "Sabrina", it will cause you to love the city even more, as she applies her voice so sweetly to the already captivating lyrics. Sabrina's description of the rain on the Bois de Boulogne, and Paris smelling its sweetest then, always seems so veritably apt too. I think I fell in love with Paris the moment I set foot on its hallowed ground. If I were to marry again, I pray that it will be to a lady who will share my love for Paris.

The city, of course, was made all the more magical by the fact that I got to spend time touring various parts of it with Rachel. She was such an amazing and generous host and showed me the city as viewed by a Parisian. It was a spell-binding experience, and one that I will never forget easily, as it made me fall in love with so many aspects of the city. I began to truly appreciate also why it is claimed that the city is best enjoyed in the Spring, as it held an aura of romance, further enhanced for me by fond recollections of meeting my first love there at that time of year.

Rachel served as a wonderful guide to the city. We did all the touristy things, but with a local approach. One of the first things I was advised of, was not to walk in brisk fashion as one tends to in London, but to adopt the style of a flâner. One strolled, rather than rushed from point A to point B, in order to best savour the attributes of the city. We walked virtually everywhere leisurely, stopping now and then at the various sidewalk cafés, which appeared to be ubiquitous in Paris at the time, but only became a more recent development in London.

We visited the Louvre, of course, both being passionate about art, although I would never claim to be profoundly knowledgeable on the subject. I could never explain why I liked a particular painting, nor be descriptive of the style employed, nor in some cases even remember the artist. I focused on the art, not the creator. I was drawn by the beauty of the works – the style, the colours, the textures, the overall effect, very much as one would enjoy the eye-catching splendour of nature's creations, without delving into the why's and wherefores of God's work. We also visited some of the smaller museums, like the Musée de l'Orangerie within the Jardin des Tuileries, and Musée Rodin, which is supposedly also one of the most romantic places in Paris. I should have taken Paulette there, if we could have had more time together.

I did venture out on my own from time to time, and on one occasion visited the Centre Pompidou where they held an exhibition of photographs by the extremely talented Man Ray. I was totally captivated by the stunning images he created through the lens of a camera and vowed to apply myself to creating memorable photography if I ever could. Sadly, even with the technology available today, I have only managed a few dismal snapshots, which I believe Man Ray would have, with accompanying shrieks of horror, discarded hurriedly into the trash.

We visited the Eiffel Tower but did not go to the top to attain views of the city. Rachel took me to the top of the Arc de Triomphe, instead. I must admit that the vistas were probably just as grand, carrying views straight down the Champs-Élysées. The Louvre could be sighted in the distance. The fact that the Arc sat in the middle of the intersection of several avenues, gave one the feeling of being sited at the dead-centre of a web from which all city life and movement spiralled.

We ate at home mostly, as my nephew Anthony was still very young and had strict early bedtimes to adhere to. But we did also because Rachel happened to be a great cook, and we ate well from the purchases of deliciously fresh produce from the markets.

We occasionally partook of lunch at the numerous convivial and popular bistros, where the food was reasonably priced for perfection on a plate and even the *vin de table* seemed a very safe palatable bet.

Having tried it a few times, I decided that I was not nouvelle cuisine's biggest fan. It may have started in the 1970s in France as fashionable fodder but was still the rage in the 80s in London. I absolutely loved the presentation but longed for substance. Call me a peasant if you must, but I much preferred the traditional *cuisine classique*. It was both robust and magnificently relishing.

You must remember also that these were the days when I could merrily eat a horse, and still have room for more, so substance over style prevailed for me. On the food front anyway.

What a delight it was to also progress from almost forced consumption of student plonk to partaking, through the exercise of independent choice, the various nectareous French wines. My palate welcomed the exquisite tastes from the wines of Bordeaux (especially Saint-Émilion), Burgundy, Loire Valley and Médoc (Margaux being a long-lasting favourite). Again, I cannot lay claim to connoisseurship, as my entire knowledge of wines can be easily summarised onto the back of a postage stamp, but I loved the stuff and could joyfully consume it by the barrelful.

Shopping was so much fun too. Rachel was as keen a shopper as I, and we would spend hours just browsing through the many delightful stores, with little Anthony in tow, either on my shoulders, which he preferred, or in his buggy. Galeries Lafayette was not quite my Harrods but carried that certain Parisian charm and incredibly seductive sales patter. I did buy a suitcase there, partly out of seduction, but primarily to replace the tattered one I had arrived with. Our shopping expedition included, quite necessarily the *haute couture* boutiques along the rue Saint-Honoré, where I treated myself to a couple of shirts and a pair of St. Laurent trousers, throwing myself wholeheartedly into capturing, as best I could at least a partial Parisian dress sense.

One of the keys to blending into Parisian society was to be well, but not overdressed. Both men and women dressed with classic elegance, and with a *je ne sais quoi* that was not immediately apparent in London.

Fortuitously, I had Paulette's assistance during my college years, where she began the process of capably influencing my style of attire. It is safe to say, I dressed reasonably well. But I still needed a little further guidance to develop a truly Parisian chic.

The way the women in Paris dressed reminded me of my great screen love, Audrey Hepburn, who epitomised a successful transformation of style from ordinary to elegant in so many of her on and off-screen appearances. She had that inherent ability to dress with understated elegance and accessorise in style, always appearing so exquisitely and aesthetically alluring. Ever since I fell in love with her and worshipped her from afar, I have held great admiration for women who possessed this ability to dress with subtle sublimity and accessorise simple attire to create a look of quintessential chic and desirable femininity. I had such a girlfriend, once.

I found the Parisians wonderfully hospitable in all the places I visited. Beit to the lovely little *magasin's* for milk and bread, or one of the non-tourist-filled cafés for a croissant and *grande crème* (cappuccinos had not entered my life at that point), where I was always made to feel welcome. As I was keen to practice my French too, I would attempt a little more conversation beyond the extension of a polite greeting. I hoped also that my English sense of humour would translate well. But as my French was probably poorer than that of a village idiot, I am sure the patrons may not have fully appreciated what I hoped to convey with a sense of joviality. They would have possibly only wanted to pat me on the head for the laudable attempts made to converse in their language.

My conversational French was truly tested when Rachel took me to a dinner party, where they deliberately avoided English, (and why not, as this was Paris after all), and I battled to comprehend much of what was said. I resorted to immersing myself in the delicious wine, smiling politely and showing gratitude to whoever would lean toward me occasionally and offer a translation.

I lost my heart to Paris. It filled me with an empyreal sensation of *joie de vivre*. It was no surprise that I visited Rachel there twice more. I was grateful to her for being kind enough to show me the delights of this beautiful city, and more importantly for me, as seen through the eyes of a local. It was wonderful that we got on very well as siblings too, which is why it was probably inevitable that we would end up sharing a house some years later.

My only frustration, during those visits, was not being able to converse fluently. I was insistent on using the little French I had knowledge of, mostly to the unexpected amusement of those who interacted with me but failed to engage too intellectually. Rachel recommended a course of study, which I happily subscribed to with the intention of improving my schoolboy French as rapidly as possible.

The trips to Paris were enhanced further by Rachel being particularly supportive of my relationship with Paulette when I met her again in Paris and rekindled the long-held feelings, we had for each other. I appreciated the efforts she made to ensure that Paulette was made to feel part of the family when she spent the weekend with us. Perhaps Rachel, Paulette and I did look at life through rose-coloured lenses at the time, but I shall always treasure those memories of visits to Paris. *La vie en Rose*, indeed.

When Rachel returned to England, and I had obtained reasonably paid employment ('reasonable' given that Engineers are paid an odious pittance in England relative to their qualification), we opted to buy a house together.

When our quest for a home began in around 1985, prices of houses in Fulham were in the £150,000 mark or thereabouts, would you believe. I would hate to think with the spiralling demand in London, what that same house would now fetch. Well in excess of ten times that, I assume. Crazy!

Anyway, we did find something eventually that was a little beyond our budget but suited us in every other way. We set about refurbishing the house on a room-by-room basis, with the little spare cash we had to hand. We made it homely, primarily with Rachel's stock of furniture and furnishings acquired over the years. My contribution was a bed and a stereo system.

Rachel thankfully did most of the cooking, on the basis that Anthony had a good appetite, which was preferably directed toward good home-cooked food. I did participate every now and then, rustling up the odd delicacy within my limited culinary repertoire or manning the barbeque. The aromas of good food certainly contributed toward making ours a very welcoming home.

I must say that our family has generally, probably as a result of our parental tutelage, made each of our places of residence as warm and hospitable as we remembered our home with our parents to have been. We may have moved many times, but everywhere we stopped and metaphorically laid our hats, we made a home. Was there some magic formula we applied? I wouldn't know, but it was nice to be told by friends that our homes exuded a warming welcome and cosy comfort. We, therefore, entertained a lot. At least, it certainly seemed that way, given the constant stream of guests, as well as family. We even had our parents stay for a while when they travelled back and forth between England and India, frustratingly unsure of where they should finally settle.

It was much easier to entertain in the summer, particularly on a warm sunny day when we could open the door from the large kitchen-diner onto a large garden, by London standards. The sound of Gershwin's "Summertime" from the opera Porgy and Bess played as many times as possible, particularly on a long sultry afternoon. Gershwin, although a favourite, was not the only music played to keep guests entertained though, as we would also include much other jazz and opera. And Piaf too!

Music with which to enjoy the several gin and tonics or glasses of wine, whilst food mouth-wateringly sizzled on the barbeque. I think that this is actually when I began developing my skills at the barbeque - during those long, mainly warm summer days in England. A skill, I might add, I have now honed to such a fine art that friends in Zimbabwe currently wax lyrically about my barbequed chicken.

It was also during our time in the Fulham house together that we took up horse riding. I had found a place near Newbury, which was not many miles from Reading where I happened to be working. We did not mind the hefty trek from London though, as it made for a pleasant drive on a Sunday morning when the traffic was light and deemed it well worth the journey when we arrived at the picturesque village on the borders of Hampshire and Berkshire.

As soon we came off the motorway, the beauty of the English countryside began to unfold in front of us. Driving along narrow roads shaded by trees on the one side and close-cropped hedges on the other, with gaps offering occasional glimpses of fields of lush green beyond, gave one a fleeting but striking glimpse of the beauty of the English country landscape. Very much like the brief glimpse one gets of the silken skin on the dainty leg of a woman wearing a beguilingly slit skirt.

But it was not only the scenery that was enjoyable, as the riding was too. It felt majestic being atop the horse. You could understand why kings adopted these creatures as their preferred mode of carriage. I loved riding. I was totally sold on this endeavour, and resolved after our very first hack, that it should become a committed pastime. Without further bidding, I subsequently invested in a pair of designer jodhpurs, boots, gloves, mac and crop, with all items bar the jodhpurs satisfyingly procured from the equestrian department of one of my favourite departmental stores – Harrods.

This regular Sunday pastime for Rachel, Anthony and myself, soon became one for Carole too. It was therefore a great family occasion also, and we would make a day of it, by having lunch at one of the local village pubs, where we were greeted as effusively by the pub landlords, as they did their village regulars. Just thinking about it conjures up ambrosial aromas of the homemade steak and kidney pie, Lancashire Hot-Pot, Battered Cod or whatever happened to be the on the special's board that afternoon.

Even the Guinness tasted especially wonderful after a long hack over the Newbury downs, which sometimes included a gallop across the ridge with the wind brushing against our excited faces.

Fair weather or foul, we turned up at the stables without fail, much to the delight of our trainer. Would you believe that she even thought us sufficiently competent to try our hand at some jumping too? If there was any aptitude demonstrated in this area, I feel it may have been more attributable to the horse rather than to my limited control of the reins. It felt very good in looking the part of a seasoned rider however, particularly with my riding mac billowing out majestically behind me on a gallop.

Our house was not far from John and Maureen, so I continued helping them out at the Singapura, and babysitting for them too. My idea of babysitting my niece and nephews was to integrate them into my schedule of activities, and therefore mostly involved taking them out shopping.

They were all incredibly well-behaved, and no more so than Jamie, who was the most adorable baby to take anywhere. Carole and I sometimes used to have to vie for his accompaniment. Do all little children seem well-mannered with aunts and uncles, or is it just my fortunate experience? Jamie though was a particular delight, for there was never a complaint nor a hideous nappy to change. He would sit quietly and patiently in the changing room watching me try various items of clothing, and similarly when I popped him atop the desk at the till when it came time to pay. Very often arousing favourable comment from the staff at the shops, about how cute he was.

When he was a little older, he would invariably ask for the Pavarotti CD to be played as I strapped him into the car; comment wisely on clothes I chose as we wandered through the shops; and also provide great conversational company over lunch. In hindsight, I could have, and possibly should have, obtained a few prospective dates from some of the many women who cooed over him, had I claimed him as my own.

Rachel, in her very unspoken way, always served as a great social filter to some of the women I courted during that time. It is not as though she imposed any restriction, but I subconsciously de-selected some on the basis that they would not pass the 'Rachel' test.

So, it was only the 'acceptable' ones that I brought home to dinner or drinks. Some she took an instant liking to, and welcomed warmly, not just to her home but to her heart, as she had done with Paulette in Paris.

Besides sharing a house together, Rachel and I also seemed to have an affection for many things French, and it is I am sure obvious to you now that I still valiantly carry that particular torch. Anyway, one evening we settled down to watch a movie called "Jean de Florette", which on reflection was probably not the cleverest thing to do, as it had us both in floods of tears, barely able to discuss the movie without sobbing incessantly.

We proceeded to torture ourselves with the equally delightful and moving sequel "Manon des Sources" a few months later.

I have heard the haunting melody of the film's theme tune played a few times since and have always stopped to listen as it reminds me not just of these very moving films, but also of that painfully beautiful time together with a dear sister.

I miss Rachel. Although there were many aspects of her life I questioned at the time, she was a wonderful and supportive sibling. I am not suggesting that it was all peaches and cream, because we did have our differences, as we all did as siblings, particularly when living together. That was entirely natural with any relationship, especially as we were all brought up to be fiercely independent characters within the family with very clearly defined identities set at an early age. But we also had a very strong family bond that allowed us to bridge these differences and heal rifts quickly.

She was an amazing woman. Incredibly bright and diligent in whatever she applied herself too. She obtained A grades at school and a good degree from UCL, which happens to be my alma mater too, as you know. It was sad to see her abandon school and University success to enter into a failed marriage. She was never the same after that.

It was almost as though a beautiful bird had had its wings clipped. She did find joy in having a child but had to bravely undertake child rearing almost single-handedly. That is when our family come to its fore, with all of us contributing moral, emotional and practical support as best we could.

I was very fortunate to have such a great family. I wonder if by being the youngest, my siblings felt duty bound to be caretakers of my well-being. It may have been that, as we all considered ourselves intrepid explorers in some form or another in our journey from the security of a home with parents to the independence of life in England as teenagers. My siblings being the early settlers, offering helpful support to me, as the last arrival, to adjust to life away from home.

Whatever it was, I remember Rachel being one of the great pillars of strength in my life, particularly during my teens. I just wish her life had not ended so tragically nor whilst she was still young.

It is a pity I have to end this letter on a such sad note, because I have so many happy memories of her, particularly in Paris where she appeared to occupy a state of vibrant euphoria. I am so grateful to her for allowing me the opportunity to be similarly euphoric about Paris, and really experience *la vie en rose*.

And that my dear friend, sums up my musical journey thus far. Some joyous, some mournful, some just melodic, but all contributing to weaving what we know as the rich tapestry of life.

I hope you have not minded the few detours I took along the way, to let you know more of my family members. Until the next journey down memory lane, and as an ode to Rachel, I shall leave you with the lyrics to Edith Piaf's song "Paris"

> "Paris, c'était la gaieté, Paris,
> C'était la douceur aussi.
> C'était notre tendresse.
> Paris, tes gamins, tes artisans,
> Tes camelots et tes agents
> Et tes matins de printemps,
> Paris, l'odeur de ton pavé d'oies,
> De tes marronniers, du bois,
> Je pense à toi sans cesse.
> Paris, je m'ennuie de toi, mon vieux.
> On se retrouvera tous les deux,
> Mon grand Paris."

Bien amicalement à tu. Ton ami,

Davide

Letter 22 – In Lockdown with Schoolboy

Recollections

March 2020

Dear Geoff,

We are now confined to our homes for the next twenty-one days in an effort to contain the spread of this wretched virus. How awful it is to hear of so many being cursed by its spell.

I do hope that measures can be taken to effectively combat this awful plague upon us. I must advise you though, of my scepticism toward the approaches adopted by some of our world leaders to deal with this deadly disease, especially when injecting oneself with bleach is proposed as a possible remedy. I cannot claim to profess great knowledge in the sphere of medical sciences, but this suggested course of action worries me greatly. Until proven otherwise, and given also my fear of needles, I shall steer well clear of injecting that substance and shall limit its application for the removal of stubborn stains. It is also, we are led to believe by advertisers of a particular brand, capable of killing "99.9 percent of germs dead". This germ killing, I understand, however, takes place in the dark recesses of a toilet bowl and not necessarily in one's intravenous tracts!

I have no doubt that we will soon have much to discuss on the availability and efficacy of the proposed vaccines, but I shall leave that for another occasion and for the moment relate to you my plans for staying safe and healthy during this involuntary confinement.

I am sure that there will be much to occupy my time during this lockdown. There are several things that I had always wanted to do, and much that I need to do, but never seemed to find the time for. On the 'need to do' list, were all the usual mundane aspects of filing personal paperwork, packing up items for storage, sifting through closets for clothes to sell, etc. Amongst items on the 'creative and self-improvement' list, includes a wish to learn how to play the piano, improve my French, write some poetry, learn a new language, and improve my tennis if at all I am able.

Tennis is a game I enjoyed both as a spectator and participant but seem to be continually badly handicapped at.

It is the difficulty I have in anticipating and hitting a moving object travelling toward me at a great rate of knots that impedes my development in this arena. I, therefore, spent most of the time on the court leaping about like a deranged spider and making only very occasional contact between ball and racket. It was a pity, as I thoroughly loved this sport. Given that both my parents, particularly my father, were fantastically well coordinated, it is disappointing to note that their genes do not appear to have combined very well to work effectively for me on the sporting front.

I remember vividly an occasion of discovering this vast ineptitude for certain sports when appearing for hockey team trials on arrival at boarding school in England. I had mentioned in passing, that my father played hockey for his university and also Madras State in his youth, and you can imagine how skilled he must have been, given the highly competitive nature of this sport in India. I think that, next to cricket, hockey was the most revered sport in India. I had no doubt about his ability, as besides being the English Language and English Literature teacher, he was the school's preeminent hockey coach. I had mistakenly assumed that a little of that ability resided in me. His skill, I learnt much later had skipped a generation and appeared in my daughter, Holly.

I turned up for the trials looking the part. You could almost sense the palpable expectation from the others as I strode purposefully toward the practice field and the other players clustered around the coach. With my hockey stick held casually over my shoulder, bearing a hubristic demeanour and confident gaze in my eye, I felt that my audience was totally engaged. I wondered if a few of the seniors in the team were quivering in their boots at the thought of being upstaged by this confident young Indian lad.

I made sure that I wore the appropriate practice garb, from shirt to sock and shoe, in a manner that came across as well presented as possible on my slender frame. I do not know what guided my thinking, but I truly believed that one must be suitably attired if attempting any new sport. A practice, I seem to continue to this day.

Whether it was horse riding, which I took up in my twenties and felt duty bound to make the purchase of the best kit I could afford (purchased at none other than one of my favourite departmental stores, namely Harrods); fencing taken up at school, but thankfully with all of the required kit purchased by the school and therefore required one only to turn up in one's clean underwear; or golf when the bag, glove, shoes as well as a pair of plaid trousers occupied space in the list of must-haves. In other words, I had to look the part.

I felt that a lot rested on my young shoulders. But I felt up to the challenge and truly believed there could not be much to it, despite never having played the game. The youthful conviction was soon shattered.

Despite Herculean spirit and considerable enthusiasm applied to each physical effort, I was awful. It would have been a painful sight to have witnessed. My coach looked stunned! He looked as though he was reeling from the aftereffects of witnessing a horrific car accident at which some vehicular debris had struck him with force.

My dribbling skills, rather than being sublime, were grotesque. You would have assumed from the word 'dribble' that it was an action easy to execute – the accidental discharge of liquid from the side of one's mouth, and said discharge traveling rapidly toward the chin, causing one to reach for one's handkerchief to deal with the offence. Not so, I disappointingly discovered whilst I attempted to keep the ball as closely attached to the hockey stick as possible and moving all the while.

A satchel full of handkerchiefs would not have helped me out of this particular dribbling debacle.

My ball striking skills were marginally better, but only if one considered the word marginally representing the thinnest of thin separations and bordered on hopeless inefficacy. Even a blind man with a gammy leg and broken arm would possibly have struck the ball more accurately.

After much expectation, I could see sore disappointment etched across the face of our coach and some of my prospective teammates. If any of the seniors had indeed quivered, their fear was now replaced with utter astonishment and some amusement. The coach called me aside after a little while, probably prompted by his wish to see the first team pitch preserve some of its turf, and for me to retain some remnant of dignity. He politely suggested that if I wanted to continue playing, it was best that I acquired considerably more practice prior to any aspiration to obtain a slot within the First Team. As a result of my continued enthusiasm for the sport, but in recognition of my lack of ability, I was relegated to the Third Team, which was also affectionately also known as the 'Spas(tics) League'.

The 'Spas League' basically comprised anyone forced to play hockey as they had no other elected sport to showcase their sporting ability (or inability in the case of some), and those who considered themselves able, but disappointingly unrecognised and with a wish to prove themselves.

Thankfully I fell into the latter category, and every game we played was with great gusto and a wish that one day we would also have our names called out at assembly for a First Team tie.

I never got the tie. I should have, alongside some of my colleagues, at least received medals for bravery. Getting on the hockey pitch with a bunch of guys lacking even basic hockey skills was highly dangerous. Films on mortal combat, like the "Mad Max" series could well have been based on the activity of a Spas League game. No one paid much heed to the rules of game, raising the stick well above shoulder height to strike the ball for instance, and very often striking an opponent's foot instead. There was generally no means of telling who exactly struck the ball, and in which direction it would head. All hell broke loose at these games. We considered ourselves lucky to leave the pitch with our torsos and limbs only mildly bruised and all our teeth present and correct. But we did laugh a lot in compensation when discussing the game in a post-mortem of our efforts.

I really liked my sports coach. He was a good soul. He could see that I was disappointed not to make the grade at hockey but directed my attention toward athletics instead. I was not too bad at these athletics events, and gleefully took part in everything from sprints to the long and high jumps. I excelled at these events and recorded some of my better sporting achievements, largely I think because I was considerably taller than most in my class at the age of fourteen. Many classmates would soon catch up to my height by the time I got to my sixth form, but I enjoyed towering over them in the meanwhile.

Our coach discovered that I was fast. But only in short bursts. It was a pity they had not invented a 30m sprint, as I would have won many races! He felt that I would be a good addition to the Colts Rugby team. I was actually an asset to the team for some time, would you believe. The tactic he applied was one of getting the ball to me so that I could leg it down the field as fast and far as my young legs would take me. I never really learnt much about the rules of rugby, but enjoyed playing it, for most of the time anyway. The only problem I encountered was sometimes being so far away from my scrum that I had to endure the pain of being pinned down by several bodies before any relief from the late cavalry arrived. This tactic of a fast run down the edge of the field worked well for a time when we played against other schools, but they soon wised up to this manner of play, and I soon found myself the target of the opposition team with an intent to disable me with or without the ball.

My rugby career would end as quickly as it started, when I began wearing contact lenses. I am not sure what induced me to try contact lenses. I believe that it had much to do with my desperation to get away from those thick-framed NHS glasses that I had been given to wear as a result of my need for optical aid, which was discovered when my teacher spotted me looking at the blackboard through binoculars. My riotous days at the back of the class, passing notes across to friends were now well and truly over. Those thick-framed glasses are now in vogue, but at the time were a ghastly fashion *faux pas*. Contact lenses were calling out for my consideration.

During one of the school holidays, my sister, Carole and I chose to try these 'new on the scene' contact lenses. They were an answer to my immediate prayer to get away from unsightly spectacles, I thought. Unfortunately, not so. I had so much trouble inserting and removing the lenses, as my eyes would invariably shut during any attempt however patient, to place my finger anywhere close. It was a delicate operation and took several attempts and a considerable amount of time.

I really struggled as even the smallest speck of dirt which could, in most normal instances of eyewear, be wiped away without much ado, caused me many painful eye watering exigencies. I wonder if my eyes, which are now very prone to getting tear-filled, are as a result of this epic struggle with hard contact lenses.

I did try wearing sunglasses as a protective cover for a while, thinking that I could look cool, whilst dealing with the dust syndrome effectively, but reliance on this even on a cloudy day caused me to being likened to a Ray Charles lookalike, and I soon abandoned this as a long-term solution.

If the battle with contact lenses had been tough on a day-to-day basis, it was ten times worse on the rugby field.

I must have spent more time on the side-lines crying than I did on the field. There was little hope of seeing well enough to catch the ball and make a quick dash to the goal line with tear-filled eyes. Sadly, I had to hang up my boots.

It probably was a good decision anyway, as my peer group soon began to grow as tall and fill out sideways too, and I would probably have suffered much more pain than that obtained on the hockey pitch. I could no longer refer to them as my 'little friends'.

For as long as it lasted, my height relative to theirs, also made me popular amongst most of my classmates as I could reach the top shelves at the magazine display with ease and with the beginnings of a moustache, could get away with buying pornographic magazines for us all to share. It was either me electing to undertake this daunting task or paying one of the seniors a large premium to make the purchase on our behalf. This was never a good idea, as it would get to us several days later, and deprived of many pages. I offered to play the hero for my peers.

I remember the first time reaching casually for one of those magazines and attempting to look unperturbed as I sauntered over to the counter at the front of the Newsagents store. I could bolt for the door if things got awkward, I thought. I could feel the Newsagent's eyes bore into the back of my skull as he stared first at the magazine and then back at me. He in all likelihood hoped to test my resolve. I might have been inwardly fearful, but remained unshakeably resolute. He continued his inescapable gaze from top to toe, to ensure I was not some gangly underaged youth standing on a box to appear taller to validate the age restricted purchase. It could have been the faint growth of hair on my upper lip that finally convinced him, or the fact that it was one of the tamer of pornographic magazines, whichever it was, he finally relented and just asked if I wanted a bag. Much as my upbringing required a 'yes please' response, I simply muttered an abrupt 'yeah'. I was at this point totally absorbed in my wish to convey an uncouth and rugged countenance and could have even spat on the floor to emphasise this, but thankfully didn't, and merely accepted the change offered with an appreciative nod, before walking confidently out of the store. My friends who had waited outside patiently, and most probably nail-bitingly apprehensively also, were naturally delighted that I was allowed to make the purchase along with a few bars of Marathon chocolate and a packet of gum.

I use the word 'tamer' to describe the magazine, as there were other titles such as 'Orgasm', 'Rough Rider', 'Busty Babes', etc., in this genre of publication, which I think may have raised an eyebrow or two and prompted closer examination of my credentials in any purchase attempt.

As schoolboys, I would like to think that we held some lofty ideals and avoided the cruder publications wishing to view nudity presented in a more polished manner and in a refined setting. But even magazine titles can be misleading, I was to learn later from my brother.

One of his holiday jobs entailed an administrative role for a company publishing a magazine called 'Peaches'. As with any normal human being, he had no idea that a totally unassuming name like 'Peaches' would be associated with a magazine specialising in featuring naked women with particularly enormous breasts.

Beyond this discovery, I also learnt from him that all the stories we read in the magazines about guys managing to bed their neighbour's beautiful daughter or their sexy teacher, nurse, etc., were apparently largely made up by the editorial team working for the magazine and not by readers as we had assumed. That was such a disappointment to me and my friends, to whom I felt duty bound to convey the story, as we had always dreamt that those stories were true, and that such opportunities would one day present themselves to us. Regardless of this disappointing news, my friends were highly respectful of my brother's position at Peaches and considered him the luckiest man alive to have access to 'free porn' as he did. I took every opportunity to bathe in his reflected glory.

To someone who previously only had accidental sight of naked breasts in my father's copy of National Geographic, the contents of 'Penthouse' and 'Playboy' magazines were great revelations. I could never have imagined a sight more beautiful than that of a lovely woman naked or in various stages of undress. Up until that point, my imagination captured only images of the sagging breasts of the half-naked indigenous Amazonian lady featured in that article, and to my great satisfaction, I soon learnt that not all women had breasts hovering close to their waistline. My reaction to these wonderful new images was, of course, that of any red-blooded teenage boy.

Whilst I must necessarily confess to breaking the rules at school with regard to pornography purchase, I had never expected to also face Hell's fires for this illicit material. Unfortunately for us, our RE (Religious Knowledge) teacher considered images of naked women, which we had often paid good and hard earned pocket money for, highly sinful, and moreover that masturbation was the act of the devil himself.

And would you believe that he made this declaration in our very first lesson. This, to a group of boys with testosterone levels hovering dangerously at DEFCON Two. To say we were perturbed, would be a gross understatement. Looking around the room, there were a few smirks, but most were in shock. Had a poll been conducted, I would say that more than 85% of us were very disturbed.

The ones who smirked probably had annual subscriptions to 'Bondage for Beginners' or some such journal and were likely to go to Hell anyway, so we were not troubled by their reaction. A few were probably too saintly and likely to have been shocked even with saggy breast images from National Geographic and may have agreed with the teacher on this matter.

The majority of us were absolutely aghast and looked at each other in abject horror. We were now additionally traumatised, as there was now not much to make life a tad more bearable as fourteen year-olds in boarding school, given that the food, except for the puddings, scrambled eggs and tea, was of prison quality; the dorms were freezing, as the strict rule was not to have any heating on until the first of November no matter what the ambient temperature; the lessons were either laborious or taxing, except for the interesting teachers in the History and Art classes, and Maths too (for me at least as Mr Bolt the teacher thought me a budding genius of sorts especially when it came to calculus); and the best seats in the TV room were always occupied by the seniors.

What a blight placed upon our young lives, especially the more Christian and gullible amongst us. It is not as though he planned to offer comfort by shipping in a few ladies to help relieve, (in every sense of the word), our teen suffering. We were fearful of consulting our seniors, especially the ones we held in high regard for their perceived sexual exploits, dreading a label as 'no-hopers', so we had only ourselves to derive solutions to this frightful predicament. It was a dilemma I hope no other teenage boy has to confront – the possibility of facing the scorching heat of Hell's fury on the one hand (I use the word 'hand' purely illustratively) or depriving oneself of a little gratification on the other.

After much debate, we agreed that it was vital, in order not to disfavour our future partners, to carry on this important activity as deemed practice for the real occasion.

And besides, there was nothing that we could now do, as we had already blighted our copybooks in the eyes of God from previous misdeeds in this regard. We resolved that, if need be, we would seek absolution upon arrival at the Pearly Gates. It may have been the ardent prayers I whispered in my sleep, (as a contingency arrangement to the group-felt bravado), but I obtained an A grade in this subject in the 'O' Level exam!

I loved sport at school but wish I had more of an aptitude for it. I threw myself into most new ventures with great enthusiasm. I was good at a few things but close to hopeless at most. At PE classes, I could climb up a rope rather efficiently for example but struggled despairingly with the vaulting horse. In fact, I spent much time nursing my battered testicles after landing squarely on top of said vaulting horse than over it as was required. I often wondered then, if the cumulative battering of my private parts on the vaulting horse, would affect the prospect of my having children in the future. Thankfully it was not the case.

In the pool, I swam better under water, than on the surface, but sadly, there was no event to showcase my skills in that regard. I was not too bad at diving, if I recall correctly, but never made a selection for the swimming team.

Such was my aquatic inability, that I would never have been selected even if the entire swim team and their replacements were simultaneously suffering food poisoning or lumbered with some other ailment. I did enjoy messing around in the pool with my friends though, playing Marco Polo mostly.

And then to my great joy, I discovered fencing. I do not mean the process of erecting a boundary wall, but the true gentleman's endeavour. I took to it like a duck to water. I was somehow reasonably able to apply myself well to this sport. Unrestrained by the lack of likely harm to life and limb, or tear-filled eyes I threw myself wholeheartedly into this sport, rejoicing wildly with every strike of the opponent's torso with Foil. We were but a mere handful of boys at the school willing to give up time for this, but enthusiasts we certainly were with ambitions to progress to Épée and thence to Sabre. I looked forward to gaining notoriety at this event. As a result of my enthusiasm for the sport, and my untiring efforts in organising events for the team, I was rewarded with a role as Vice-Captain. Hurrah! And added to that glory, I soon obtained a further elevated status as one of the school's Prefects.

I digress again. Forgive me. It was on the subject of improving my tennis that I got distracted. But as a result of my digression, you now at least, have a flavour of my sporting prowess on anything that required at least a modicum of coordination. As I mentioned earlier, I hoped to use this time under lockdown, *inter alia*, to improve my game of tennis. It is a rather sociable sport after all, is it not? Something we can play well into our sunset years. I just wish I had spent my time at school more usefully, at least in acquiring some semblance of a reasonable game as a basis upon which to build.

How best to learn to play the game by myself? I was tempted to enlist the help of Enoch who had coached Holly and Chloe but was not sure that my current frugal budget which now already excluded many luxuries, could extend to a fee for a tennis coach too. My plan was therefore to hit the ball against the practice wall to begin with, in an effort to develop an eye for a moving ball, and also practice my service.

I dressed and got ready to go out to the court, dusted off an old racquet I fished out from the 'sports box', and was all set, until I discovered a crucial missing element – there were no balls to hit. The only ones that Dunmore and I could eventually find were two that my dogs had adopted as toys, and now only had a very vague resemblance to their former existence. My eager hopes to improve my tennis had now been disappointingly dashed even before the very first strike.

Anyway, not being one to give up easily, I decided to see if I could use the stochastically available time to improve my golf instead. I had always assumed, given that my hand-to-eye coordination was not my greatest asset, that it would be much easier to hit a ball when stationary. It was true to some extent.

I took up golf when I was working in Jealott's Hill. I joined a group of colleagues who decided to make the most of the facilities and amenities there, including that of having a choice of golf courses within easy vehicular access.

Lessons were had and some of us decided to equip ourselves with at least the basics to commence our golfing adventures. Out came the handy credit card and we left the pro shop equipped with the shoes, glove, half set of clubs, golf bag and a few sets of balls. Some of us went a step further and decided we needed covers for the club heads, despite them being entirely optional for beginners. Being me, I had to equip myself with some trending golfing attire as well. As I had mentioned to you earlier in this letter, looking the part was a key approach I chose to employ in every endeavour I felt worthy of participating meaningfully in.

We had so much fun, despite the fact that many of us spent an inordinate amount of time searching for lost balls or hitting multiple divots instead of the ball. What a great relief it was to finally reach the green and hear the clump of the ball sinking in the hole. Although complete novices, one of my colleagues felt that we were able enough to enter a competition.

We enlisted, and against all odds and expectations, I won a prize for the longest drive! I cannot remember the yardage, but the ball flew straight and true for a considerable distance, as was verified independently. Apparently, there was another ball that had been hit about ten yards further than mine but had been discounted for being on the edge of the rough. I was thrilled! I was now a complete convert to the game. My prowess at golf cannot really be a boast, however as, other than the occasional great shot, (and you can hear it – the club head meets the sweet spot of the ball at the right velocity and sets it off on lofty flight in the desired direction), my game never really improved.

I had Dunmore dust off the clubs and decided I would attempt to re-learn the art of hitting a ball well. The driving range was closed, as part of the lockdown regimen, so I had little choice but to confine my golfing efforts to the garden. As the garden was of reasonable width, I felt it appropriate to practice my chipping and putting. It was surprisingly not too bad. I just had to keep reminding myself to keep my eyes on the ball and resist the constant temptation to anticipate its flight. I hit the ball generally well and even noted a slight inclination to hook which I progressively corrected. I enlisted Dunmore's assistance to not just fetch the balls, especially as many were lofted beautifully into the swimming pool, but also to film my efforts. One such recorded effort proved worthy of an Instagram post.

Next, I followed up with putting practice. That went rather well too, and I felt reasonably cheered by my attempts. I now look forward to the lifting of the lockdown so that I can head to the golf range and hit the ball a little more forcefully. Who knows, I may soon feel confident enough to throw my hat in the ring for consideration in a four ball. It would be nice to take you out on the course when you next decide to visit me here.

I must also take you to the gun club here. Keith, who is another friend who had welcomed me back warmly on my return to Zimbabwe, was instrumental in introducing me to the excitement of clay pigeon shooting. I took to it immediately and with unabated enthusiasm. And although my shooting was, as is my golf, very similar to the weather forecast for a poor summer's day in England, i.e., mostly cloudy with a chance of rain, but the occasional glimpse of sunshine, he and I had enormous fun planning the club's monthly magazine content over several beers and whiskeys alongside much laughter. Sadly, I haven't been clay shooting in a very long while.

What I have done though, is increase my workouts to a 5 day a week routine. As you know my trainer Givemore comes for 3 of those days and puts me through a punishing ritual. I sometimes wonder if he has been hired by the 'Mob', or whatever the equivalent may exist in Zimbabwe, to deliberately cause me pain. To be fair, I do appreciate the fact that he pushes me to achieve more than I would otherwise, if left to my own devices. I am not exactly gentle on myself on the other two days though, as I use the motivation of wanting to get in shape for that much talked about a beach holiday. It was Mallorca we were headed to, was it not?

Although I am using the time available to keep both mind and body occupied and in an improved state, I hope that this lockdown ends soon with some degree of control over this virus spread.

I really do have my fingers crossed, and my toes too, as any spread of the pandemic here would be devastating, and rain chaos at best. The medical facilities are not the greatest, and unless the quest was for a mere aspirin, we would be placing our lives very much in the hands of our gods.

I assume that matters are a little more comforting where you are.

I shall of course be writing to you again soon. Take care and stay safe.

Love,

David

Letter 23 – Hair & Mon Frère

March 2020

Dear Geoff,

I went for a haircut today. My usual hairdresser was unavailable, so I decided to try a lady called Tabitha, who some friends had recommended.

Their recommendation was not limited to her hairdressing skills, but her likely candidature for an amorous intent. My hair was getting to the point of being progressively more difficult to brush and keep in some orderly manner. So, reluctant though I was to break the lockdown regulation for a seemingly poor reason, my wish to tame the unruly tangle became more urgent, and I made an appointment with Tabitha. To some extent, I was also curious to meet her, as I had only previously gained a brief glimpse of her at an Embassy function. I did note, at the time, that she seemed to have a nice figure and a great pair of legs, and you are well aware of how susceptible I am to those.

You may not be as particular about your hair as I, but I am always averse to trying someone new especially when I have, through painful trial and error, finally found someone who knows exactly how I wish to have my hair cut. I feel similarly about the selection of dentists when it comes to caring for my teeth. I am very nervous about changing dentists as I would rather stick to the one who knows me well and has a very good understanding of my sincere and intense wish to avoid pain at any cost.

I mentioned as much to Tabitha when I did finally sit on the proffered barber's chair, ready to have her deal with my mutinous mop. She seemed to understand my concerns, but as she reached for the clippers my nerves began to twinge with concern.

Perhaps I am too much of a traditionalist, but when it comes to cutting and shaping hair, it is something I always associate with an orderly process. The stylist first assesses your hair expertly, examining the length and shape with their fingers, proceeding then to ask you what you wish to achieve, followed swiftly by a rinse of your hair as its wet state allows a more precise cut with scissors. Yes, scissors. This is this implement that I feel defines the more accomplished hairdresser or stylist. I am not for a single minute suggesting that the barbers who have attended to many a male scalp with clippers are inexperienced amateurs in that field.

In fact, to the contrary, I think that many should be revered for sheer dedication to the task and for tirelessly attending to the many men who occupied the seats desiring nothing more than a quick trim, or a regulation cut.

It was no reflection on the barber. It was just me. I had developed a paranoia for clippers, associating them with imprecision and have feared them ever since my parents once decided to cut my hair at home with this savage instrument, and I ended up with a monk's hairdo. It was horrific! I shed so many tears that I would have easily filled a water tanker or two. Crying brought no relief. The humiliation was compounded by the endless teasing from my siblings. I must have only been about eight, but my hair and how it was best shaped was obviously something I felt rather sensitive about even at that tender age.

I realise that this is probably an aspect more relevant to our opposite sex, and to be honest, I am still unclear as to why I was then, and to this day, become so precious about my hair. What I am certain about is that it was never an issue of vanity. I never even really considered myself good-looking, even by the most generous of definitions, which is why I always feared approaching the pretty girls almost certain that any attempt to solicit interest from these winsome creatures would more than likely end in dismal failure.

The only time I felt confidence of sorts was in the latter part of my primary school days, when I captured the interests of the prettiest girls in the class. My earlier primary school days, as you will recall from my previous correspondence, were occupied with playing marbles or fishing, and preferring the pursuit of butterflies to pretty girls.

However successful the latter part of primary school may have been, my fortunes in this regard have faltered ever since, and if I ever did summon up the courage to approach such girls or women, I relied heavily on my sense of humour to see me through. I became the sort who, if by some misadventure or misdeed, found myself entered in any beauty parade, would immediately anticipate being thrown out at the earliest point, or rejoice if found to be at the bottom end of any tabulation of entrants. My humour, dress sense and my hair were the only aspects, I could reliably lean on to pass for at least a vague facsimile of a desirable male.

As I grew older and my hair turned progressively grey, I regretted the passing of the days of my long black locks even more. I took comfort from friends and hairdressers paying compliments on my distinguished looking greying hair. "Silver fox" I believe was the term sometimes applied. The minute I gained compliments from a respected hairdresser, I was sold, and happy to place my hair, and therefore my life in their hands.

Sometimes the more creative ones would apply a little dye to make the grey less pronounced but deliberate. Dyeing soon became part of the hairdressing ritual if I ever got around to making it to a reputable stylist.

Unfortunately, once children appeared in my life, my visits to high-end hairdressers became less of a priority, and I resorted to finding just a decent barber. And yes, I began to accept clippers as an inevitable part of the hair-cutting practice. I considered myself lucky to escape with a bearable cut, and just prayed for the day my fortunes would change for the better so that I could afford to provide for the family whilst simultaneously treating myself to entry into a half-decent hairdressing salon.

After an incident when the dyeing went disastrously wrong, I had to reconsider its exclusion for good. I had gone to George whose premises were always tired and unkempt in appearance and full of a million people packed into a small space seeking plaits, perms and pampering. It was not the sort of environment I would normally like to be in as I am freakishly concerned about hygiene and space around me at any hairdressing premises, even in darkest Africa. But I opted to go there as he had been cutting my hair for a while now and knew exactly what I desired by of a haircut. The trade-off was experience over environment. George was by no means what I would term a high-end hairdresser but was able enough with a pair of scissors. And cheap. I had taken the girls with me on this occasion. He offered to dye my hair applying a different technique to the scalp cap he usually used. That should have been warning enough for me, but with the girls' encouragement, I accepted.

It was an absolute nightmare. Sections of my hair had taken on a greenish brown hue.

There was no semblance of a natural pattern and made me look like I was sporting a comical wig as part of a fund-raising initiative. Had the BBC been notified, I would have had a team of reporters at the doorstep wanting to know more of this catastrophe. I had to live with this shame for many weeks before I could eventually have sufficient hair cut away to show the emerging roots of natural but very grey hair! I never look good in hats, so, sadly, I was not able to disguise this horrific hairdo for even part of the time. Many teased me mercilessly over my hair and I was even labelled a 'Bollywood porn star' lookalike by some. Understandably, I stopped going to George, and that was also the very last time I had my hair dyed.

Part of my desire to have long hair was to detract from possessing such a prominent nose. I had hoped, when I was young lad, that as I grew older my nose would remain small so that it did not occupy most of my face. The gods must have decided, however, that it would be fun to see if my nose could grow at an even greater pace than the rest of my features. It now cannot be missed.

The long hair worked to some extent, as people would comment on my hair rather than remarking on any other feature. Or do I delude myself? This may have been a polite way of them avoiding making comment on my nose. To this day, it remains the one feature on my face that I would gladly apply some form of surgery to moderate its significant presence. It is interesting that one of my daughters is equally obsessed with her nose. In her case, I can see no cause. It is consistent with her face, narrow and aristocratic, as was my father's. I do not object to the slight curvature at the tip of my nose, as much as I do to the fact that my nostrils appear to be enormously flared and look as though a once acceptable nasal feature was squashed with a hefty blow from a brick, and never repaired.

My focus was my hair. I discovered the wonderful world of Vidal Sassoon. Thanks to an introduction by my brother, I began to frequent their studio during the school holidays. I say studio rather than salon, as our student budgets were limited to say the least, and the studios offered cuts at a token cost if one was prepared to offer one's scalp as a practice pitch for aspiring stylists. You would have assumed, given my nervous disposition with respect to this aspect, that I would be the very last likely volunteer for such an undertaking, but not in this case.

My justification being that most of those who did cut my hair were aspiring stylists and therefore could not afford any mistakes in order to progress their careers.

I also took comfort from the regular attendance of their watchful supervisors. And for further comforting consideration, the studios were well lit, immaculately clean and open planned and well located in a prime position in London's West End. Even the smell of fresh shampoo, as one walked in was noticeably alluring. It all made for a great hairdressing experience, especially as the hair washes were with the best shampoos and conditioners, and all the cuts were with scissors. Not a dastardly clipper in immediate sight.

I went so regularly that I soon got to know some of the supervisors quite well. They seemed to enjoy my attendance too and always commented on how great they thought my hair was. I tended to grow my hair to a length that stretched the definition of what the school permitted, which in my final year at school meant that I generally got away with sporting it to shoulder length. During one such visit, I was asked if I had any Native American Indian blood as the supervisor thought I looked like a member of the Cherokee tribe. He was new and very obviously gay. But then so were most of the men at that studio. It mattered not to me. They were such a wonderfully entertaining, friendly and charming bunch. Besides, I was flattered by the attention, clear that there was no desire to court my interests. I loved their compliments. I do feel, though that the aquiline nose alongside the long hair may have played a part in his suggestion of a native American Indian lineage. Whatever his basis, he remarked on the beauty of the thick and long black locks that adorned my head. Soon a crowd of stylists surrounded me, and I had my fifteen seconds of fame. They did not want to cut much of my hair as they wanted me to participate in a fashion event to showcase various hair types and styles.

How exciting this was. As I had mentioned to you earlier, I never prided myself on my looks, but was delighted to be selected for such a glamorous assignment. Off I trotted to the Lancaster Gate hotel excited but also a little apprehensive, as I had never modelled before. I have appeared on stage a few times in school plays and been as nervous as a skittish cat, but usually comforted by the thought of a few supportive and forgiving fans, by way of parents at the least, in the audience.

Having suggested that they were supportive. It was not always the case. I once was teased endlessly by my parents when I had been selected to play the part of Macduff in the school's interpretation of one of Shakespeare's finest works but appeared instead in an inconsequential small role. I had taken sudden fright and ducked out at the last minute. I was, as a result, subsequently relegated to playing one of the 'trees' in representation of Birnam Wood. It was literally almost at the point of curtain call, as we had successfully completed a dress rehearsal and were psyching ourselves for a performance to a very large general public audience.

Perhaps that is why my nerves gave way? Rather than admitting to stage fright, I feigned a sore throat and convinced my teacher that I would not recover sufficiently from this ailment to provide the necessary vocal delivery on stage. I had hoped that giving up on a key role would at the least obtain a non-speaking part which would allow me some stage presence. I offered to be the Standard Bearer. It may have been a punishment for my letting him down at the penultimate moment and causing a chaotic rearrangement of personnel, but the only part on offer was that of a tree! I was sorely disappointed as I had read well for the part of Macduff and was cheered for a good delivery on stage at dress rehearsal. It was tree or nothing.

It was humbling! I did learn something from playing a tree though and am able to offer you good advice as a result - if you are ever selected for such a part, be aware that walking in costume is more difficult than you are led to believe.

I never discovered what exactly caused my stage fright for the role in Macbeth, but I was not able to recapture the performance I produced previously when playing the part of Sergius Saranoff in Shaw's "Arms and the Man". I was so confident on stage then. The performance was 'imperious', I believe I suggested to you in one of my earlier letters. Those were indeed the words used by my teacher – "convincing and imperious", if my memory serves me well. I wonder whether it was, on that occasion, purely driven by my desire to impress my lovely Fawzia who played Raina so beautifully opposite me. Whatever the reason, my acting career had come to a humiliating and abrupt end.

As you can imagine the apprehension for this forth-coming fashion show was understandable. I took some comfort from the thought that my role required no speech, and that I was very unlikely to be the focus of any attention. After all, there were several of us who had been selected for the assignment. I assumed that we would appear for a minute or so at the most.

It was a great experience! We were only three boys amongst several girls, and the added delight to this wonderful assignment was that we were thrown together in a single prep room. Hair and make-up together with a troop of many pretty girls - hurrah! We were told to leave our personal items in the prep area and called to the stage, where we were provided with instructions on what was required of our appearance. All it entailed was to walk as instructed to the edge of the platform, turn and return to the back of the stage. What could go wrong, I thought to myself as I strode confidently down the stage when called. My walk may not have been perfect, but sufficient from a quick lesson on how to do so. The girls who must have rehearsed this several times over, looked and behaved like absolute professionals. I kicked myself for not applying the same preparation for this moment. I did however, get an encouraging pat on the back from one of the organisers, so I remained upbeat about my forthcoming performance.

We had our hair and make-up done, and I enjoyed all the pampering. How wonderful it would be to do this on a full-time basis I thought, as I had my hair brushed caressingly and had a little make-up applied to my face. I presume they felt they could do little about my hideous nose and concentrated on my hair instead. I realised that I was not selected for my looks but my hair, but I nevertheless wanted to provide as positive a presence as I reasonably could, in the hope that I would be considered for future roles.

We dressed in the primarily black attire provided and lined up backstage ready for our walk on stage. All I now had to do was to conduct myself as I had done in the trial and avoid a misstep and fall. I had no control over a possible misstep, but I prayed that there would be no dust catching in my eye to cause tears and ensuing disaster unfolding *à la* rugby field experiences. There was no need for concern. All went well. Not only did we receive profuse thanks for our attendance but were paid handsomely for our efforts. I would have gladly done this modelling for free but was happy to add this unexpected benefaction to my rather meagre student budget, nevertheless. Money was always welcome in my life, providing it was earned in an honest manner.

It was the boys who appeared the shyer in the changing area, as the girls seemed happy to stride around the room half naked. That was a novel experience in itself. Trying not to stare at these heavenly bodies clad mostly in just their panties during costume changes was akin to being asked to disregard the contents of a Playboy magazine to focus only on the adverts. It would be virtually impossible to expect any red-blooded teen harbouring raging levels of testosterone to remain unperturbed when sharing space with a bevy of half-naked pretty girls, but I tried my best to avoid staring, by feigning nonchalance.

Whether it was for fear of being accused of staring too intently, or a wish to appear professional in order to impress, I cannot be too sure, even in hindsight. What I can admit to, is being incredibly shy. I lacked the confidence that other boys in similar conditions would have ably applied, and probably secured dates from one if not more of the girls as a result. I had obtained no telephone numbers, and other than fiercely clutching the ten-pound note given, I left completely empty-handed. The experience of modelling, however, albeit brief, remains a memorable one!

Almost all of us in the family signed up with the Joan Tree Agency and managed to land well-paid work during our holidays. We were always given first preference because we were diligent, attentive and hard-working.

In many cases, employers felt that we were often better than the permanent employees whom we replaced temporarily. This marginally added income allowed us to splash out a little on luxuries – a meal out at a better restaurant, a better item of clothing, a visit to a chiropodist, or a haircut at a proper salon. My brother, John was yet again instrumental in discovering and recommending Roxanne. She worked at the Vidal Sassoon salon in Knightsbridge. John was waxing lyrical about her attributes, and it didn't take much persuasion to decide that I too could part with a little more cash than usually budgeted for, in order to give Roxanne a trial.

She was everything John had described and more. Long dark curly hair framing a face with a virtually perfect complexion and beautiful big brown eyes. Dressed in tight black trousers she left little to imagine of the lovely figure it reverently clad, and a low-cut top drew one's eyes immediately to the perfectly shaped breasts.

As you know, I am more of a legs man, but her breasts were so perfectly shaped that they were worthy of several lines of poetry!

She took her time with her cut, and when she ran her finger through my hair to check length and angularity they felt like caresses. I could just imagine her kisses being as gentle as the touch of her hands. I was inclined to shut my eyes and just picture her peppering my face with soft kisses from those perfectly shaped lips. But I did not, for fear of missing out on seeing her beauty in person, albeit through a reflection in the mirror. I just smiled and tried to avoid looking like a love-stricken gargoyle, as I was generally inclined to on such occasions.

The ultimate joy, as my brother rightly described was when she got you to tilt your head back to rest comfortably on her breasts, as she continued her thorough examination of her work. It was more than bliss to feel one's head rest on those heavenly cushions she called her breasts. If one were to perish, that would be the absolutely perfect moment to do so! If only I had been a little older or preferably better looking, I would have been sorely tempted to ask her out on a date, but the best either of us could do at the time was worship her from afar and make as many hair appointments as we possibly could with her. Roxanne's was a scissor cut. I rest my case, with regard to this aspect.

She left Vidal Sassoon's, and we were unable to track her down. She was probably bikini-clad and sipping cocktails, whilst luxuriating aboard some millionaire's yacht harboured in San Tropez. no doubt. Oh, the lucky man!

I was grateful to John for the Roxanne recommendation. I can honestly say that I have never found any hairdresser who looked as special as she did, nor cut my hair as well. I could always rely on *mon frère* to look after my interests well.

It was great to have an older brother during the formative teen years, especially as neither of us had a male role model easily accessible to us. By way of guidance on everything from shirts and aftershaves to luring girls' attention, and the best application of one's financial resources, he provided me with good advice. For guidance on fashion, finance and females, I salute you, *mon frère*.

You have met John only relatively recently, and probably think of him as a mild-mannered and gentle soul. But under that calm and quiet exterior beats the heart of a rebel. At school, he was considered one of the beer-swilling lads and beyond the capacity of any teachers to tame into the confines of an ideal boarding school pupil.

There was one memorable occasion in which his wild side was highly evident.

He invited me up to his student digs at Keele University for a lad's weekend. I set off by train with great excitement at the thought of posing as a university student and meeting some great liberally minded girls. I was now in my lower sixth form and allowed to wander into town in civvies for return by the curfew hour. I am sure that the schoolmasters knew that we tended to sneak straight out again to rendezvous at the various pubs but may have chosen to turn a blind eye to these nefarious activities.

Did you know that there were fifty-two pubs within the city limits in Canterbury? We had a challenge of sorts to visit as many as we could and collect beer mats as proof of our conquests. But beyond the beer, our quest was to chat up as many girls as we could. We had to pass as university students to stand any chance of gaining their attention. We had some success but scored best in the summer when there were many foreign students on exchange courses, and we could use their lack of familiarity with the English language to better camouflage our posturing as university students. The Scandinavian girls were the best-looking and greatest kissers. It was one of the causes I may have mentioned in one of my previous missives, as to how and why I fell for the pretty and special Danish girl, Madeleine.

My brother was now going to give me an insight into student life at university. This knowledge was of course to then be communicated to the eagerly awaiting crew back at school, so that we could be better armed to chat up girls in our *sojourns* into the city centre.

I met John at the given train destination where he had come together with one of his flatmates, who had a car. We drove back to their flat on the campus. There was a disco on that evening. The excitement was palpable. I could already feel my heart beating faster with excitement. I was introduced to the rest of his flatmates and offered the floor as my bed for the night. I wasn't disappointed. On the contrary, I would have been happy to sleep in the bath or atop the kitchen counter in exchange for the valuable real-life experience I felt was obtaining.

I followed their conversation with great interest trying to absorb the manner in which they spoke and tried to copy also the way they carried themselves - the assurance in gait that only University students seemed to possess.

My school was not a military academy, but I felt that even boarding schoolboys walked and generally moved in a more disciplined way. Perhaps it was the orderly queuing in the dining hall or for the team bus, but there was a distinct difference. I had to try and adopt as many of the casual mannerisms and confident postures of these University students as I could.

I tried smoking and nearly choked. I decided to leave cigarettes for another time, but carried one in my pocket, thinking that I could have it unlit and casually attached to the side of my mouth. This, coupled with some microscopic stubble around the chin and upper lip, could convey sufficient maturity, I believed. I could merrily sink a pint or two of beer without collapsing in a heap, so I felt confident that I could carry off a fairly credible facsimile of a university student.

John made dinner for us. I think it was a Beef Stroganoff. It was one of his specialities. He was actually a good cook and still is, although it's not required of him these days given what a great chef Maureen is. We set off for the disco. John had lent me one of his shirts. These were the days I almost completely followed his fashion advice. The shirt was patterned and wide-lapelled.

I know it sounds decidedly hideous now, but at the time it was the height of fashion to wear shirts with lapels that reached the edge of one's shoulders, preferably with a couple of buttons undone to show some chest hair. Unlike John, I had nothing to display in this area unless viewed with aid of a magnifying glass, so other than opting to insert a bathmat under my shirt, I had little choice but to dress my buttons more conservatively.

Attire completed with the vital flared trousers and platform shoes; I stumbled out of the flat together with them making up a party of four. Other than at school where this footwear was specifically prohibited, I wore platform shoes, everywhere, and for the most part, struggled. How women wear heels elegantly, I will never know. I walked for miles in these stilts, or more correctly staggered along, but remained resolute. I even danced that evening in them without falling over. A feat that should have received commendation in my view, as it was a very hard thing to do, especially after consumption of many beers during the course of the evening.

The plan was to arrive when things were getting interesting. Only the uninitiated and nerds turned up early, apparently. We were part of the 'cool crowd'. I tried to calm myself down and act as casually as the men I was with, but the heart of the schoolboy continued to beat excitedly within me.

Most of the rest of the night was rather blurry, except for a few stand-out moments. One of them was watching my brother on the dance floor as they played "Layla". He strummed an air guitar in a manner that would have Eric Clapton applauding frantically. John went completely wild! He took centre spot amongst the group he was with and danced without a care in the world. Fully bearded, with hairy chest on display and long hair swaying madly, he looked the part of a rock star, albeit an Indian version of one! Had it been in the days of camera phones, it is a video that would have gone immediately viral and achieved worldwide acclaim.

The other memorable incident was my success in soliciting the interests of one of the girls there, with whom I exchanged a plethora of lingering kisses. Please note that this was after quite a few alcoholic beverages, so I have little recollection of anything about her. Neither name, nor face, neither figure nor attire. I do think that some discussion was had about going back to my room, which would have provided a better prompt to memory.

Alas, I had no room to offer, other than a careworn sleeping bag on the floor. I had hoped to make it to her place of abode, even if it constituted a stable in Bethlehem for privacy's sake, but this offer was not very forthcoming for some unknown reason. Had I been more seasoned or astute, a desk, chair, back seat of a car, or against the door to an empty lecture room could have served the purpose. I was no veteran and had to accept a dance of tongues and some petting as sufficient sexual engagement for that evening. Pity, but it was better to have gained some gratification than left with no success at all.

I toyed with the idea of slight exaggeration of this encounter when relating this tale to school chums, but decided that they would easily see through me, and that any claim to have had sex when I had no prior experience of it would be foolhardy. Regardless of the measure of sexual success, I had a great weekend, and enjoyed the opportunity to bond further with my brother also. Visions of John on the dance floor still always make me smile when I hear "Layla" being played.

Although generally kind and supportive to me, I do remember an occasion when he allowed his less benevolent side to enjoy laughter at my expense. It was the evening of my prospective brother-in-law's stag do. I begged to be included in the party headed for the pub. They felt that I could pass for eighteen, given my height, enhanced further with my preferred footwear of platform shoes, and agreed.

Unknown to me, John and his friend Arthur, kept adding shots of vodka and whisky to the pints of beer I was happily pouring down my throat to keep pace with the adults. Their admission was only made after the event, and therefore of no help in rectifying my resultant hopelessly drunken state that evening.

I do not even remember how much I drank or what took place afterwards. I just remember being asked to make my way from the car to the front door by myself. I could hear John and Arthur chuckling as they kept calling for me to join them at the front door. Walking in platform shoes was a difficult task in itself for me as I have mentioned before but made considerably more challenging when faced with what appeared to be a mirror-like appearance of several front doors in my line of sight, caused by the swirling in my head. Valiantly though I tried, the simple task of placing one foot in front of another suddenly appeared an impossible one without veering off-course many times. I must have eventually made it in.

It was not my favourite receptacle in the home to occupy, but I hugged the toilet bowl in welcome relief. My sister Rachel nursed me that evening. I felt the room spinning when I was eventually put to bed. My head felt as though it had been smacked several times by a battering ram, the next morning, and I swore solemnly that I would never touch another drop of alcohol again for as long as I lived. The very mention of beer made me feel positively ill. At Rachel's insistence, John apologised to me the next day, but the sly smirk suggested that he was not being terribly sincere.

Have I strayed notably away from the subject of hair again? Forgive me. As always, when talking to you on one subject, I am inclined to immediately hold forth as soon as I think of another. I was telling you about my hair and trying by way of a letter to you to understand why it appears to be so precious to me.

Why am I so protective over, and attentive toward the follicles arising from the top of my head? It may be partly attributable to the fact that having a loved one run their fingers through my hair offers much solace. It was something my mother did when providing comfort to me as a child, which a few of my past loves particularly Paulette, Madeleine and Ravinia adopted and subsequently developed into an amazingly loving and soothing art form.

Although there is no provider of such solace apparent in my life currently, it may be a subconscious desire to safeguard it as a source of future delight and comfort with prospective lovers. And given my current circumstances particularly, there is an understandable wish to hang onto every hope for assuagement possible!

It is possibly also due to it being a characteristic of mine that has generated many compliments over the years, (other than for the dip in ratings due to the dyeing disaster), from the time of positive appraisals of my 'long black locks' at the Vidal studios to the more recent 'silver fox' references with others thereafter.

And to some extent also due to the delectable Roxanne, as ever since she convinced us to invest in good haircare products, (which would not have been too difficult to do when making a sale to a couple of besotted teens), I have generally abided by this advice.

A little extraordinarily perhaps, but I therefore, even took the loss of my hair into account as part of my deliberations on cancer treatment, and finally chose to decline the recommended chemotherapy. I inarguably and eventually decided that I would rather risk and face death if I needed to with a full head of hair. Is it because I feel that it is now such an integral part of me, and that it somehow almost defines who I am? Possibly. Does that seem shallow? It is a rather peculiar view, I grant you, but I hope that you do truly understand.

It will not surprise you, therefore, that when I suggested that my nerves were on edge when Tabitha reached for the clippers, I was truly in fear of what she may do to my hair. She was happy to concede to my preference for a scissor cut and promised to use the clippers only for some minor edging. She was quite thorough though and seemed to apply a good understanding of what I wanted to achieve. It was good to note as there are many hairdressers, particularly those who work in factory-like settings, who nod agreeably when discussing your wishes, but proceed subsequently to do exactly as they chose. Tabitha's cut was not a bad one. I shall certainly consider her again, if I fail to get hold of Charlotte, who usually does my hair. But I did enjoy talking to Tabitha too, as Charlotte was not one for much dialogue beyond the exchange of pleasantries.

Conversation with your hairdresser is essential, is it not? Barmen and hairdressers are the people you speak about the entirety of your life; or turn to for an outpouring of grief, or sometimes just to obtain wisdom on a particular course of action in the pursuit to win over the target of your ardour. I am sure John and I had recounted every aspect of our lives to Roxanne.

In hindsight, I should have sought her counsel on my love life also, but I think I was too captivated by her beauty to contemplate thoughts of other women. I probably would have willingly offered my right arm to be wrenched from its socket just to have the opportunity to be with her and rest my head on those delightful breasts for an eternity.

Tabitha had an incredible tale to tell. Hers was a story of broken dreams and senseless brutality. It is amazing that she had the strength and the will to bring herself out of the depths of unbelievable poverty and engagement in abusive relationships, to establish a relatively firm financial and emotional independence. It would be nice to take a leaf out of her book, but not literally of course, with a view to re-directing my life also.

I look forward to learning more about her, but I am quite convinced, as with every other lady I have met recently, that she could not hope to occupy the place in my heart that seems to be almost permanently reserved for someone else *en ce moment*.

I shall of course write to you soon, and let you know what transpires, but will bid you adieu for now.

Love,

David

Letter 24 – Renewed Conversation

April 2020

Dear Geoff,

I spoke to H today!

Her voice was so beautiful to hear. Its musicality made my heart melt.

I had not spoken to her in so long, but I knew that it was a voice I was happy to hear constantly without any interruption. I practically clung to her every word. I could not have pressed the phone closer to my ear without causing severe auricular damage.

It felt so good to be in touch with H again. We had exchanged messages since my return to Zimbabwe, but not very frequently. She enquired of my health, and I felt obliged to send her recent photographs, including one of myself after a workout. She appeared to be very impressed with how I looked.

If she had previously pictured me looking careworn or emaciated, given knowledge of my illness, she seemed suitably impressed with my state of health and more particularly my shape.

As you know, I have been working tirelessly, and sometimes painfully also, to get into some level of fitness and shape. Each view in the mirror of continued unwelcome signs of fat, provided me renewed vigour to apply myself to exercise to the point of complete fatigue and breathlessness to achieve some good physical form. Why was I driving myself so hard? Was it merely to please H? I think not.

I was doing this for myself, largely. I wanted to somehow rid myself of the demons that occupied my mind from the day I was diagnosed with cancer. I keep telling myself that if I can develop a healthy body, I would be better equipped to fight this disease through natural effort rather than medication. It is without doubt, that I am terrified. I am sure that its return would be devastating to both mind and body, so I feel I have to try. Chemo or any other invasive and debilitating therapy will not be for me. I am hoping that a relatively healthy diet to accompany my efforts in the gym will allow me to prevail. God willing, as they say, but only if God does in fact exist.

My efforts to get into better shape are also motivated by a wish to recover some semblance of dress sense. I have written to you previously of my interest in clothes and my various flirtations with fashion – from a childhood of stubborn insistence on particular attire to requiring adolescent guidance in my teens, and thence to trendy college days, followed by modest vestments whilst in darkest Africa; a fashion revival and my trendsetting twenties on return to England; the post pneumonia hospitalisation days with conservative but attractive dressing and then a fall into the dark days of fashion *faux pas'* during married life and arrival in Zimbabwe!

I have no wish to denigrate the entirety of married life. Some of my happiest days were during those times. I absolutely adore my children and would gladly relive some of those days. But not with the same approach to fashion. Looking back through some of those photographs from that time, I appeared to have completely lost any sense of suitable apparel.

I seemed incapable of creating any attractive ensemble, which was previously of second nature to me. I was voted the most fashion-conscious and best-dressed man at Cranfield during my time there. Those days now seem to have retreated into a distant past. I dressed reasonably well in suit and tie for work in Harare but failed dismally in the casual wear front.

When I left corporate life to start a new business, I sunk to greater depths in the pit of fashion failures. A dire lack of resources, coupled with an abdication of personal health and acceptance of business and marital difficulties relegated any fashion desires to the lowest of priorities. My wardrobe at the time was made up of a ghastly combination of cheap brightly coloured Slazenger polo shirts and progressively larger trouser sizes, in what can only be described as a peasant's ensemble.

I am surprised that I actually chose to venture out in such awful attire, let alone be photographed in it. I often shudder at the thought. Even the horrific days of hideously patterned polystyrene shirts and flared trousers seem a welcome imagined sight. At least I was trendy then!

A modest recovery in business fortune and regular visits to London at the behest of my then-client allowed me to improve my wardrobe a little. My motivation to improve my fitness and figure returned. And then came the diagnosis and hospitalisation, this time for a far greater illness.

I was shocked at what appeared as my reflection in the hospital mirror. I could not recognise the man I thought I had begun to slowly recapture. Not only was the man who stared back at me patently ugly, but devoid of even the smallest of redeeming features. Even a once bright smile was a grotesque distortion of the lips. There was no muscular aspect whatsoever. I made sure I addressed these matters after I was discharged. The ugliness, however, I could not do much to alter.

It was hard at first to undertake any strenuous exercise with the limitations of carrying a stoma bag, but the trainers at the Soho House gym were wonderful. Giuliano, Jake, Viktorija, Ferdinando, Gaia, Ellie, Adriana, Ron amongst others, were always smiling and warm in their welcome. Giuliano, Jake and Viktorija also gave me sets of exercises to do and supported me constantly in my efforts to regain my fitness, and with it some confidence.

Viktorija, who is also a very gorgeous young actress (I am convinced that she will be very famous one day), was when not training, so supportive also of my intended literary efforts. In fact, when I told her about my wish to write a book, she immediately bought me a copy of Seneca's "Letters from a Stoic", which served as such a great inspiration to me. The literary gulf however, between my letters to you and those of Seneca to his correspondent is an unbridgeably immense one. But the spirit is not too dissimilar, I assure you.

I soon became addicted to exercise again and could easily have spent every day at the gym, but I limited exercising to about three or four times a week. I was eager to regain form to my post-pneumonia Luisa days. I was slowly reaching my goal in terms of fitness but was under strict doctor's instruction not to exercise my core. I was also doing a lot of walking and my step count according to the FitBit I wore, always exceeded the target ten thousand steps a day. I was, I thought, both mentally and physically prepared for the operation to remove the stoma bag.

It was supposedly a relatively simple procedure. Haha! Perhaps for the surgeon. I felt that I retreated physically to a point before square one. Square zero. I felt that I had aged significantly all of a sudden. I looked and felt like a physical wreck, mentally unable to cope with the damage inflicted on my person; and emotionally at a point where even death would have provided welcome relief.

As always, the optimist in me took hold again. It took a few weeks, but I began to heal. I opted to restart my days at the gym and am again so grateful to the team of trainers, and to some of the gym members also with whom I had become acquainted, for all their support.

When I got back to Zimbabwe, I tried to make what I could of my life, as I mentioned to you in an earlier letter. One preferably, where I could begin to chart a new course for myself. It was a time also though, that I could really have done with a soft and loving shoulder to lean upon. Someone like H.

But before I attempted to court her again, I needed to regain a little self-esteem, which had all but disappeared from my life. And if as a result of my sweat and toil, I was able to win some of her admiration, I would be very happy.

Just hearing her voice was sheer pleasure. It would have been even nicer to have gazed into her lovely eyes as she spoke, but I was glad to hear that she was prepared to give up some of her time for me. Our conversation lacked the gaiety of our very first-time flirtations but was pleasant enough as the basis upon which to build further rapport.

Could I still be in love with her? I have met several women on dates and indulged in the occasional fling since, but am firmly of the view that I have no serious interest in many of them, other than that of pursuing friendship. Am I still applying her qualities and attributes as a yard stick? I probably am, but now with a sense of pragmatism. I just hope that any future prospect must at least come close to creating the sort of emotional stir within me that H does so successfully and easily with a phone call or a message.

I have to make the most of her intended trip to visit me here in November. Who knows? I may even be able to, as a result of having her undivided attention for a few days, be able to either create a spark of mutual interest within her soul or dispel the surreal affections I hold for her. If all comes to nought, this will not be a love lost through any action or inaction, but an acceptance of what must prevail, given the current state of my seemingly un-requited love.

I have yet to chart an itinerary for her visit but would love to show her around as much as possible, and not just the tourists' round of sights either. I would like her to see some of the projects I have worked on and completed. A view from the top of the Joina City building with vistas across Harare, for example.

It is a pity that there are limited places to take her to dinner or lunch given how wonderfully well she dresses, but perhaps a few dinner parties are called for. I love en-tertaining anyway, and this would be a perfect setting for her to meet some of my friends here. I shall of course write and let you know more of her visit.

She had sent me a video of a belly dancer, previously, and I took this conversation as an opportune time to quiz her over this. She apparently can belly dance very well too. She indicated that she once had all the delightfully exotic costumes for this purpose. Is there no limit to this wonderful woman's abilities? If I marry her, Geoff, she will not only be my companion, wife, and lover, but my very own private dancer too!

Prior to this conversation, we had also exchanged some amusing memes highlighting the obvious incompe-tence in the handling of the pandemic by politicians in some countries. She appeared to be amused. I did not realise that such a negative press could unite us more meaningfully, but it veritably does. She has little regard for extremism in politics, as I do. I feel that I could spend many a jolly hour with H discussing just how we could put the world to right.

I must admit that I have become very disenchanted with the global political environment. It appears that many countries have elected to adopt extremes of politics, mostly, and sadly toward the extreme right. Once the bastions of democracy, many seem to now prefer to lean toward autocracy. But I am not a fan of the politics of the far left either.

Did you know that I flirted with communism once? To be more precise, I flirted with a Communist once. It only came about because I met this rather attractive girl at a party, who was rather impressed that I had read "Das Kapital". I was impressed that I secured her interest. I had just started at university and was keen to explore life more broadly. And you guessed it. I was also a highly charged hormonal teenager who was desperate to get into her pants, even if it meant attending the odd rally or two with her.

If you were wondering why I was so desperate, I must tell you that I was still harbouring many of the schoolboy ambitions to spread my oats as often, and as widely as was humanly possible. This spread was to be selectively undertaken of course, given my fervent wish to avoid regrets as much as possible, and also amongst those who would be willing and eager recipients of the oats I wished to scatter. So, when I use the term as widely as possible, I really mean within the scope of my limited appeal.

Sandra, if I recall her name correctly, was one such eager recipient. She was a self-confessed communist, who stereo-typically feasted (and I use the word generously), on lentil soup and vegetarian burgers, and drove a Citroen 2CV. The Citroen I must admit to thinking of as very charming at the time. The rallies were not really appealing though, and I point blank refused to carry a placard, nor chant nor cheer wildly, as I was merely there to keep Sandra suitably happy.

She was very attractive, and quite charming in a politicised way, but her tree-hugging enthusiasm soon began to irk, as did the insubstantial shared vegetarian meals, and the wish for me to attend many marches and protests with her. I believe that the final straw though may have been her practice of continued conversation during sex.

I would not have minded in the least had it been words of encouragement or utterances of pleasure. The last thing I wanted to do was discuss trade unions, or some such subject that has my eyes glazing over at the best of times, in the midst of applying my best endeavours to make love to her. "Less talk and more action, please" is what I should have said at the time. The cigarette after sex was probably the best part of our entire performance. It was all rather unfulfilling, and this little flirtation with Communism ended almost as quickly as it started.

Anyway, you will be pleased to know that I no longer now feel the desperate need to get into anyone's pants, by claiming political affiliation. Except for H's pants of course, but that would be more for her overall appeal, not political affinity.

I had never mentioned to Sandra that I had read "Mein Kampf" too but had no inclination to sign up to any Fascist party as a result. As I said earlier, my objectives were very clear. Although the intellectual debate was stimulating at the time, it was primarily a physical attraction.

And that is where it remained.

My reading did not guide my political beliefs. I was neither Communist nor Nazi. I was just interested to learn of various ideologies and their derivations. It was soon very clear that I was not attracted to either extreme. Nor am I now. In fact, I find politics rather unpalatable at the moment, and sometimes actually enjoy being in Zimbabwe, where I have no desire whatsoever to get embroiled in the political environment.

There are books that I felt influenced my thinking greatly, at least in the political sphere, and those are Orwell's "Animal Farm" and "1984". I am of the view that his suggestion of the "two legs good, four legs bad" perpetuation of failed political ideologies is still practiced to this day as is the concept of "Big Brother". What an amazingly insightful man he was.

If there were any environments that I am drawn to, it would be New Zealand, where Jacinda Arden seems to be doing a wonderful job of managing the country. Why on earth are not producing more world leaders like her, Angela Merkel or Sanna Marin or even our very own remarkably wonderful and reliably steadfast Queen[1]? Several more women leaders are called for, wouldn't you say?

I don't know how a letter on the subject of an enjoyable conversation with H appears to have veered into politics, but it is strange how my mind works. It is not dissimilar to some of my shopping trips, I fear. I would start with a very clear focus on buying a shirt, but end up straying into book and jewellery stores, antique shops or galleries, and then end up wondering what it was that originated my outing in the first place. So it is with this letter, it seems.

---

[1] Sadly we now mourn the loss of Her Majesty The Queen.

The entire point I wanted to convey to you, in this instance was how wonderful it was to converse with H again. Given the physical distance between us, I could not enjoy gazing into her lovely eyes as we talked, but I did so much enjoy hearing her voice again.

Messages are all very well, but they can never truly replace the joy of conversation. Hers is a voice that I would love to hear every day of my life. And not just in idle banter, which is wonderful as she makes me laugh with her dry wit, but in profound discussion also, as I find her thoughts on various subjects so rapturously engaging. Besides her beauty she appears to possess an equally wondrous heart too, making her probably the most desirable woman in the world today. Perhaps this will give you an understanding of why I am so besotted with her.

My best to you, as always.

Love,

David

Letter 25 – *Fleeting Italian Romance & Mia Sorella*

April 2020

Dear Geoff,

I spoke to my friend, Kate, today and was reminded of a wonderful wedding we both attended in Italy.

Everything appeared to be magical in that summer of 1991. July to be precise. The weather was marvellous, the occasion blissfully romantic, the setting charmingly rustic, the food indescribably delicious, and the company delightfully engaging.

I had not spoken to Kate in a while, and I think the subject of Italy only came up because I had mentioned feeling rather lonely in Zimbabwe. To be very honest, I do actually feel rather peregrine at the moment too. They say that one's home is where one's heart is, which is so very true for me. I miss my girls. I appreciate that they are all grown up now, but I would like to be somewhere within reasonable access to them, especially as I am now without a partner in life. We spoke about my wish to find somewhere in Europe as home. But where best, remains unanswered.

I have grown progressively more disenchanted with matters in England. It does not feel any longer like the wonderful country that I grew up in and love so much as a home. I feel that there has been such a great dumbing down in society generally, and that we possibly were now catering for the lowest common denominator, in terms of societal behaviours and intellectual capability.

Whilst the embracing of technology has to be applauded, it has sometimes been thoughtlessly applied in instances where human interaction, and with it, the show of understanding, empathy and compassion, would be more desirable.

It has also become progressively more harshly divided, along economic and political lines. The economic divide was growing by the day – the rich becoming enormously richer and the poor decidedly poorer – more typical of one in the list of Least Developed Countries, incidentally. Brexit, I fear, has now hardened the political divide.

It was sad to see that everything was developing with a lack of personality and humanity. Money was the only language people wished to understand. That and aesthetic appeal. Everyone could be famous, if they could display a beautiful face or figure, sometimes with a little digital enhancement. No one seemed to place value on principle or ethic.

The days of the gentlemanly handshake to confirm agreement were also over, and one now had to now ensure commitment in writing, and in a form acceptable to the courts of law.

Banking was no longer relationship-based and was now almost completely call-centre oriented. I longed for the days when I knew my bank managers well. I had opened my bank account with NatWest at the age of fourteen and became the proud owner of two cash withdrawal cards, each with a ten-pound limit, which was a sum of money that kept me adequately clothed and fed in those days.

I got to know my managers well, especially during my days at university, as I would be called in quite often to explain an overdraft or two. They believed in me and grew to understand that I was a good investment and a good credit risk. In fact, when I decided to embark upon my MBA, my bank manager was so very supportive, to the point of extending a very generous overdraft as he felt that I would obtain a better career and earning prospects as a result of this further educational endeavour. And I did.

Even after completing my MBA, I continued to have the wonderful support of bank managers. There we many such wonderful managers, who were so helpful in dealing with all of my banking needs, and even helping me arrange my first solitary mortgage for a flat in London over the phone from Zimbabwe, amazingly!

I shall be forever grateful to them and to the many staff at the North Audley Street branch, where I had held my account for many years. These days, I have no idea who I speak to when I call the bank. It is usually a 'Sharon' or 'Kevin', who never disclose their surname, but feel at ease to ask one a gamut of questions in the interests of 'security', excluding only those pertaining to the size and colour of one's underwear.

It became so utterly ridiculous that on one occasion I had such dreadful trouble convincing them that I was the rightful owner of my very own account, which had been defrauded. All because I could not remember a particular password.

I am sure you can relate to a situation where one thinks of oneself as awfully clever in deriving a seemingly unfathomable password, and then proceeding to forget it completely almost immediately afterwards. The one I had set had obviously been deleted from my memory bank and replaced with some inconsequential recollection like the name of the chap in Waitrose (Albert) who indicated that crisps were shelved in aisle 10 next to the drinks (which makes sense), and potentially cost me the loss of a long-standing bank account.

I often wonder if as part of their cost-cutting endeavours, one may soon have trained parakeets and hamsters working alongside each other to provide this customer service in future. The parakeets required only to repeat a taught phrase several times over, and the hamster on a wheel providing the required turning of dials to transfer calls. One would be no worse off than what one experiences currently. Better, perhaps, in having one's call dealt with a little more swiftly. You probably have gathered by now that I am not the biggest fan of my bank's current service provision.

In order to re-obtain a 'relationship manager' at the bank, as they are called these days, I must demonstrate earnings, which I could not even begin to aspire to at the moment. Such is the state we have arrived to.

I fear that Brexit has not only created a political divide, but serves the cause of greater racism, despite progression over many years toward creating an integrated and cross-cultural society. A friend of mine was recently shouted at and told to return to her country. She is a well-heeled Spanish lady, blonde and extremely well-attired.

I was rather disturbed when she told me about it, particularly as it happened not once but twice, and on both occasions in London. As you well know, I have always considered London to be very much the only truly cosmopolitan environment in the entirety of England, and felt completely at home there as a result, so it was disappointing to note that the political divide exists so harshly there also.

I had considered France as a possibility. Property there was still reasonably priced relative to London. I would love to live in a city, but Paris may prove unaffordable.

Lyon? A lot really depended on who I was with. My ideal arrangement would be to have a sustainable business in Harare, which would allow me to spend some time luxuriating in the lifestyle here, whilst allowing me time capturing some culture and sanity in Europe, and time with my girls too. Kate mentioned that I had expressed a love for Italy also, which I had to admit harbouring to this day.

I met Kate at Peter and Barbara's wedding in Italy. To be more specific, we met at a pre-wedding dinner and got on like a house on fire. I could not help but be captivated by her charm and incredibly infectious laughter. I have to admit that beyond her scintillating company, I did find her rather attractive too. The sort one experiences great difficulty in taking one's eyes away from, if you know what I mean. But on this occasion, I was not tongue-tied, as is my usual want.

She knew Barbara from the Chamber of Commerce in Milan where they worked together briefly. She spoke Italian fluently and it was as much a delight to listen to her talking in Italian as it was talking with her. As with my idol Audrey, Kate's perpetually present broad and winning smile was enough to win hearts. Mine certainly.

It was a lovely setting, the weather kind – warm without being oppressively sultry; the ambience merry with much laughter and gaiety; and the food beyond delicious. The wine flowed as easily as the conversation, and I felt very comfortable in her company. For once I met someone who was gorgeous and charming, but who did not leave me unable to form reciprocally engaging conversation. I hoped that Kate and I could pick up where we left off the next day.

There was no call for a morning suit, and I had struggled to think of what best attire to pack before we left for Italy. The weather and setting would have called for a beige or cream coloured linen suit, which I unfortunately didn't possess at the time. I think I eventually settled for a pair of white linen trousers and a blazer. If I had known better, we could have raced into Florence to pick something up from the multitude of the most wonderful fashion stores there. And what better than Italian fashion for a wedding in Italy. I shall just have to wait for another set of friends to arrange a marriage there and plan my wardrobe and visit a little better.

The wedding itself, I must say, ranks as one of the best I have ever attended. The service was held in a little private chapel, called the Chiesa di San Giovanni Battista in Camporsevoli, about a hundred kilometres from where Carole and I were staying in Siena. It was conducted in Italian, which mattered not as it largely followed the form of most weddings which require negligible participation from the congregation other than to be in enraptured attention.

And we were totally enraptured by the beautiful service. Peter and Barbara made for a handsome wedded couple. Barbara as with all brides, the perfect picture of a dazzling fairy tale princess, and Peter the rather dashing knight. Their smiles as they walked down the aisle past our pews, conveyed their matrimonial bliss.

Wedding services are always so moving and wonderfully romantic in my view, which is why I loved being invited to these events and thrived in their amorously charming setting. You will have gathered from my previous letters, that I consider weddings to be my 'happy hunting grounds', but that would somehow coarsely suggest that I attended with the sole and specific intention of capturing the attention of a single lady attendee. Not so, my dear fellow. It just seemed to happen. So, it was at this wedding also. I just 'happened' to meet Kate, and like her enormously.

The reception was held a little distance away in Radicofani in a beautiful palazzo suitably named "La Palazzina". I wonder if this is the same place where your daughter was married also. Anyway, the journey of twenty-odd kilometres from the chapel began with cars tooting their horns and being in receipt of considerable cheering from the crowd gathered outside, to whom we waved gaily, as would parting celebrities. The party had begun.

It was early evening by the time everyone had gathered at the reception, but still light enough to enjoy the stunning views. It was another picturesque setting, with the sky portraying the wonderful colours of a summer evening headed toward a late dusk.

The picture would have been beautifully completed with my arm around Kate as we watched the sunset on a largely cloudless sky. Alas, not so, but I was equally happy to be stood by her side with a glass of champagne in hand.

Neither Carole nor I had eaten much of a lunch before leaving Siena, worried that we would be late for the wedding, and we were therefore ravenously hungry. So, it appeared, were Kate and her friend Tracy. Cigarettes and champagne kept the hunger at bay for a while, as we awaited the dinner gong. The call to dine, finally came and we trooped into the dining area. Long tables were set out for the guests, reminding me of the dining hall at school. But that is where the comparison ended. Once seated, we stared wistfully at the menu, anticipating the arrival of the food with great eagerness.

To say that the food was good would be cruelly unfair to the chef. It was heavenly. If the dinner the previous evening was enjoyable, this surpassed any previous standard, and was worthy of several stars on the Michelin guide. They began with the courses of antipasti, which we practically inhaled given our hunger, and asked for more. We had lost sight of the long list of items yet to be served, and we paid the price for our early gluttony, as by the time the further courses arrived, we were fit to burst.

At one point, Kate, Tracy and I walked outside for a much-needed break from the endless consumption. We stood outside massaging our tummies to speed up the digestive process and hopefully create room for more. We were also unable to stop laughing.

Perhaps the champagne had played a part, but we were caught up in a very jovial mood. Kate, as I said, had the most infectious laugh and it was difficult to contain one's mirth. Anyone observing us would have assumed that we had been smoking dope and were consequently as high as kites.

The unending laughter was further exacerbated, when one of the guests walked down the dining hall past our table with her dress tucked into her pants. She had obviously been to the powder room but not realised her clothing mishap on leaving the privacy of the chamber. We were a totally uncontrollable rabble by this point, practically rolling around on the floor in stitches. She did have a nice arse, though.

I think it was Carole who finally took it upon herself to approach the lady and discretely suggest that she needed urgent attention to her wardrobe.

The cake cutting and dancing that followed took place under the superbly moonlit sky. The evening was enchanting. We drank, chatted, danced and merrily celebrated Peter and Barbara's marital union. I flirted with Kate, but in a subtle manner, and she may have been completely oblivious to my amorous advances. She did accept the offer of my blazer to keep the chill of the night air off her shoulders and urged me to stay on longer when Carole signalled that it was time to leave.

It was a long drive back and Carole opted to drive, as I was well established in my state of joyous inebriation.

However, by the time we got back to the hotel, after a few hairy turns around hairpin bends, which had me clutching my seat in abject terror, the effects of drink had well and truly worn off and I was completely sober. I did fall asleep quickly though, smiling at the prospect of seeing Kate the following day. She had promised to take Carole and I for a long walk in the countryside. She was due to meet us late morning.

Carole and I were sharing a room at the hotel. This was the second holiday we shared together. The first was a trip to Greece a few years previously with a group of her friends from the London Business School. There were six of us on this trip, Barry, John, Eric, Efie, Carole and I.

Of the six, I was the only one who was not an MBA alumnus at the time. After an overnight stop at Efie's parents' home in Athens, we headed off to Skiathos. It is certainly near the top of the list of my best beach holidays.

The food was great, once we discovered wonderful niche restaurants outside the boundaries of the hotel; the weather offered unlimited sunshine during the day in all the time we were there; and vast stretches of sandy beaches, which became pleasurable surfaces to spend entire days upon. We all got on well and had a wonderful time there together. I look forward to visiting these absolutely glorious Mediterranean islands again.

We were having a lovely time in Siena also. The hotel was strategically placed a short walk into town, allowing us to take in all the tourist must-do's in the short time we were there. The Piazza del Campo could of course not be missed, unless we deliberately chose to, as it was placed slap bang in the middle of this beautifully preserved medieval city. Sadly, we were not there at the time of a 'Palio', as that would have been, if judged by the scene in the James Bond film 'Quantum of Solace', a sight very well worth witnessing.

We stopped at many of the cafés situated around the Piazza, some a little more inviting and cosier than others.

The Duomo, was utterly awe-inspiring and spiritually uplifting and the Piccolomini Library with its Pinturicchio frescoes, can only be best described as spectacular. We also took the many steps up to the top of Torre del Mangia, and the breath-taking views of the city that lay before us were well worth the arduous climb.

Beyond the tourist element, there were many delightful shops along the several brick paved alleys leading away from the Piazza, in which we whiled away a good part of the morning. We stopped every now and then at one of the many pastry shops to purchase a bag full of scrumptious delights including several biscotti and the local recommended favourites of Cavallucci and Ricciarelli. I am a sucker for anything with almonds and scoffed as many Ricciarelli as I could lay my hands on.

We had hired a car for the drive from the airport at Florence, as we knew that it would make us truly mobile during the period leading up to the wedding and after, so we made the most of the time exploring other towns in the region. We drove to Montepulciano for a whistle stop tour of the Piazza Grande, Church of San Biagio, and one of the wineries to procure a bottle or two of the superb local wines. We did the same in San Gimignano, and at a winery there.

If we had more time, I believe we would have taken up the many generous offers to taste a seemingly endless supply of the various wines and acquire greater knowledge than I possessed of Italian wines.

Kate and Tracy appeared at what seemed like the crack of dawn the next day, as they had promised. Except that it was not the crack of dawn, but late morning. Carole and I hurriedly showered and dressed, taking turns in the bathroom whilst entertaining our guests in the bedroom in the interim. We drove together to this area, recommended by Kate, after arming ourselves with a picnic of sorts, including a delicious bottle of wine.

We had a wonderful afternoon together. Tracy was marvellous company too, as she had been at the wedding and the pre-dinner the night before. Kate took us on one of the walks she had been on previously as she was planning to create walking tours as a full-time job in Italy after she left her role at the Chambers. I was sure that she would excel at this task, as she had as good a grasp of the terrain as she did of the language, and more importantly, was very charming and entertaining company with it.

I carried on my subtle attempts at flirting with her, and at one stage held her hand as we walked a little unsteadily across a dry riverbed, and she seemed happy to allow me to keep holding it, past the point of footfall uncertainty.

A good sign I felt.

The girls were setting off back to Milan the next day, and Carole and I were leaving too, stopping only in Florence to return the car and spend the night before our onward journey back to London. It was sad to part, but Kate promised to be in touch on her return to London. I kept my fingers crossed for this. She did come. We serendipitously met again. They do say dreams occasionally come true.

Carole and I set off early to Florence, on what seemed a shorter journey back. We had time to meander around the shops after checking into the hotel. The hotel was better than we had expected, but their recommendations to restaurants were poor. We had experienced similarly in Siena and should have learnt our lesson there.

The concierges obviously favoured the restaurants who tipped them with generous commissions, but unfortunately did not provide the fare or service we had enjoyed at the smaller momma and poppa establishments. The restaurants catered almost entirely for tourists who had poor taste for local cuisine but prepared to pay high prices for mediocre fare. We vowed we would be more sensible on the next occasion.

The shopping we had undertaken earlier was much more exciting. The Italians knew their fashion and the shops were an absolute delight. Carole and I loved popping into the various boutiques, where everything was immaculately arranged on display and the sales assistants were polite and extremely helpful. I could have spent an absolute fortune there but restricted myself to a pair of Ferragamo shoes.

As with the French, the Italians were obviously well trained to sell – they do it so beautifully.

I suppose they do have the added advantage of having the most charming accent with which to persuade one to make a purchase.

I loved shopping in Florence and intended to do so again at some point. I had the opportunity to do so recently. Well not exactly in Florence, but from that delightful and charming city.

I ordered a Margaret Howell sweatshirt online but was advised that the only store that held my size was the one in Florence. I was contacted by one of the staff there, Annalisa, who sent me a charming email to begin with. And when I called to provide my card number over the telephone, I was greeted with the sweetest and most seductive Italian accent – it was Annalisa. She thanked me profusely for my purchase, even though it was by no means significant.

I was so charmed by this gesture, and thrilled to receive the shirt, within the stipulated period, wonderfully wrapped in the most beautiful packaging. It reminded me of how impressed I was by the attention they paid to the packaging of all our purchases, when we were in Italy, no matter how small.

This applied generally in our retail endeavours there, and not just in the couture stores either.

Although brief, as we had gone for no more than a week, it was a wonderful holiday. It may have been the occasion of the wedding and its subsequent goodwill and sentiment, but I enjoyed catching up with some old friends; meeting and making some new ones; visiting the delightful little towns with all their unique and wonderful attractions; treating my palate to some marvellous food and wine and experiencing the joy of shopping in Italy.

Unfortunately, I did not have a camera with me to take photographs to remember this trip by.

Incidentally, it was not just meeting Kate that caused me to fall in love with the country. I had a special time with Carole too.

She proved to be yet again the patient, generous and genial holiday companion, I had always known her to be. I thought that our holiday together in Greece was good, but this short trip overtook that one slightly in terms of scenic pleasure and overall enjoyment.

As siblings, we have got along generally well over the years, and developed a closeness through shared accommodation during most of our teens, and after that also through the university years. But, in all honesty, we had been close when we were kids too. Any rivalry only existed because she played marbles better than I did! There were times, when I felt that it would have been easier all-around if I had just handed her my bag of marbles than pretend there was any real competition in the play for them. She also had the habit of beating me and most of my friends in all our sprint races. Many times. Boy could that girl move!

We remained close, however. I believe that the closeness between us may have perhaps existed also because we were the two youngest in the family and had an exactly two-week separation between our birthdays.

After University and completing her MBA, Carole went on to have a successful career in the financial sector. Ah, if only I had followed in her footsteps.

Carole was kind enough to support me through the difficult period, after my return from Nigeria, when I was at my most vulnerably itinerant. I wonder if she sometimes feels too much of the burden, especially when most of us in the family have depended on her to be the emotional and financial rock upon which we built our lives around.

She was especially supportive of my parents in the latter part of their life, when all of their hard work and investment came largely to nought as a result of being both unwittingly swindled, and through their own self-defeating generosity.

I am not suggesting that the rest of the family made no effort, as we all pitched in with whatever we could and assisted in a million different ways, but the financial burden tended to fall largely upon Carole. She was generous enough to manage this for several years without a single word of complaint.

This wonderful sister of mine has been kind enough to help me through almost every single difficult period I encountered in my life. Including this one. She not only contributed considerable emotional support through the pain of cancer treatment and divorce, but also stepped in to bridge financial gaps when my income evaporated. She has also generously provided monetary support and accommodation to my children when I was unable to.

She was away on a trip to New York when I broke the news to her about my diagnosis, and she told me immediately that she had sensed that something was wrong, which would suggest a closeness that was real and not merely imagined.

Carole has done much to keep our family close no matter what the circumstances, sometimes singlehandedly. What a gem of a sibling!

Family means everything to me also. I love all of my siblings, even the ones that have sadly passed away well before their time. I loved my parents dearly too, and only wish that I had spent more of my time telling them that I did.

I know that you have a close and loving family too, and I am sure that you are all equally demonstrative in this regard.

I would urge you to keep it that way.

In closing, I shall wish myself back to that magical time in Italy also, to recapture the sublime moments of a remarkable holiday with a treasured sibling and a fleeting romance with a charming brunette that never came to pass but allowed me to benefit from a soulful journey, nevertheless.

Love,

David

Letter 26 – Spanglish & the Ideal Woman?

April 2020

Dear Geoff,

I felt I had to write and let you know about the profound impact a movie had on me recently.

I was bored. The night was still young, and I decided to scroll through and find something on Netflix that I had not watched previously. I selected a film called 'Spanglish'. It was a strange choice, as I do not really enjoy Adam Sandler movies and try and avoid them if I possibly can. I was not even sure that the summary of the movie had any appeal, as I had watched a movie with Catherine Zeta Jones earlier in the evening of similar ilk and not been enthralled. "Nothing to write home about", as one would say, which now makes me wonder why I am even now mentioning it in a letter to you.

I think I was captivated from the very commencement. I was surprised to find myself, glued to the screen, ignoring even the constant pinging of my phone with message receipts obviously from insistent callers. I loved the film.

I was so captivated by the character of this Mexican housekeeper. I had to look up the actress. It was Paz Vega. A Spanish actress I had never come across in my life before.

As you know by now, when it comes to screen idols, there is only one who occupies pride of place in my heart, but Paz, did a fine job of capturing a small piece of it as a result of this. She played the part so beautifully that even watching Adam Sandler in the lead male role was tolerable.

I loved the character. Here was a woman abandoned with a young child and scarce resources, but who held firmly to her principles and toiled away desperately to make ends meet and educate her daughter well. There appeared so many points in her life where she could have given in to the opportunities presented to accept monetary reward but chose instead to stick to what she believed was right, and not sell her soul. It resonated so well with me. I was so struck by that movie because that is exactly the sort of woman I long to meet and have a relationship with.

I am so tired now of these dating sites. I feel that it all appears to be more an escape from humdrum existences, and not really an inclination to fulfilling any quest for true love. I just long to meet someone who shares my ideological view of life and is prepared to stand by me no matter what my circumstances. Is that not what an ideal partner does – stay together with you no matter what circumstances prevail? A burden shared... and so on. But along with sorrows, joy and celebration are to be experienced together too, if partnerships are to work in a truly equitable manner.

This applies to my business philosophy too. You cannot have shareholders expecting profit only and shying away from carrying loss during the lean years.

I accept that the lovely actress Paz only played a fictional character, but it was the manner in which she came across that had such a profound effect on me that evening. It was, (at least in so far as they were competently conveyed in this movie), her principles, that she adhered to so resolutely, despite the offer of easy lucrative alternatives, that registered as a quality I unequivocally seek in any prospective future relationship. She happens to be amazingly attractive too, which of course helps considerably. Could I ever hope to find anyone like that – both loving and beautiful? I wonder what it is I need to do to secure someone's interest in me emotionally, with the prospect of being loved endlessly in return. Preferably one easy on the eye and not merely seeking pursuit of material comfort.

As my head has been in the clouds with thoughts of H all of this time, I had to think hard to determine what it was that I actually found appealing and attractive about the opposite sex. More specifics than the usual generalities. Preferably someone like the character played by Paz V – i.e., someone who combined beauty with a moral fortitude? A combination of style and substance.

I felt that the best way to start the definition was to interrogate each and every aspect of previous loves or desires to see if there was some form of recurring theme or trait.

I can't think of anyone better than you to ask what it is that causes me to be attracted in the first place as you have known me well, for an inordinately long time, and have also been at the receiving end of so many discourses on my romantic liaisons. I hope that you could, after this missive, identify and alert me to any common threads that appear to be the determining physical or other characteristics.

Without wishing to appear completely depthless, I have to say that the outward appearance is what causes the initial draw for me. Isn't that entirely natural though?

Reciprocally, I would like to understand what it is any lady beholder would consider an attraction to me as I currently assume my appearance would be largely uninteresting other than for the crown of almost white hair atop a dark complexion which draws some comment. But we shan't go into that for now and focus on aspects of her appearance that matter to me. Yes, the beauty of the soul matters, but I quite like the qualities of the packaging it comes in too.

I can almost hear your cautionary advice ringing in my ear, but I can assure you that no matter how beautiful she may be, if the beauty is not also resident within her heart, my interest fades nearly as quickly as the onset of initial enticement.

In developing an understanding of my ideal in totality let me begin, therefore by providing you an understanding of the physical attributes of the opposite sex that causes the initial capture of the eye and subsequent rapid beating of the heart and stirring in the loins.

In terms of facial features, I do get easily attracted to women with large or inquisitive eyes. A part of me is fascinated with the combination of blonde hair and green eyes, but is that merely me adopting a screen star-driven stereotype of what a beautiful woman would look like?

I don't think that I am particular about the colour of eyes but penetrating and glittering blue eyes have captivated me more often than large doe-like brown eyes. Is there something more mystifying about blue eyes? Why glittering? Is it reflective of my draw to the sea? Why inquisitive? Perhaps because mine are? I may not wish my face to be as thoroughly inspected as I would theirs, (rather unfairly I might add), but I would be happy for her eyes to be more inquisitorial of my soul.

I think that I have been attracted to large or inquiring eyes ever since I, alongside a billion other people, fell in love with Audrey Hepburn. As she herself has indicated, "The beauty of a woman must be seen from in her eyes, because that is the doorway to her heart, the place where love resides."

Audrey had the most exquisite eyes. Greenish brown, with an unflinching and penetrating gaze, that even in a photograph makes one feel that she sees directly into the depths of one's soul. To be quite honest, I am sure she had the most exquisite everything, and would be my dream woman. One who looked more beautiful with every passing year of her life.

In summary, it would appear that the appeal is for large or inquisitorial or sparkling ones, with a slight preference for blue.

The nose is a feature I have never really cared to be as judgemental over. Perhaps it is because I am so conscious of mine, that I do not pay particular heed to theirs. If somebody were to ask me how I would describe this feature in my previous romances, I would find it rather difficult to do so other than to say that it was never noticeably big and would have sat juxtaposed very admirably between her beautiful eyes.

I suppose therefore that for as long as the is able to breathe effectively with her nasal attribute, I offer no preference.

When it comes to her lips, however, I do have very clear preferences, as I have indicated to you in my letter which speaks of kisses. Because this is the one feature most often interacted with intimately, I believe it to be of the utmost importance. From experience, it is not with great joy that I have kissed a girl with thin lips. In those instances, one is almost kissing for kissing's sake; to acquire some further technique; or to merely accept some simple gratification for a night's dating effort.

The thicker set of lips has absolutely no appeal whatsoever either. It amazes me, therefore that some women, appear to pay good money to have their lips enhanced.

Why, Geoff? What drives this insanity? Am I in a sad minority, or even completely unique in this regard? Whatever the fashion drivers are, I shall remain attracted to an average thickness of lips, and preferably ones which suggest perfection of shape. After all, if one is to kiss one's loved one from dawn to dusk, the fit of lips is ideally one of compatible width.

Her teeth, I would assume were largely her own, well maintained with some regularity in form and appearance, preferably not buck-toothed, for example. A good smile tends to reveal all in this area right at the outset, so it is unlikely to be a hidden or unpleasant discovery at a later stage.

Ears are not a feature I have focused on much, which is strange given how I am usually drawn to comment on beautiful earrings adorning them. I suppose that, for as long as the ears remain closely affixed to the side of the head, they do not warrant a remark. I have to confess to the fact that my ear lobes are one of the most sensitive and 'erogenous' parts of my body. Ever since some girl, (to whom I owe much for being the pioneer), nibbled on my ear lobes whilst dancing at some party or the other, I have been driven insane from this sensation by most girl-friends since, Paulette, Madeleine and Ravinia in particular.

Hair colour is again a feature that does not determine attraction in itself. I do tend to often apply my default choice, which is that of a blonde, but that may in part be due to Paulette, who was the first woman I fell madly in love with, being blonde. If asked, Shingai would adamantly insist that blonde is my clear and regularly applied parameter for attraction. But in all honesty, I truly have no partiality in this regard and am very conscious of the fact that this element is going to be necessarily associated with skin colour.

Being absolutely besotted with H may indicate a slight preference for an olive complexion, which in turn invariably suggests dark hair of a certain length. Gal Gadot, Jessica Alba, Aishwarya Rai, Salma Hayek, Paz Vega to name some of the women I consider true goddesses in colour, style and length of hair.

But then again, I could fall headlong into love with blondes or brunettes equally easily too, and my guiding lights in this arena have been Claudia Schiffer, Marilyn Monroe, Brigitte Bardot, Catherine Deneuve, Monica Bellucci, Claudia Cardinale, Cindy Crawford amongst many others. As for hair length, I definitely have some preference for long rather than short, but this really is a choice best left to each individual. I do think that some carry off both looks equally well, and there is none more devastatingly charming and alluring in a long or short coiffure than Audrey Hepburn. As long as it is a gloriously soft and sweet-smelling mane that frames her face beautifully and leaves me visually entranced, I will be very happy.

Rather bizarrely, visions of a long curly-haired brunette seem persistent lately. A future love?

Having grown up in a largely cosmopolitan environment and spent formative years in much the same, I have no decided preference for complexion. Although many of my loves have been primarily of Caucasian ilk, I also apply very favourable consideration of the complexion of lightly browned toast – territorially I would assume everywhere from south America to Spain and across the Mediterranean, Italy, north Africa and the Middle East through to the Indian shores.

I realise that she is only partly of Mexican origin, but in terms of having such a perfectly light-toned complexion, there is none better than Jessica Alba.

It is rather ironic discussing complexion currently seated in an environment like Zimbabwe, where skin colour has created so much of a polarised society. I have friends over the entire spectrum of colour and creed but find it incredibly fascinating that despite advances in technology and communication, which should bring about more of a global society and bridge differences, we still find ourselves with some who insist on maintaining division on the basis of skin tone, and in many cases driving them deeper.

It is a very sensitive subject, I grant you, and perhaps a debate for another time. In the meanwhile, all I can understand of my choices is that they may be borne out of an indefinable subconscious selection, but I do tend to be automatically drawn toward a creamy complexion to compliment my rather dark tones.

What is about a woman's legs that has me almost obsessed? I could dwell for hours on a lovely face, but as soon as my eyes capture sight of legs not meeting a qualifying standard, the magic somehow disappears. How could one's interest evaporate so quickly? It works to the reverse also. I could be fascinated by the shapely legs of some lady or the other and then have immediate disappointment register, should the face not bear the same degree of attractiveness. This sounds absolutely fickle, I realise, but it is a practice I cannot seem to depart from.

Again, I would prefer to be honest with you, rather than proclaim sainthood by suggesting that these things do not matter to me.

The reason I consider a good figure independently from good legs is that it appears very possible for women to have great legs but almost no correspondingly good figure. In one case, almost square, and a bit like Sponge Bob Square Pants, I fear. It is decidedly disturbing, I advise you, especially as it is sometimes not quite immediately obvious, and certainly not after several glasses of champagne at a wedding. So yes, a good figure is a must, beyond possessing nice shapely legs.

An ideal figure, for me, would be that of Audrey H – slim and sylph like. Is there anything about her that does not appeal so much to me? She had the most attractive shape that suited the most fashionable and classic of clothes. She kept that figure for the entirety of her life, post-children, miscarriages, etc. The perfect frame in my view.

In terms of attraction to an overall body shape, therefore, it is really and very simply one of symmetry and balance. A nice perfectly rounded arse and breasts of corresponding curvature, and appropriateness of size.

Speaking of breast size, I feel, that this is best determined on a BSH (British Standard Handful) basis, a measure that we used to apply as schoolboys, and I think very applicable for my current day considerations too.

Her bottom, ideally a little rounded over flat, but not too wide or overly exaggerated, as seems the fashion these days. 'Big booty', I believe is the term. It does absolutely nothing for me, no matter what my desire to be fashionable is. A bottom that illustrates some sensual curvature in a pair of jeans, and one that provides a hint of a dreamy sway in a dress is all I request in this area of anatomy.

Her arms are fine as long as they are neither too muscular nor flabby. Preferably of lengths corresponding to overall bearing, to avoid having any simian-like appearance.

A flat tummy please. I do accept however, that the toll of childbearing, etc may cause a degree of difficulty in achieving the ideal. But, having said that I do know several women who, subsequent to childbirth, still manage to obtain surfboard like appearance in this area. Unless of course they disguise this very well in which case they should definitely be entrusted also with all of NATO's secrets.

I should really be a little forgiving, as mine can still only be best described as a 'work in progress' despite my untiring efforts with a combination of a low-carb diet, boxing, and several 'ultimate core workouts'! It may be the result of many years of overindulgence in my previously described passion for mince pies, but I seem unable to shed that final sebaceous layer around my middle.

In fairness, all my dietary and training efforts have yielded some reward, as I am currently back down to a pre-marital trouser size of 32 inches, and would like to believe that, when clothed, my appearance of a thirteen-stone carrying weight translates into a relatively lithe frame.

Perhaps to be more equitable, 'flattish' could be a preferred requirement? The 'ish' allowing some degree of latitude in the strict definition of the term?

Her hands are a feature that should really be at the top of most lists of consideration of physical attributes as they are almost as important, if not more so, than her legs. To me at any rate. Slim, long fingered and well-manicured hands are always a racing certainty for attraction in my book.

As you can imagine it is probably the one aspect of her anatomy that one finds oneself interacting with a considerable amount of time. Her touch. Her caress. It is so important therefore not just to have wonderful hands to view but, to feel. One must also determine the fit at the earliest opportunity. By that, I mean that having one's fingers entwined with hers must feel like a natural coming together of an anatomical puzzle.

Her feet – you may think me rather bizarre, if you don't already, but the shape of her feet is also a rather crucial consideration *pour moi*. You may recall my mentioning this in my letter when I spoke of my accidental shoe shopping expedition with H.

Although they may be clad in something or the other for most of the time, it shouldn't suggest that they be overlooked. On the contrary, it is imperative to establish the daintiness of the foot at the soonest hour. Can you imagine the sheer horror on the face of the prince had he been confronted with a foot of an Ogre when he eventually tracked Cinderella down? Even if the glass slipper had fit her perfectly, it would have left him decidedly disturbed in their happy ever after. I feel therefore that the trace along a marvellously shapely leg should ideally culminate in the discovery of an equally enchanting foot. A slightly arched, 'Greek shape' of foot, if my search to provide you a description of sorts proves technically correct.

You can imagine rightly, therefore, that I take great delight in the opportunity to caress the dainty foot of a loved one when placed comfortably upon my lap.

My beloved Audrey by her own admission had feet too large for a ballerina, but I could not even for a single moment imagine that they were not as beautifully shaped and enticing as every other part of her splendid physique. Find me an Audrey Hepburn, Geoff I beseech you.

Anyway, my dear fellow by concluding on word of her feet I believe I have veritably and comprehensively covered all aspects in the description of my ideal from top to toe - very literally.

Onto other characteristics, therefore.

Education. Ah, this is a difficult one! There is naturally a wish to share intellectual debate alongside emotional sustenance; but should the lack of academic achievement be a determinant? Is the knowledge gained from the 'university of life' not to count for anything?

Although, as I mentioned earlier in this letter, I was in admiration of this amazing character showing gritty determination, and more importantly, maintaining moral fibre, despite being largely of limited formal education and working as a housekeeper, I do feel some partiality toward the academically clever. But I believe though that these decisions mostly come about as a result of one's shared experiences and expectations.

I must also add that I feel rather strongly about the direction of their moral compass and their ability to think with their hearts as well as their heads, and attraction, therefore, is not determined solely by academic orientation. Also, no matter the base of education, I think that desirability is greatly enhanced when discovering that the object of one's interest is driven, and has ambitions to accomplish something in their life. As was the case in the character played by Paz V. A woman who wishes to contribute to others by imparting their wisdom, skills, principles or whatever it may be.

As I had indicated in my previous letters to you, I think that women have the amazing ability to exercise their minds to several tasks simultaneously, whilst showing great compassion with it, and thereby possess the capacity to be great leaders – in industry and otherwise. And it would be terribly sad to have this potential unrealised. Not just for my sake!

Should she be politically aware? Yes, ideally though not necessarily actively, nor to any extreme. It would be nice to know that one's partner is guided by some political conviction rather than drifting through life aimlessly and directionless in what appears to be a progressively more divided and fragmented society.

In similar vein, I would also wish for a woman who is well travelled, broad-minded and happy to understand as well as embrace other cultures and customs.

I have my heart set on meeting a fellow foodie and preferably a good cook too. I love entertaining, as you know, and am happy to share the task of food and décor preparation in hosting dinner or drinks parties. One of the nice things about entertaining in our family household, was that guests were always welcome to contribute and participate. In fact, the more hands-on deck the easier and quicker tasks were completed and the more involved everyone felt, whatever the occasion.

Being of Indian origin, I would suppose that the desire to have a prospective partner deriving from a good family is important. Sadly, I do not have my parents around to make that determination for me, but it is something that seems to be at the very core of our culture. It is equally applicable to British society too, I believe, if one just considers the issue so specifically and wonderfully raised in Austen's "Pride and Prejudice", for example.

I am sure that there is a clutch of other literary works in both English and Indian cultures stressing the importance of origins from a 'good' family. I presume 'good' in this instance means persons of similar social standing as opposed to any anything akin to the long-standing feud that existed between the Capulet and Montague households.

But would it matter so much what her parentage was, if she has through supreme efforts of her own, and with the application of some skill and good fortune managed to create a better life for herself? One of my favourite films ever is 'Sabrina' - the story of a girl who is the chauffeur's daughter, but who without any wily manipulation, captures the heart of Linus, a smart and very successful businessman.

From what I remember of recounts from my parents, we are descended from established landowning gentry, and supposedly one such relative had considerable wealth and ownership of vast tracts of tea estates.

Sadly, it appears that a combination of family feuding, nationalisation, etc., put paid to the trickle-down of his wealth to other generations. Some explanation of my current financial malaise, I guess. Oh, how cruel fate can be at times! On my father's side, my grandfather was apparently a great scholar, which would explain my father's abilities in this regard. I shall avoid for now an investigation into why this scholastic ability seems to have bypassed me somewhat and appeared in my children instead and focus only on the past for the purpose of confirming genealogy.

There appears to be a 'good family' tick in the box from my side from what I understand, but sadly it is not accompanied by the expected corresponding economic substance. Not yet anyway. I do have much hope for redeeming my fortunes soon, but only if the guiding stars are aligned with me for a change.

In terms of personality, what better than a woman who bears all of the traits of a caring, compassionate, empathetic, sincere, faithful, loving, devoted, assured, witty, generous, kind and forgiving individual. I know that alongside all the physical attributes, it may seem a big ask, but I sincerely believe that this person exists!

And some other aspects for consideration would ideally include:

Make-up – I really admire women who require and generally applied very little. I say this with immense feeling because I had a rather horrific experience once which has alerted me against its over-use. I had walked into the bathroom inadvertently on the girl I had spent the night with. We both screamed. She, because of the unexpected interruption, me because I was horrified by what I saw – unmasked she was not the most wonderful thing to behold at dawn. In future, I decided I would rather be dazzled when the 'she' in my life felt the need to 'go big' on special occasions but had universal appeal for most of the time. A woman easy on the eye straight out of a shower is the best determinant, in my view.

Smell – having waxed lyrically in previous letters to you of how much pleasure I derived from the perfumed skin of previous loves, it would be very wrong of me not to mention how important this aspect is also to my deliberations. A lady, therefore, who knows exactly what perfume suits her skin and how much of it to apply without it being somewhat overbearing will undoubtedly win my unwavering attention.

Posture and dress sense - having an awareness of her own sensuality, but not overly so, would add to the allure of any prospective partner. The subtlety will be obvious from the way she dresses and carries herself, to express her elegance and femininity.

Languages – I am definitely impressed by anyone who is fluent in more than one language. I feel so hindered by the fact that I never really exercised myself to acquire skills in the linguistic arena and am by default, therefore always attracted to a lady sufficiently capable in this aspect.

Accent – I love the various European accents, but I don't know why I just go weak at the knees when it comes to the French one. Given how naturally seductive the Italian accent is, what is it about the French accent that floors me every time? I feel that I could listen to the music of her voice for hours if only it were laced with a French lilt. Perhaps I had an affinity to France in a previous existence? A mystery indeed.

Dancing – this may sound rather perplexing, but I am inexorably captured by someone with more than just a basic ability to move to the rhythm of the music, and who loved the idea of dancing, even if it were on a whim in the rain. I am currently very keen to learn the tango, so a partner interested in this wildly sensual dance to rhythm would be a godsend. Seeing one's prospective amorous interest flop about on the dance floor like a poorly trained performing seal although humorously mesmerising, would have all desires for future courtship evaporate almost instantly. Amusing perhaps, but not endearing!

Tidiness – I like being tidy, as you know. Not obsessively so, but I really could not bear the thought of daily life with anyone unable to keep things in some semblance of order. When speaking of this, I am reminded of an episode from "Friends" when Ross dates a rather divinely gorgeous blonde but reacts with sheer horror when he is invited back to her flat and discovers that she kept her premises in a manner reminiscent of the local municipal landfill. I can relate completely to that. However, if it helps secure an amiable companion, I could easily abide with a little 'lived in' clutter.

Dogs – she must like them, or at least show some affinity toward having them as pets. I do accept the fact that dogs are generally attention seekers, but they can also be fairly independent. I find their show of devoted and unconditional love in return for a mere pat on the head, hard to resist for inclusion in my life. As you are aware, I had three of them recently until Nougat passed away, and they served as my constant and amusing companions. Audrey loved them too! Not mine obviously, but dogs generally.

So, what I seek, my dear friend appears to obviously be a reincarnation of Audrey Hepburn. I appreciate, however, that this is nigh on impossible, as she was truly one in several billion, and unlikely to be found again. But I firmly believe that there is someone out there who comes close to fulfilling or even exceeding some of my expectations. The key would be in discovering if this particular 'someone' finds me reciprocally desirable. That 'someone' would be a very special find indeed. Aren't the best love stories the ones of falling in love with someone unexpectedly and at the most unexpected time or set of circumstances?

Anyway, I was thinking that if H is not to be my dream woman, I should perhaps give fate or destiny a gentle nudge in my quest. Based on my wish list, therefore I was planning a personal advertisement of sorts to save myself the hassle of registering on dating sites and partaking in the ensuing lacklustre communications. It would read as follows.

"Charming, witty and youthfully minded man, from a good family seeks attractive lady of similar ilk for a serious relationship. Nice legs and slim figure, bright blue eyes, slim hands, dainty feet, long dark hair and beautifully shaped lips, a must. Currently a trifle economically challenged, but oozing with considerable potential/aptitude, and therefore desirous of women of immediately

accessible financial substance. Successful applicants may be asked to remove make-up, dance and demonstrate an ability to fold clothes. Preference will be given to French speakers and dog lovers..."

What say you? Would such a posting gain any interest, or merely laughed off? Am I hoping for too much? Should I be happy with anyone who comes along with even a modicum of interest in me?

I look forward to hearing any ideas you may have in addressing my problems in this quest, preferably other than one involving stepping in front of a fast-moving bus.

I shall leave you with some wonderful quotes from my beloved Audrey Hepburn. I realise that I have mentioned her a thousand times already, but she really encapsulates beauty for me – physically, intellectually, emotionally and spiritually, and has delivered profound and enduring thoughts:

"For beautiful eyes, look for the good in others; for beautiful lips, speak only words of kindness; and for poise, walk with the knowledge that you are never alone.", for example.

"... I believe in kissing, kissing a lot..." is part of another quote, which applies so readily to me too. I long to win the heart of my wished-for love, having her fingers entwined with mine as I gaze longingly and lovingly into her eyes, and then kissing her sweet lips several million times.

Kissing helps enormously. Why move lips to utter only sentences when pressing them onto the lips of another speaks in richer and louder volumes?

And finally on humour, she said *"I love people who make me laugh. I honestly think it's the thing I like most, to laugh. It cures a multitude of ills. It's probably the most important thing in a person."*

That is my greatest asset, Geoff. I may not have the nicest nose, or most admirable physique, or the material possessions to impress, but I can promise to make a woman laugh.

I eagerly await your thoughts on this.

Love,

David

Letter 27 – Death, Despair & Dreams

April 2020

Dear Geoff,

I awoke to a message conveying horrific news.

A very good friend, Justin had passed away the previous afternoon. I stared at the message in complete disbelief. The shock of the news left me gasping for breath. I felt a great heaviness in my heart also. The weight of immense sorrow. I wanted desperately to cry.

I felt I needed to speak to someone, just so that I could share the immediate pain. It was awful. I wondered why life was so unfair. Why should he lose his in the prime of his life when he had still so much yet to give?

I was also truly saddened to hear of his passing as it did not seem that long ago that Justin and his wife Jacqui were one of the first to welcome me back to Zimbabwe. As you will recall I arrived with great trepidation, as I was not sure how people would react to my divorced state, illness and the fact that I had been away for so long. I need not have worried, Justin and Jacqui made me very welcome in their home.

When Nougat died a few months ago, I was a wreck, as you know. I was so sad and carried the same heartfelt pain. So much so, that I found it difficult to cry. Me, not crying? It beggars belief, does it not, especially when I so easily begin shedding tears at even the slightest of lachrymose moments. But I have learnt that when faced with such deep sorrow, my immediate reaction is usually one of denial. It is only when I comprehend the true extent of the news later, and the realisation finally sinks in, that the sorrow finds release in the flow of tears.

I really do not understand how fate or religion or life for that matter works anymore. Is it that good people that die first; having proven that theirs are the purest of hearts? But my parents were truly wonderful people. Generous, kind, caring, devoted, loving, and (especially in my mother's case), God fearing. How did they enjoy reasonably long lives? My dad lived to the ripe old age of ninety-two, and Mum to eighty-six. In fact, when my sister Rachel passed away tragically at a relatively young age, my mum questioned us as to why she could not have been taken instead - it seemed unfair and illogical to her to lose the life of her child before her own.

Why is it that good people like Kennedy, Luther King, Audrey Hepburn, and so many others of their ilk including my sisters, and now Justin, have their lives cut so brutally short, whilst those of villainous dictators and criminals prevail? Justin was still young. In his late forties.

He was a kind and generous man, with a great sense of humour. He belonged to a group of men friends, who got together under the banner of the 'FoC Club', the primary purpose of which was to meet over a meal of chicken and chips on a Friday afternoon and review life in a humorous vein. As one of the founder members and Chairman of this esteemed grouping, I was, together with the Club's Treasurer and my able lieutenant Keith, required to ensure these lunches took place with reasonable regularity.

Justin was an avid attendant. I shall miss his continual guffaws at the many lunches we shared together. It did not seem right at all to me that his life should end so unexpectedly and swiftly.

I was feeling wretched for most of the day. I hated the thought of losing anyone close. I hated even discussing the subject of death and found it very hard to cope with it even when my parents were elderly and spoke of theirs.

As you know, I lost several members of my family in a short space of time and am still not sure whether I have had sufficient opportunity to grieve them properly.

I mourn his death, as I ponder mine.

I am now just tired. Tired of crying over the graves of others. I am beginning to feel that for as long as I have some time to say my goodbyes, I am happy to explore what lies on the other side of mortality on this earth. Perhaps all my questions, including my now constant one of whether God truly exists, will be answered. It is not that I no longer value my life. I am just no longer scared of losing mine.

At the moment, I would say that the fear of not being able to provide for my daughters is greater than the fear of death itself. I feel so trapped by the dire circumstances I find myself in now, that I wake up every day fearful that my daughter's university education is in jeopardy unless I find some means of funding her through it. Almost constant harassment from divorce lawyers and creditors served only to compound a daily anxiety.

I have never usually feared the peaks and troughs that occur naturally in life, but it seems so different this time. I am generally strong enough to cope with suffering, but at this particular juncture I truly feel the weight of the world upon my shoulders.

I believe that my sorrow on this occasion was compounded by the culmination of several things going wrong in my life simultaneously. Although separation and the onset of divorce proceedings were painful, it was a set of stresses I felt I could manage and still see my daughters through to the start of their own careers and independent lives. But then shock after shock struck in rapid succession or so it seemed, as I had to deal with getting diagnosed with cancer, whilst having my expected income curtailed because of the parsimonious act of others. Medical costs then mounted, and to add further misery, the economy in Zimbabwe collapsed and I had to rebuild business opportunities. I felt I was already suffering enough. If God existed, I had no comprehension of his actions – one setback at a time, possibly, but several simultaneously? Surely that is an odiously harsh punishment by any standards.

It is awful, Geoff. There are times when I wonder if I should just stay in bed and hope that when I eventually choose to awaken it would all seem like a bad dream, and I can open my eyes to recapture a life of love and laughter.

Thankfully, the optimist in me gets me out of bed each morning with the hope that something happens in my life that could see me turn my misfortune into success. The sad thing is that despite so many attempts on my part so far, I keep being disappointed by others failing to keep to their obligations and promises. But, for as long as a single bone of optimism resides in my body, I shall continue trying.

If it were not for friends and family, I don't know how I could have coped over the last year. I sometimes even feel guilty that I should eat well. I have no wish to acquire material possessions beyond those I have, which is good, as I no longer place value on material things, but on people – friendships and love.

So, I do not fear death. In fact, I think that in my current frame of mind, I would welcome it. Yes, an otiose surrender perhaps, but I would rather at this point die, and leave whatever value applies to my estate to the children. I would have provided something for them to be able to begin their adult life, by happily giving up my own.

All I would hope for is that I leave them with no more emotional suffering than that which they would experience anyway, at my eventual demise.

I really have no desire to be the architect of my own, although there have been some days when it has been sorely tempting. I think I fear the shame it would bring upon my family more than the act itself. It would add to the mental anguish my girls have already had to suffer – divorce, moving and financial hardship. No, that is definitely not the answer.

I also think that it would have indicated a considerable weakness on my part to do so. Whilst I may have no control over external factors, I feel generally happy with the way I have led my life so far, and dealt with its previous predicaments, albeit with some regrets.

As Frank Sinatra would suggest –

I've loved, I've laughed and cried
I've had my fill; my share of losing
And now, as tears subside
I find it all so amusing.......
For what is a man, what has he got?
If not himself, then he has nought
To say the things he truly feels
And not the words of one who kneels
The record shows I took the blows
And did it my way!

Did you know that I had once dreamt about my own demise? It was very strange. I had these dreams shortly after the ones I had about H and I having our third child.

429

I would have expected to have such dreams before my operation, as that is when I was at my most vulnerable in terms of consideration of death, but it was peculiarly sometime after the first operation and recovery. I had not mentioned anything to you earlier, as it may have caused unnecessary concern on your part.

The dreams were bitty, snapping quickly from one scene to another, but I recalled them as I had done the others, with the greatest of clarity. I shall describe these dreams in the same manner as those in my earlier letters.

Scene 1
We were now living in London.
I was happily married to H with 3 children.
I had spent the day with my son in my study.
He sat on my lap as we chatted together for a long time.
I felt that it was to be our last such occasion, and I held him close.

I assume that we were living in London, as that is where the funeral was apparently held. I also assume the happy marital state from the visions that followed.

Scene 2
H is in the kitchen, preparing supper.
She tells me that I should spend as much time with my girls, as I did with my son.
I tell her that she seems too partial to our last born, and she laughs knowingly.
I am astounded by how beautiful she looks to me, even after several years of marriage.
I hug her fondly from behind, and she turns to me to suggest having a fourth child to even the spread of favouritism.

430

I laugh with her.

<u>Scene 3</u>
I said goodnight to the girls after reading them a bedtime story.
They insist on several hugs before they would let me leave.
I give them each a kiss on their forehead and tell them that their mother will be along shortly to bid them good-night too.
I feel tearful as they smile and promise to be good but smile back at them.

<u>Scene 4</u>
My son was fast asleep.
I stroked his hair and kissed his forehead.
He murmurs something in his sleep.
I left a little note for him together with my gold cross and chain.

I could not understand why I would not have left a note for H, knowing of my pending demise rather than to my son. I decided to leave him something that he admired greatly. It was a parting gift from my parents at the age of 13 before I left Brunei for school in England, and therefore meant a lot to me. I think in part my vivid dream of leaving my son with my chain and cross relates to my wish to continue a legacy through his life. I would want all my children to continue to cherish and apply the values and principles I hold dear, much as I have been conscious of how important they were to my parents and the generations of inspirational individuals in their families before them. But why would I not leave something for my daughters too?

Scene 5
H was at the church with the children and my family.
She was wearing a black dress and a black hat with a veil.
A lot of friends attended.
A friend stood up to deliver his eulogy.
I was supposedly seventy-six.
It was then H's turn.
She walked to the podium and had taken her hat off.
She struggled to speak.
The children were ushered to join her to help her complete her words for me.
She did, with tears flowing unendingly down her cheeks.

The suggestion was that I passed away in my sleep. I do hope that when I do, it will be painless, and I suppose this dream reflected that wish. If at all my dreams of marriage to H do come true, I know that I would have left her still young enough to be married again, and my children old enough to remember me as their father.

Scene 6
This last scene was at our home.
My older children Chloe and Holly were comforting the little ones.
They were sat together on the stairs as the guests at the wake mingled.
Chloe and my son sat together on a step in the middle of the staircase, and she held my little one on her lap.
Holly was on the steps just behind with my middle daughter, Sara, sat next to her.

It appeared a wonderful scene with all of my children together. I could sense much love between them binding them all together, despite the large age difference between the sets of children. If there is one legacy I hope to leave and be remembered for, it would be one of a close and loving family. It puzzles me though, that if I were no longer of the world, how would I picture such images? Had I returned as a ghost? It is all so very bizarre.

Anyway, it seems rather peculiar to be talking of death when all I see in front of me is a garden bathed in beautiful sunshine. Ollie, my black spaniel on the chair in front of me keeping me company. Ollie, although very naughty and lazy with it, has been a wonderful companion, especially since Nougat passed away.

So, if I fear death no longer, let me speak candidly about aspects of mine that I would hope to be addressed. I hope you will not find it a morbid subject if I were to tell you of my wishes in this instance.

I realise that this may be a rather unusual request, but I would greatly appreciate a handful of my ashes, (the reminder buried alongside my parents and siblings), being scattered by the grave of Audrey Hepburn, in a town called Tolochenaz.

Other beautiful actresses and models may have caught my eye at various times in my life, but the one constant and continual draw has been the beautiful, loving, kind and generous woman that Audrey H was, beyond the charming characters she played. I just hope, in so doing, that my soul may get to dance with hers even for a moment, and that she may guide mine in any future loves.

I have often thought about what songs I would like played at my funeral. Besides the Hallelujah chorus, and the joyous "Jerusalem", I would love to have included the songs "The Living Years" and "La Vie En Rose" played to remember me by.

And no one performs the latter better than the great Edith Piaf. She sings it so beautifully. It fills my heart with so many different emotions – joy, pain, hope, love. How she manages to evoke both complementary and conflicting emotions within me with her words, I do not know. I could feel myself wanting to smile at the thought of wonderfully amusing things discussed over lunch with friends, whilst simultaneously wanting to cry with pain at the loss of many good souls. It is my wish that this song causes my spirit to soar to the heavens alongside theirs.

'La Vie En Rose' as a concept also summarises me well. I have generally been a dreamer all my life, and often chose to look at life through rose tinted glasses. Does this optimism not run contrary to my wish to accept death now, I hear you ask? Not at all. We all have death awaiting us as a certainty. I have just learnt to accept it, whether it happens now or a few years hence.

If seventy-six was the age I would leave this world for the next in accordance with my dream, I shall cherish each year from this point until that time.

I just sometimes wish that I had accomplished something truly significant enough to point to as a legacy, but I hope nevertheless, that I would have made some small differences in the lives of people I have known. We have been friends for a long time now, I hope I have in some way influenced yours too.

The two things I do feel extremely proud of though, are my two children. Whilst I cannot claim unilateral credit for them, I would like to think that I have helped shaped their thinking and created a value platform upon which they will hopefully develop their own ideals. If I will live on only in their hearts and thoughts. That is enough.

I leave you with these words from the poet Rumi. They seem so particularly apt in my life at this point. I really could not have conceived a more appropriate expression. If my dreams of H, even those of my demise, were to come true these words would be all the more germane, as I would have passed away in love.

"Don't be without love, so you won't feel dead. Die in love and stay alive forever."

Adieu,

David

Letter 28 – In the Dentist's Chair
& Forgotten Sibling

May 2020

Dear Geoff,

I had an appointment with the dentist today.

When I made the appointment on the prior Friday, I was in such searing agony from a toothache that I would have resorted to having Dunmore crudely apply a pair of pliers to remove the offending article if necessary.

It seemed such a good idea at the time. Not the pliers, but making the appointment with the dentist, I mean, and I looked forward eagerly to his attendance and application of pain relief. Little did I know that when the day dawned, my overwhelming fears of a visit to the dental surgery would return with such unmanageable vengeance and overtake any consideration of toothache. It had been a while since my last visit to a dentist, and I began quaking in my boots, or whatever footwear I happened to be adorning at the time.

I was rather impressed by this particular dentist's recommendation to procure some medication for interim relief over the weekend until he could attend to me. He had prescribed a course of antibiotics and a strong painkiller, which took a little while to act, but I awoke the following day with little discomfort. By the day after that, I was as 'right as rain', and in fact, after procuring a bunch of flowers, headed off to a birthday party at Karen and Shingai's with fervent anticipation of good company, and the ability to now partake meaningfully of the good food that I knew would be on offer.

I did eat my food a trifle gingerly just in case I bit into anything that would have me writhing about the floor in agony, but I need not have feared, as all went well on the deglutition front. By the time the sun arose on the day of the appointment, I began to feel so well that I had every intention to call off the appointment. I felt obliged, however, to meet and at least say 'hello' to this splendid fellow, as he had been so concerned about my well-being over the weekend. Therefore, when his assistant called to confirm the appointment, I decided to toddle along dutifully to his surgery.

It amazes me to think that I had approached my major operation in England with less trepidation. At the time thoughts of H comforted me. I felt at the time that destiny would be my guide eventually into her loving arms and that any suffering was to be accepted as part of that journey of love. This time, I was similarly accompanied by feelings of longing. I smiled at the thought of kissing her sweet lips one day. Visions of her beauty quelled my fears to some extent.

My fear had been exacerbated by the fact that my regular dentist, a chap called Milan, was out of the country and not due back for another fortnight hence. I had to obtain a hasty recommendation for an alternative from a friend.

I had known Milan for many years now and had complete trust in his election to do me no harm whatsoever. We bumped into each other quite often socially too, and he had become a friend of sorts. Could one really befriend a dentist, I hear you ask. Funnily enough, I think despite one's inherent fear of their ilk, it is indeed possible. I suppose that with the amount of trust we place in them, it is almost inevitable that one regards them with a little affection as well as respect. Is it not better to have some affection than harbour dislike? Can you imagine if that dislike were to be reciprocated? The sheer amount of anguish that could be caused. The accidental slip of the drill hitting the nerve at its rawest, for example. Ouch, it pains me to just think of it.

Before Milan, the only dentist I trusted was a chap called Philip who had a surgery in the West End of London. Bang in the middle of Shaftesbury Avenue to be exact. He was a rather wonderful chap. I am sure that his dental charges included for the very extended foreplay of much friendly conversation even before work started. I believe that I may have divulged more secrets to him than anybody else who was not a close friend. He was more of a barman than a dentist in this regard, and I felt comfortable making him privy to all matters relating to my amorous adventures or misadventures for that matter. His conversational charm was a rather good tactic I think, because it had the desired effect of putting me completely at ease.

I recall several instances where he would hold the horrifyingly large metal syringe behind his back as he asked me several questions concerning my well-being, and in the midst of full flow, casually ask me to open my mouth wide and then insert the odious needle for a bit, before allowing me to continue as best as I could with a consequent progressively numbing set of gums. He was instrumental in the removal of all of my wisdom teeth over several visits, employing this procedure. My wisdom teeth were stubborn. On one occasion he had to resort to placing his foot on the chair to provide himself sufficient leverage to extract a particularly difficult lower molar. He dismissed me that afternoon with a swab to keep in my mouth for a bit, and his home telephone number in case of an emergency.

I should have been troubled, but he had such a reassuring manner about him that a clearly bleeding mouth left me mostly unperturbed. In fact, I ended up having to help my brother on a busy night at the Singapura that very evening. The conversation was, understandably a little limited as I had to keep my teeth clenched for most of the time.

I miss Phil and his tactics.

I really have no idea how I survived many years without ever going to the dentist, as I only began appointments with 'Phil the drill' in my early twenties after returning from my expatriate stint in Nigeria. I trust you recall my letters to you on my time in that country, and meeting one of the true loves of my life, Madeleine?

I must have been very fortunate during my college days and my time in Nigeria, as I have no recollection of ever needing medical attention in any form, dental or otherwise. Heartbreak yes, but no other ailment of note. Interesting, if come to think of it, as I wonder whether it was just good fortune or if I had obtained the right balance in my lifestyle. I could certainly do with a similarly long period of ailment-free life right now!

Was it merely good fortune that I benefitted from during this barren ailment period, or should I also attribute it to my sense of duty in taking good care of the pearly whites? As I have mentioned to you on many occasions, I love kissing. In pursuit of this endeavour, practising good oral hygiene was necessarily a must. I flossed and brushed my teeth regularly. I could think of nothing more off-putting than encountering offensive breath in the midst of an amorous encounter.

My fear of dentists was not entirely imaginary, as I had the most horrific of experiences with a particularly sadistic specimen during my early teen years at school. I remember very clearly the torturous moments and the period after. It was whilst enduring a very cold first term of boarding school.

Much as I recall with great clarity the actual visit to the dentist, I cannot remember what led to the making of an appointment in the first place. I was generally in good health, as I had been in Brunei also. As I had mentioned to you in my previous missives, I was in fine fettle, and had in fact signed up to play hockey, rugby and other athletic endeavours. In hindsight, it may just have been one of those routine check-ups required by the school of all its pupils.

Not that I never had any dental mishaps in my youth. I lost both my front teeth simultaneously. They were my milk teeth and therefore par for the course, but it dealt a huge blow to my self-esteem at the time. I was probably about eight or nine, but my teeth were an integral part of what defined me.

Although just at primary school, I was regarded as the leader of a gang of sorts. You can imagine the sheer frustration I had at the time, waking up to find both my front teeth literally hanging on by a mere thread. Had I been able to, I would have resorted to gluing them back in place.

Despite my valiant efforts to keep them in place somehow, they eventually fell out onto my breakfast plate. I howled in anguish. How could I face my comrades in arms in this state? Who had ever heard of a toothless gang leader? Although I was still more enamoured with marbles, butterflies, etc than girls at the time, it still mattered to me that I could attract the attention of a couple of admirers from the opposite sex. Toothless, I had no hope, unless they were also!

441

I had only one option, and that was not to bare my teeth at all. I, therefore, refused to smile. This was far more difficult than I had imagined it, as smiling came rather naturally to me. I was a happy kid and smiled rather a lot. I had to consequently adopt a broad smile without display of teeth or a deliberately sullen demeanour. It seemed to have had the desired effect, though, and I managed to keep my place at the top of the food chain amongst my peers.

My broad 'no-teeth-displaying' smile also headlined in my passport.

Things were going well with my buddies at the time, and I imagined myself getting gold teeth to replace the ones I had lost to garner further respect and emulate the menacing appearance of the villainous characters we were enthralled with as kids. I desperately wanted this glittering appendage as my dental feature also. I suggested as much to my parents who laughed it off. I was emotionally wounded by their facetious dismissal of my suggestion and vowed to save up to procure them for myself. Thankfully those childhood desires did not continue into adulthood.

The sullen look I adopted prevailed and seemed to have a draw on the girls too. Perhaps that should form a key part of my dating strategy now. Could I reinvigorate H's loving attention if I smiled less? I think at times that women do prefer bad boys, so I need to give some serious thought to this. I shall henceforth be working on a new look of casual indifference over the course of the next few weeks. In the case of any woman of interest happening my way, I shall be adopting a slightly haughty 'I'd like to do a number 24 from the Kama Sutra with you if I may' gaze, providing of course that she does interpret this correctly, and not assume it a wish to share 'Butter

Chicken served with Onion Bhajis & Raita' as item 24 from the local Indian takeaway.

Said haughty gaze applied in preference to my usual beseeching one of 'I'll worship at your feet until the dawn of infinity and beyond'!

I am not sure I can carry it off, but I promise to keep you advised of developments in this regard, nevertheless.

On the rare occasion that my parents took me to the dentist, it only involved the obligatory opening of the mouth, feeling a little probing here and there, and then being offered a choice of sweets. Ironic, in hindsight, as sweets were the very things that would have aided my tooth deterioration. So, you see, my childhood experiences were not ones associated with fear of any major kind. A mere routine irritation.

On the occasion of my teen experience, however, I had some premonition of doom. I pride myself in possessing perfectly good instincts, which I rely upon to this day. But sometimes, as you very well know, the rational being gets in the way and disrupts the continuity of concern initiated by these instincts and serves instead to quell them.

That frightfully painful day arrived. I took the bus into town, as the surgery was beyond reasonable walking distance. By requirement I was attired from top to toe in my school uniform, which still exuded the freshness from the laundry room that morning. I returned the many smiles I was greeted with by the occupants of the bus there and sat quietly looking out of the window pondering the future with a nagging anxiety I found very difficult to shake off. How injuriously accurate my instincts proved to be!

I was led into the surgery by a rather scrumptious looking dental assistant and watching the entrancing sway of her hips certainly helped dissipate some of the anxiety. She was so gorgeous that even when she put her surgical mask on, I was drawn to the sparkle in her eyes. Pity she was not the actual dentist, as I would have gladly sat in the dental chair for all eternity allowing her to do to me as she wished.

Sadly, the prodding about in my mouth was by an elderly gentleman of withered appearance who failed to bear the kindly smiling face that my previous dental interactants did. This alone should have alerted me. My rational thoughts though continued to suggest that there was nothing to fear, despite his tut-tutting as he inspected my teeth with all manner of instrumentation. When I was finally allowed to close my mouth, I took it that the session had concluded and was ready to disembark from my perch and seek the expected sweet.

No such luck! He almost forcibly held me back on the chair, now declined to an almost horizontal position, and aimed the light directly onto my face once again. This time the light seemed even more blindingly fierce, and his mocking smile looked positively evil. He began drilling without application of an anaesthetic. The pain was excruciating. I screamed. If it were possible to scream effectively with one's mouth open and full of dental instrumentation, I proved it so. I tried to think of anything to distract me from the pain of the moment but couldn't.

There were things I feared as a kid, particularly snakes in our garden, or total darkness because of the ghost stories that my mother insisted on gifting us with every now and then, but this pain took fear to another level altogether. It was in the premier league of fear. Do you remember a film with Dustin Hoffman called "Marathon Man"? In case you don't, I shall inform you only of the relevance. In this film, Hoffman, who plays an innocent good guy, gets tortured by a baddie, (played convincingly by Laurence Olivier), seeking to extract (pun unintended) information by way of drilling onto the nerves of his teeth. I could so relate to the imagined pain. I wince even now when I think of that particular scene.

I was in so much agony, that tears also formed and began to pour unendingly down my face.

I held my cold hands onto my cheeks on the way back, aiming to ease the continued hurt. On arrival at school, I headed straight for the sanatorium. My face must have taken on an equivalent of an ashen hue. The duty nurse took one look at me and before I had said much led me into one of the rooms and had me immediately tucked comfortably and warmly in a bed.

I recounted my tale of woe as she soothed my brow. She ran her fingers gently through my hair as my mother always did when comforting me. If only she had been as pretty as the dental nurse I had seen earlier. Nevertheless, her gentle caress coupled with the medication she provided began to take effect.

She was so outraged by the treatment I received that she immediately called the dental surgery to register a complaint. She told me later that they had issued an apology, but I am sure it was more because they feared losing the school's account than any concern over my well-being. It took me two whole days in the school san to recover from the ordeal. I hope you now understand better the deep-seated fear I have of dentists. Even the sound of the drill whilst sat in their waiting rooms has the effect of prickling the hairs on the back of my neck.

Thoughts of H have such a soporific effect on me. If I could bottle it in sufficient quantities for sale, I could make an absolute fortune. She makes me dizzy with bliss. I wish I knew what exactly it is about her that causes me to feel the way I do. Her beauty, obviously, but it seems so much more.

Forgive my straying to the clouds again. Back to my present-day occupation of the dentist's chair. Adrian could sense my anxiety from my fierce grip of the arms of the chair and, I assume, the look of sheer unadulterated terror on my face. Despite his gentle requests to relax and open my mouth wide, I was by no means comfortable. He asked me to think of something that would help me relax.

I closed my eyes and resumed my contemplation of H.

I thought that if I were to expire then, I would rather leave with images of her beauty embedded in my mind's eye, and her name cast on my lips. I immediately felt a sense of calm wash over me. The underlying fear remained but only to a limited extent and supposedly completely natural in so far as Adrian was concerned. I obediently opened my mouth and relinquished all authority for its care to him as he applied all manner of metallic implements in the cause of managing my dental health.

I am happy to report that there was no major drama other than a much-needed filling. He indicated that my teeth were generally in good repair, and also expressed his happiness that, given my nervous disposition, I was not in the habit of grinding my teeth. I assured him that my nervousness applied only to unkindly dentists and slithering reptiles, and certainly had no cause otherwise for the gnashing of teeth. Other than a promise to visit him again in a few months for a routine review, I was free to go.

It was interesting though that he mentioned grinding teeth, as I was never a candidate for that practice, but my eldest sister, Isabel was, and I was immediately reminded of her.

I am sure I mentioned her to you in previous letters but had probably forgotten to speak of her in more detail. It is only right that you have a good understanding of all my siblings as she was an integral part of our close-knit family.

Isabel was the eldest of the five children my parents so beautifully raised. An incredible extrovert, she made friends easily and quickly and usually brought home as many strays as my parents did, both human and animal.

What do I mean? Well, my parents had this habit of befriending people easily and sometimes invited them home on a whim. One stranger they met at a travel agency ended up staying with us for three months! Isabel had obviously inherited this trait and would bring home many a friend to be fed and clothed.

Also, anyone with pets they could not manage themselves or surplus to their needs found willing recipients in my parents. We ended up with a veritable zoo.

According to Isabel, who learnt of this from our mother, there was a very particular arrangement to the order in which we were born. Isabel was born on the first of the month, and thereby being the number 1. Rachel who was next, born on the twenty-ninth was number 2 (2+9=11, 1+1=2, for reduction into a single digit). John was next, born on the third, and thereby number 3. Carole after him born on the twenty-second (2+2=4), and finally me born on the fifth – number 5.

There was an approximate eighteen-month to two-year separation between most of us except between Rachel and John, where the gap was wider. This, because my mother lost a child in between. Although obviously and naturally deeply saddened, she apparently was rather philosophical about it and was accepting of the notion that the numbers (in terms of sequencing) didn't quite add up – literally.

It has always rather baffled me that for someone generally fact-based and so scientifically minded, (she was a science teacher at a girl's senior school for most of her working life), my mother exhibited a tendency to believe in the intangibles of astrology, ghosts, etc. My father on the other hand dismissed most of it as utter nonsense. As I have mentioned to you previously, I am somewhat mystified about my tendency also, despite my mind's general mathematical and analytical bent, to be sometimes unhesitatingly susceptible to soothsayers and those of similar ilk. Ever since my run-in with that Indian fellow who stripped me off a hundred euros, you would have assumed that my move to scepticism would have been very swift, but not so. I may have inherited this trait from my mother, I fear.

I believe that Isabel also tended to take after my mother in this regard. If you felt that I appeared occasionally to be a card or two short of a full deck, Isabel was a complete suit short. She was a nutter. A very kind, caring, generous and loving soul, but an amiably eccentric one.

She was very dear to me, but perhaps not as close as I had been to the other of my siblings. This may have been because the rest of us experienced more together as teens. Also, perhaps because she chose to study in India, whilst the rest of us opted for England, creating a small cultural divide.

After university, she decided to follow in my parents' footsteps and trained to become a teacher. Shortly thereafter though, she met and married Bob. Children followed, as did their move from Brunei back to England, from where Bob hailed.

She had two sons, Billy and Raji. I cannot remember Isabel being a terribly stern parent, but together with Bob, raised them to be very well-behaved and adorable nephews. I enjoyed their rare visits to London, as they were a delight to take charge of, being easily occupied with

448

games of cricket comprising nothing more than a rolled-up piece of paper and a wooden spatula for a bat. They ran around gleefully as I 'bowled' paper balls to them from the comfort of an armchair. They did not benefit from many shopping expeditions with me as my other nephews and nieces but seemed to hang onto my every word and appeared particularly keen on the wide variety of infantile jokes I had in my repertoire at the time. I enjoyed watching them practically rolling around in stitches to simple jokes like "What's yellow and goes 'round and 'round? Answer: A banana in a washing machine." Or "What's yellow and swings from cake to cake? Answer: Tarzipan!"

How quickly time has flown by though, as they and the others of the next generation of our family, other than my youngest niece Maia, are all fully-fledged independent adults. Many cutting a very dashing figure and in the process of creating the generation after.

Sadly, as you would have gathered from an earlier communication, Isabel, shortly after my other sister Rachel, also passed away at a relatively young age. Isabel may have been a little barmy at times but was a very sweet and gentle sister to me.

I apologise for ending yet another letter on a sombre note but am still not clear how I departed from advising you of the welfare of my teeth to speaking sadly of a beloved sibling.

I shall endeavour to be of greater cheer when I next write.

My love to you as always,

David

Letter 29 – Lost Pathways & Humsafars

May 2020

Dear Geoff,

The lockdown is to continue for a further two weeks under an edict delivered by the powers that be.

I have to assume that they know what they are doing, but this continuing pandemic is causing absolute havoc to an already weakened economy and may eventually bring the country to its knees. I remain cynical of any miraculous recovery in the short-term, but am optimistic about the country's longer-term future, and therefore continue to focus my efforts on improving my fitness and diet and keeping the business afloat in the meanwhile.

The time away from work is of course an unexpected blessing in my wish to continue writing several letters to you, which I would otherwise find little time for. And how wonderful it is that we learn something new each day, as I was fortunate to, when I spoke to a friend in India this morning.

Monisha is rather attractive and a very bright Indian lady whom I have known for many years. She may normally tick many boxes between beauty and wit, and be very appealing in almost every sense, but she is just a very good friend, and one who remains very much committed to her marriage.

After an exchange of the usual pleasantries, we got on to the subject of love. Partly, as a result of her enquiry into latest developments on my dating endeavours. We agreed that for all long as I was in Zimbabwe, any prospects looked rather bleak. I needed to look further afield.

But how, and where? We shall deal with that matter at another time.

This was the very first time that she mentioned being disillusioned with love and of heartbreak. I cannot profess to know the details of what took place as she has been rather private as a person, and I never like prying for information, unless it is freely volunteered. I was sorry to hear that she felt that way and told her that she should not give up so easily on love.

We accepted that love takes many forms. I am sure I would have written to you on the subject previously. For fear of too much repetition, I shall merely summarise. The love we feel for others varies; I would assume quite obviously, according to whom. The love we feel for a partner would quite understandably not be the same as that felt for members of the family, or friends, pets or even something inanimate – I love Paris, a case in point.

The discussion was less about the varying forms of love, and more about the issue of whether we get to an age when we sometimes feel resigned to accept only contentment from the sentiments shared with children, family and friends. Was that the right thing to do? Do we no longer wish to rekindle the dying embers of a passion that once burnt so brightly? Was it due to emotional fatigue or its erosion?

In an attempt to be philosophical, I suggested to her that a partner's love was like having paradisaically added guidance in our life's journey. They become our unfaltering witnesses in this odyssey. The providers of added illumination to the paths we take through the provision of unwavering trust, untiring respect, devoted care and endless emotional sustenance. The ones we stand indivisibly with at love's altar.

However, there are times when we share our journey for only part of the way, and we learn, or should do as was my case, that after some time the paths our partners wish to tread may diverge from ones that we wish to follow.

The lucky ones find partners for the whole of the journey. Some journeys have pitfalls not of our making, but those are best undertaken if our partners stay alongside us, helping each other navigate the most difficult terrain until we reach firm and even ground. But if we fall and are left to effectively journey on our own, we must pick ourselves up, dust ourselves down, and, with or without the accompaniment of others continue to the journey's end, wherever and whenever that may be. Ideally though, in my view one found a partner for the entirety of the journey or whatever its remaining portion.

She mentioned that there was a word in Hindi that would capture what I had described – Humsafar. Hum meaning 'we' and safar – 'journey'. What a lovely word! That, my friend, is what, if we have not already found, should all seek - our lifelong Humsafars!

Lao Tzu famously declared that *"a journey of a thousand miles begins with one step"*, and there is nothing to disagree with in this statement, except to suggest that one must be clear on the direction and intended destination, surely. Or am I missing the point entirely?

It would be foolhardy to journey aimlessly for a thousand miles, would it not, as that would only lead to extraneous fatigue or worse, death? Lewis Carroll once indicated that *"if you don't know where you are going, any road will get you there."* Is this to suggest that fate has preordained certain destinations for each of us?

I really wish I knew what has been ordained for me, as I do really feel that I may have 'lost my way' somewhat in the last few years. I have no understanding of why, yet, but as a result of this period of reflection, feel that I know when.

I think that I have been blindly stumbling around for the last several years, when I was left to journey alone, and I knew not where to. In my blinded search for the right paths, I therefore only found even more pitfalls.

I think I have finally realised what I have been missing all this time. My compass. My sense of self-worth. Without this I could only continue to meander through life, never having charted a true course. It was not anything that others could provide. They could help enhance it, (or cause it to diminish for that matter), but that spark of realisation or enlightenment had to come from within.

I have made many mistakes in my life, as I would argue most humans are prone to doing. But I believe that I have learnt from many of them, and to a certain extent also recovered. The mistake, however, of returning to England when my career was at its peak here, was the worst retrograde step I took. I was very happy in Zimbabwe at the time. There was political turmoil, I accept, but considerable opportunity alongside. The innumerable projects were merely awaiting the guidance, control and management that I was more than capable of providing.

And I proved it several times over. I was brimming with confidence, at the time. I could have sold ice to the Eskimos or oil to the Arabs, such was my self-belief.

It counted for nought in the return to England. I had to spend considerable time and effort seeking gainful employment in a market that had changed significantly in my time away. I assumed that the challenges I had helped overcome in realising opportunities in Zimbabwe would be sought after, especially as I had dealt with many project complexities and interacted with international organisations at very senior levels.

To have all my great achievements disregarded was soul-destroying. Even more so, when the adjudicators were fresh-faced youths, unlikely to have understood the complex issues, or successfully overcome even the most minor of the challenges I faced. Good interpreters of Balance Sheets, and nothing more. Soulless bean counters in my opinion.

Although I did the best I could to provide a comfortable roof over our heads and kept the family well-fed and clothed, the damage to my morale and self-esteem was severe. I was bright, capable, qualified and hardworking, but deemed too old, would you believe?

England's industry was placing greater emphasis on youth over experience. I sometimes failed to make it past the first hurdle in proving my capability. It was rather fortuitously that I found some rewarding employment in corporate life again through a friend, John, thanks to his belief in me. Sadly, that career journey was a short-lived one for both of us thanks to rabid corporate politics at play.

I muddled through somehow, until tragedy struck our family with a series of deaths, from my ex's mother to my own parents and siblings. Trying to deal with grief as well as economic concerns; career adversities (I was attempting to keep three different businesses on the go simultaneously, all of them dependent on me solely); and managing the needs of the family, both immediate and other, finally took its toll. I was broken.

Providentially a return to Zimbabwe allowed me an opportunity to make great headway in recapturing my old self - my confidence in my capabilities. Alas, as with life's usual cycle of good and bad fortune, events and circumstances frustrated and limited great achievement. I was in great need of voices of reassurance and faith, but I heard only criticism. I retreated into the engulfing emotional darkness once again.

It was very difficult not to want to give up when the darkness was compounded further by learning of my illness. Continuing a journey, blinded and wounded is not an ideal one. It was time to heal as best one could, and search for light.

I needed to rediscover the faith and belief I had in myself, for that to shine through for others to see. It was, and still is, hard work, as I feel that I have had to work through from under a large pile of self-doubting rubble accumulated over the years.

But I am getting there. Slowly. It just frustrates me occasionally that it is more difficult than I had initially assumed to convince others, more than myself. It was happening though, albeit gruellingly.

And then the damned virus raised its ugly head and struck a hefty blow to all the stalwart efforts.

I must persevere. I could just do with the assistance of lady luck planting her kiss of good fortune on my forehead, now and again.

On the matter of seeking love also, I, therefore, do not or should not wish to tire. I must seek my Humsafar to continue to the journey's end but armed more capably with a compass to guide me.

With the right Humsafar, I feel that I could once again enjoy the delights of loving reciprocally and unconditionally. I shall continue to seek the one who will accept the same path to our journey's end, no matter what the intervening terrain or obstacles we need to overcome. Through "thick and thin, for richer for poorer, and in sickness or health...", etc. As my lovely Audrey Hepburn once aptly declared, *"The best thing to hold onto in life is each other."* Will this be with H? I shall jolly well hope so!

Why do I remain optimistic about love after such a painful separation, when many people I met in similar marital circumstances had succumbed to cynicism and disillusionment? I am not sure. I had also felt indistinguishably similarly for a while. And then I met H.

Even if she were not to be my ultimate Humsafar, I will be grateful to her, for re-awakening dormant feelings of love within me, to such incredible magnitude.

I now feel more capable of sharing a great love again. I shall never tire of it. It is a wonderful feeling. And to quote my wonderfully perceptive screen idol again *"If I get married. I want to be very married."*

In reviewing my past and taking consideration of the future, I have learnt much about the value of creating a balance in life.

Without wanting to sound too much like a boastful lifestyle guru, I believe that we must approach life with a sense of balance in every facet of our lives: eat neither too much nor too little; avoid overworking and aim to create an optimum balance with our social lives; exercising to maintain our health but not driving our bodies to injury; maintain a political balance, as neither extreme (as proven) offers economic value or social justice to abound; drive neither too fast nor too slow (although I have to admit to enjoying speed!); enjoy music at a volume for it to be neither too loud nor too soft for lasting enjoyment; drink to one's clement state of inebriation – drunk enough to enjoy and contribute to the enjoyment of others, without passing out or causing concern and harm; gaining an optimum return on investment, by deriving profit without incurring damage to the very resources applied to achieve it; and in a relationship, always adding value without losing your own, by managing to maintain an equity of expectations.

Everything in life conducted within reason, and with a view to maintaining balance, except for love. This, in my view, must be provided and enjoyed limitlessly, unconditionally, effortlessly, joyfully, wholeheartedly and endlessly.

There is no harm whatsoever, as we journey with our Humsafars, in occasionally looking back. These occasional backward glances, provide points of reference, and also allows us to express gratitude for what we have experienced in getting to where we are. Sometimes even the difficult terrain that we have traversed prepares us to better appreciate what may lay ahead – fear or fortune.

During this time of vigorous cogitation and profound contemplation, I have realised that despite my many woes, which I have possibly recounted to you *ad nauseam*, I actually have much to be grateful for. It is far too protracted a list compile, but in summary:

Family – I have two of the most wonderful daughters in the world. They truly are a gift, for which I shall be eternally thankful. As for the rest of my family, I could not have asked for a closer-knit unit of people. Parents of great stock who taught us well and raised us to conduct our lives upholding principles and values. Siblings who have shown considerable love, understanding and support through dark days and bright. Nephews, nieces, et al similarly providing love.

Friends – I have been so fortunate to have met and retained so many people whom I could call friends. They are too innumerable to mention by name. And you, my stalwart dinner companion, chief provider of much needed laughter, as well as the recipient of a myriad of my musings, occupy a special place.

Lovers – I have sadly not as many as I would have wished, but am heartened by the passion they have shown, which easily surpasses any boasts of scratches on the bedpost. It is the quality, in my life, that has been of greater significance than the quantity.

Music – My life would have truly been devoid of any substance without this. As so wonderfully declared in Twelfth Night, "If music be the food of love, then play on." Except in this instance, I seek not abundance to lose appetite for love, but rather to foster its limitless existence. From Henry Mancini's "Moon River" to Cole's "Unforgettable" and all the wonderful songs in between, that have so gloriously enriched my life. I applaud all the composers, lyricists and performers for their great talent.

Food – I have been so fortunate to have tasted so many marvellous dishes and foods prepared both at home and at restaurants, which have excited, invigorated and satisfied my palate to an infinite extent. From caviar to satay, escargot to dim sum, roast beef and Rogan Ghosh to Peking duck and seafood linguine, noodles to biryani, bread and butter pudding, mince pies, chocolate, baklava, almonds, cashew nuts, …. – forming an endless list of remarkable items to savour and consume.

Wine – This is surely the nectar of gods. I have been fortunate to taste these wonderful derivations of grape of so many varieties – red, white or radiant pink matters not, as they have all proven universally agreeable. My heart though must surely belong to champagne, which I could happily consume by the gallon on any given day, but being an advocate of moderation and balance, shall limit this to say, no more than a bottle a day?

Books – I should have read more! I am so glad that my father insisted on all of us reading the classics when we were young. That alone set us up perfectly to enjoy other literary works over the years. Again, my life would have been considerably dimmer were it not for the clever, profound and entertaining works of Dickens, Austen, Shakespeare, Balzac, Orwell, Ishiguro, Wodehouse, Shaw, Hemingway, Fitzgerald, Kureishi, Larsson, Ludlum, Fleming, Christie, Blyton amongst a hundred others.

Art – What a joy it has been, over the years, to view the most marvellous beauty captured on oils on canvas, water colour or other mediums. I admire such astounding creativity and only wish I possessed a small spec of their wonderful artistry. It has been an exhilarating experience to see the beautiful creations of Matisse, Chagall, Picasso, Dalí, Monet, Manet, Constable, Bacon, Cézanne, Renoir, Van Gogh, Lautrec, Miró, Klee, Lempicka, Kahlo, Munch, Gauguin, and so many others. And an even greater joy to have acquired a few pieces to own by some marvellous contemporary, particularly Indian, artists.

Clothes – What would I be without some of them defining me? As with art, I sometimes think of myself as the blank canvas upon which the clothes create the picture. I absolutely love fashion, and only wish I had either more time, but also the shape, to do this delightful array of men's clothing more justice. I do not regret any of the clothing purchases, except those made purely to fulfil a functional purpose. To all the designers who have contributed to my wardrobe and more importantly, my sense of well-being, I salute you.

Travel – how wonderful it has been to visit several countries and cities whether for business or pleasure. Some once, others on several occasions, but all adding layers of knowledge or serving as an experience to be savoured – landscape, culture, language, custom, cuisine et al. What a joy it would be to travel more extensively to far-flung places arm-in-arm with a loved one who shares this passion for always wanting to extend one's horizons.

Films – What a joy it has been to be entertained. I would admit to being partial to action films and romantic comedies. So, from James Bond's "Skyfall" to "Serendipity", and Connery, Craig, Schwarzenegger, Statham, Lee, Grant, and Brosnan to Hepburn, Ryan, Monroe, Aniston, Roberts, Hathaway, Bullock, amongst innumerable others.

I am grateful to the writers, producers, directors, actors and actresses for the wonderful entertainment I have enjoyed over the years. I need to thank in particular the late William Wyler, without whose foresight, the world may never have been introduced to the sparkling beauty of Audrey Hepburn in "Roman Holiday". I have since seen many of her films and fallen in love with her character on and off screen many times over. She has created a profound and heavenly imprint on my soul through her show of seemingly boundless love.

I believe that H has stirred within me a capability of sharing such infinite love also.

Perhaps this virus, although economically and otherwise debilitating, has provided me valuable time for much needed introspection. I have had an opportunity, which I otherwise did not appear to have, to look back on my life and learn, both from the highs and lows, the sorrows as well as the joys. Writing to you about past events and loves has given me a better understanding of who I was, and now am.

I am also beginning to better understand not just when I lost self-belief, but why.

My correspondence with you has, therefore, served as a form of therapy. I am eternally grateful for your patience in attending to the many letters I have already written - pouring out every element of my heart and soul.

Speaking of pouring hearts out, I told Monisha, during our conversation on this occasion, about my love for H. Her reaction was exactly what I had assumed it would be, as she is as much of a romantic as I am.

She thought I would be utterly mad not to pursue a relationship with H, especially as I had just loquaciously expounded the virtues of seeking life's great loves, and so on.

We shall see.

I hope that all is well with you, in the meanwhile, my dear, dear friend.

Love always,

David

Letter 30 – Understanding Love

June 2020

My dear Geoff,

Why do I love H?

It appears that despite exchanging an abundance of letters, and a slew of messages, together with participation in numerous conversations, as well as a bout of therapy, I remain bereft of adequate explanation.

It is more than two years since I saw her last, and yet all the various thoughts in my head, no matter how unconnected, always lead to H. Pictures of her pretty face seem to have taken up permanent residence in my head.

Having listened to many of my musings on this subject at the various times we have met, I do know that you are firmly of the view that nothing can come of this prospective affair other than pain and heartbreak. I feel however, that any pain, (and incidentally I do not feel any at the moment), will be worth the treasure that is to be enjoyed in one day capturing her heart, if I were ever to do so.

Hardly a day goes past without my having several amorous thoughts about her. In fact, rather than causing me hurt or pain, every mention of her name actually brightens up even the dullest of dull days.

You may think me utterly asinine. I possibly am. Perhaps I am the 'sick puppy' in the Trump Tweet, and a life in straitjacket repeatedly banging my head against the padded cell walls whilst calling out her name incessantly is just what may come to pass.

You would have realised from the countless letters I have written to you, that regardless of my own efforts at objective and practical interventions, I continue to feel so completely emotionally connected to her. Rather bizarrely, I am beginning to believe now, that my love for her could be eternal, and may survive even after my demise, into future lifetimes. Even in suggesting this, I acknowledge how rabidly disturbed it sounds and would not blame you, or anyone else for dialling the telephone number of the nearest sanatorium.

Was it love or an inexplicable obsession? What is love, anyway? I thought at my age I would be able to not just understand the emotion but provide effective guidance on the subject to my children and others who sought my counsel. Yet here I am, feeling like some pimply youth in love with a prom queen, unable to comprehend or rationalise my own feelings, and completely incapable of emptying my mind of thoughts of her.

Would these feelings for her result in matrimonial bliss with one of the most perfect women I have ever met; or merely lead to spending the rest of my life as a tortured soul, unable to understand why I felt the way I did? Unlike similarly love-struck individuals of centuries past, who had no means of gathering information on their sentiments other than to navel gaze or search their own souls, I could procure speedier guidance from the world-wide-web.

I hoped that this search, alongside all the prior objective consultations through you and a few other friends also, may provide some answers. I felt I needed to begin an independent and truly objective quest for these answers through a global search on the subject, and what better way than commencing with the very definition of the word 'love'.

Some of the information I uncovered indeed confirmed the many symptoms of love. There were some aspects that aided the comprehension of my emotions, but I have yet to unravel the mystery of why my heart continues to yearn for her, in such an endless and unrequited fashion.

Some dictionary definitions include:

Deep affection, fondness, tenderness, warmth, intimacy, attachment, endearment, devotion, adoration, doting, idolisation, worship; passion, ardour, desire, lust, yearning, infatuation, adulation, - "his friendship with her grew into love" compassion, caring, regard, solicitude, warmth, friendship, kindness, charity, goodwill, altruism, philanthropy, unselfishness, benevolence, humanity - "their love for their fellow human beings"; relationship, love affair, affair, romance, affair of the heart, intrigue, amour - "he is confident that their love can survive"; a great interest and pleasure in something. - "his love for clothes"; synonyms: liking, weakness, partiality, proclivity, inclination, disposition; soft spot, delight, passion, zeal, zest, enthusiasm, keenness, predilection, penchant, fondness - "her love of fashion"; verb: feel deep affection or sexual love for (someone) - "do you love me?"; synonyms: be in love with, be infatuated with, be smitten with, be besotted with, be passionate about; care very much for, feel deep affection for, hold very dear, adore, think the world of, be devoted to, dote on, cherish, worship, idolise, treasure; informal: be mad/crazy/nuts/wild/potty about, have a crush on, carry a torch for - "I love you, H" and so on.

A multitude of words, therefore which could aptly describe my feelings for her.

The Wikipedia definition, continued as follows:

465

Love encompasses a variety of different emotional and mental states, typically strongly and positively experienced, ranging from the deepest interpersonal affection to the simplest pleasure. An example of this range of meanings is that the love of a mother differs from the love of a spouse, which in turn differs from the love of food. Most commonly, love refers to feeling of strong attraction and emotional attachment. Love can also be a virtue representing human kindness, compassion and affection – "the unselfish loyal and benevolent concern for the good of another". It may also describe compassionate and affectionate actions towards other humans, oneself or animals.

Ancient Greek philosophers identified four forms of love: essentially, familial love (in Greek storge), friendly love (philia), romantic love (eros) and divine love (agape). Modern authors have distinguished further varieties of love: infatuated love, self-love, and courtly love.

My love for her is both ardently romantic and supremely divine. I could, in theory, extend that also to 'philia' love, as I consider her a wonderful friend and social companion, beyond being a prospective lover and spiritual partner. Would this entitle me to additional brownie points? Surely, this affectionate connection on so many levels, and so mystifyingly and speedily reached must mean something?

Beyond the dictionary definition, which provided just a litter of appropriate words, I sought clarity on the causes of the sensation itself. My question could not have been better posed than that of one of the authors on the subject.

"Is love an emotion, an urge, brain chemistry, or something else entirely? It's the one question that has dominated our culture and relationships for millions of

years. But what is love? It's powerful enough to drive us to create new life or to destroy it, but while countless books, poems, films, plays, and careers have been made out of trying to decipher it, or at least represent it, can we pin down what it actually is?".

Would the answers, I sought lie in the scientific research conducted to better understand this phenomenon?

If this has not already caused your eyes to glaze over, or had you fall into deep and dreamless slumber, I ask you to prevail for just a little longer whilst I advise you of some interesting research into this subject by the neuroscientist Gabija Toleikyte and biological anthropologist Helen Fisher.

I have noted some relevant aspects of their findings, together with my corresponding opinion, for what it's worth.

Both scientists agreed that love is not something that can be controlled, curated or switched on or off. Instead, it arises from the depths of our subconscious. "Our subconscious mind has about ten times more information than our rational brain", Toleikyte said. "So when we actually fall in love with a person it might seem like quite a momentary experience, however the brain is working really hard to compute and to produce that feeling." This is what Fisher labels romantic love, something she somewhat unromantically describes as "a basic drive that evolved millions of years ago in order to enable us and focus our attention on just one partner and start the mating process." So it's a complex series of computations of the subconscious brain that gives us an emotional experience we can't control.

Our predecessors have obviously, after millions of years of evolution from primitive ape to thinking and feeling human, (as least in the case of H and I, as some people like those particularly dense individuals at a call-centre seem to have continued to retain a more primitive inability to process thought), created the necessary computations for my attention to be arrested by only H. Science has vindicated me, I feel. I did tell you on myriad occasions that it was a feeling, specifically for her that I was unable to control. Thank you Dr Toleikyte. I look forward now to hopes of commencing the wonderful process of mating with her.

How can we tell if what we're feeling is definitely love? Everything about the beloved takes on special meaning, said Fisher. "The car they drive is different from every car in the parking lot. The street they live on, the house they live in, the books they like, everything about this person becomes special." While you might be able to list what you don't like about them, you have an ability to sweep this aside and focus on the positive. Then there's the intense energy and mood swings brought about by love - elation when things are going well, to terrible despair when they don't text, write or invite you out.

I agree with the belief that our love interests are 'special'. In fact, I had actually used that specific word both in conversation and in my messages to her. I agree also that the place they reside takes on a special quality. The hotel where I first met her, feels to me like a place of worship, for example. I could happily kiss the pavement outside her apartment, in literal adoration of the ground she walks on. I have little to my name but would happily give over the entire amount to the bank she works for. I am less in agreement, however, with the analysis of the mood swings, as I feel only varying degrees of elation.

My mood would only swing from a scale ranging from a base level of happiness following thoughts about her, to total heightened elation when she messaged or called me. The only complexity arose when I doubted my ability to ever win her heart, and the feelings were those of inadequacy and disappointment. But those were thoughts of my own making, and not as a result of her actions.

Physically, love causes a dry mouth, a feeling of butterflies in the stomach, weak knees, separation anxiety, and craving for sex as well as an emotional union. "You want them to call, to write, and there's an intense motivation to win the person - what people will do when they are in love is quite remarkable," Fisher said. "Love evolved to allow us to start the mating process with a certain individual in order to send our DNA into tomorrow" Gabija Toleikyte, neuroscientist.

How totally true! Beers all around, please! The craving for sex with H is incredibly intense. But not in a coarse sense. There exists in me a great desire to have, not just full-on gorilla sex, (although this has its place in my perceived life with her too), but the intense passionate lovemaking reserved for the most special of lovers. Let the mating process begin immediately, I say. I feel that our combined DNA cries out to be propelled into tomorrow, and tomorrow's tomorrow. Dr Toleikyte, you appear to understand me almost completely.

In one study conducted by Fisher, 17 new lovers who had been happily in love for around seven and a half months, had their brains scanned. The scans showed activity in the ventral tegmental area, a region of the brain that makes dopamine and sends the stimulant to other areas. "This factory is part of the brain's reward system, the brain network that generates wanting, seeking, craving, energy, focus and motivation," Fisher writes. This, she found, means lovers are 'high' on a natural speed.

I do not actually know the precise moment I fell in love with her. I was obviously immensely attracted to her from the moment we first spoke. Her accent drove me absolutely crazy. I hung dearly onto her every word. I flirted with her outrageously. Our conversations would sometimes run past the hour. All this before we actually met. And when I did for the very first time, I could do nothing other than stare at her imbecilically, and gulp air like a stricken fish.

I had never laid eyes on anyone more enchanting. My tongue felt so glued to the roof of my mouth that I could barely form the appropriate words of greeting. My knees held up sufficiently, but my supposed evolved brain worked painfully slowly. Instead of extending a limp and sweaty palm in a handshake, which she may have likened to holding a damp sock, I should have swept her into my arms, and kissed her with unbridled passion. Perfunctory kisses on her cheek were all I could lay claim to that day. My brow felt feverish. I could feel a bolt of electricity run through me as I held her hand, and my heart struck a rapid beat loud enough to echo in my ears. Was that the day I fell in love with her?

Does love at first sight exist? Toleikyte and Fisher are both confident that yes, love at first sight does exist and more than that, it's easy to prove. Toleikyte is a living example. She and her husband fell in love straight away, getting married after one year of dating. "I think both our brains computed that this person somehow hit each other's sweet spots of our love centres and from that very moment we were fully committed to each other," she said. But it's not something you can or should go looking for she said. It does not matter one way or another - sometimes it just happens.

Correct! It does sometimes 'just happen'. I am fully subscribed to the notion of love at first sight too, as previous romantic occasions would prove. Could it be deemed first sight with H though, given our prior engagement, albeit over the phone? She had sent me photographs of herself, so I had a good understanding of her appearance prior to our first meeting and had the added benefit of hearing her enchanting voice too. But one could argue that it was only when I saw her in person that Cupid drew his bow, and had his arrow strike me squarely in the heart!

Does love last forever? From the honeymoon period to the seven year itch, there are plenty of theories that suggest love is not meant to, or even can last. But Toleikyte suggests it depends on how we look at it. Love as an emotion, she said, has follow-on effects: a deep connection between people leads to commitment and certain habits, and establishes boundaries where people identify themselves as part of a relationship. "So love as a greater experience can last. But if any steps have been compromised, for example someone learns that a person is completely different to who we got to know, that can change the experience." She said at an emotional level, love is still a function of brain chemistry which is changing all the time. "Sometimes we're not capable of feeling emotions such as love, sometimes we go through flat moments where we can't feel anything." Fisher said a study she conducted proved that it can last forever. In one study, 15 people in their 50s and 60s who told Fisher they were in love after an average of 21 years of marriage, were put into a brain scanner. What she found was that some of the brain circuits, the basic brain pathways for intense romantic love, were still active. "These long-term partners still feel some of the early-stage intense feelings of romantic love, so yes, it is possible," she said, although with a caveat - "you have to pick the right person".

With H, I would not contemplate anything but a commitment to an entirety of life with her. She is much too special to consider as a mere fling. How many women like H exist in reality? A mere handful possibly. Therefore, if I were ever to win her heart, it would be a glorious lifetime coupling. She is the 'right person', as far as I am concerned, and very much a 'keeper' as Ed Sheeran might suggest.

Fisher likens love to the fear system of the brain. "Fear can be activated at any time, so can anger, so can joy, so can sadness, so can this basic feeling of romantic love." Not only does it occur, but Fisher said it has probably evolved to occur rapidly for a specific reason: our ancestors lived together in small groups and did not run into that many people very often. "So if there's a young girl, she's pulled up to a waterhole with her family and she sees a cute boy on the other side of the waterhole, it's adaptive to feel instant attraction to him because they didn't constantly mingle with other people."

I have, in my time, attended many a watering hole, or wine bar as some would prefer to describe it these days, but never have I been so love-struck as I have been with H. Not at those venues anyway. With Fawzia, my heart raced madly catching sight of her at school; Paulette at a shop in Knightsbridge; Madeleine at a social club in Nigeria; Ravinia at my brother's restaurant; and H in a London hotel lobby. I assume that pre-civilisation there was not much choice, it was either at the watering hole, up a tree in the forest to evade being trampled on or eaten by a dinosaur, or within the depths of a musty cave.

I also think that my feelings for H may have been derived from a primal wish to mate with her as many times as was humanly possible but are now directed in a more intellectually enlightened and spiritually awakened manner.

Are there different types of love? Toleikyte thinks not. From a neurological perspective, love from person to person is not that different, even though the journey to get there almost certainly is. "Sometimes it takes a very long time for people to be together and develop love for each other and sometimes It's immediate, sometimes it can be hot and cold, so we give different names to those experiences."

On the first part, I don't agree. There are of course many types of love, as I have mentioned on prior occasions. The love one holds for one's children, parents and siblings is seemingly unconditional, and quite dramatically different to that felt or expressed for a prospective partner. On the matter of timing, I do agree. I fell in love with some of my girlfriends only after a while. Luisa in

473

particular was one I had grown very attached to only after a considerable time, compared to others in my life. My ex was one also that I had grown to love, but sadly only to find the emotion turn later into disappointment and disagreement in a failed marriage.

Fisher believes there are three different brain systems all geared toward mating and reproduction - the sex drive, feelings of intense romantic love, and feelings of deep attachment - which she said are often mistaken as phases but can actually be activated in any pattern and exist simultaneously. "That it starts with the sex drive and then moves to romantic love and then turns into attachment, that's not true," she said. "You can start with a deep attachment to somebody in college, or at work or in your social circle and then times change, and things happen and suddenly you fall in love with the person."

I would hate to disappoint Fisher in her study, but my brain sadly works only to a two-pronged system. I either recognise a great desire to make love to a very attractive woman or fall madly in love with her. Sometimes, as is the case with H, the machinations of this twin compartmented aspect of my grey matter have become inextricably linked - I harbour both a desire to tear her clothes off to make mad passionate love to her at every available opportunity, and to simultaneously love her limitlessly to the ends of time.

What purpose does love serve? It's all about survival, said Toleikyte. "You can't survive on your own in the African Savanna, you can't survive in the jungle on your own. So perhaps love or any other emotional attachment has been serving us to be good to each other, to be

474

selfless sometimes, and to really take into account other people's needs."

It is beyond a mere wish for survival. I have little doubt that I could live a life without H, but I feel that it would be completely devoid of joy, passion, desire, ecstasy or purpose. With her, I would feel that every day of life together was spent atop a cloud in divine and unfettered happiness.

Fisher agrees that love came about millions of years ago to advance the species. "It evolved to start the mating process. 97 per cent of mammals do not pair up to rear their young, but human beings do," she said. "Human pair bonding evolved about four million years ago and along with that this brain system of romantic love…..."

As I had indicated previously, I largely agree with Fisher and Toleikyte. I wish to mate with H on as many occasions as time, space, decency and societal conformity will allow. I honestly am of the view that our combined DNA will serve future generations well. Together, we will produce offspring who will in turn provide even greater futures in coming generations for the continuation of love amongst our species.

Why H, though? Why not any of the other women I have met since my marriage ended? I still have little understanding, despite learning of the profound derivations of Fisher and Co, of what I need to do with what I feel, or for that matter what remedy I could pursue to eradicate these emotions. Another friend of mine felt that I fell in love much too easily, as I had expressed strong feelings for a lady, he had introduced me to a few months earlier.

But I had used the term love loosely I feel, for that was merely lust, or a passing infatuation, I am sure. A spark of interest, not the formidable flame that burns in my heart for H.

I thought about and concluded that I do feel rather enthusiastically about many attractive women, but for most of the time, it is usually no more than a passing fancy. I too assumed that what I felt for H would soon pass, and that I would come to my senses. I was quite sure that after a couple of weeks of mourning the demise of yet another missed opportunity, I would cheerily look forward to the next amorous adventure, which could possibly materialise into a meaningful relationship. But it does not seem to be so easy to dispel thoughts of H.

I seem to have connected with her on a level that defies all rationality. H clearly does not currently regard me in the same way, but my mind refuses to accept this position. Why? I can quite clearly understand why she would not. She is by far the most incredibly bright, stunningly beautiful, enduringly charming, inexplicably elegant and unwittingly sophisticated woman I have ever met.

She has a wide choice of suitors, and I could not realistically compete with them.

Although I do like challenges, and although I have re-established some degree of self-esteem, I must admit that a race to win H's love appears an utterly ridiculous competition to enter. She is so delightfully young, geography separates us, as does religion and possibly, lifestyle. So why do I not accept this, and seek someone more suitable? I do agree with you that this reluctance to accept defeat in a situation with clearly insurmountable odds could currently make me a very good case for being registered as fatuously unbalanced and speedily shipped off to the appropriate institution.

But my heart despairingly fails to heed such advice.

The other problem that I face in the meanwhile, is that I am very aware of using her as a yardstick against which to assess other women, and there is no one so far who vaguely measures up in any sphere – intellectual, emotional or physical. My dear friend, unless you find me the equivalent of Audrey Hepburn, my heart will continue to harbour love for H.

You will have gathered from my previous correspondence that I continue to hold much affection for my previous loves – Paulette, Madeleine, Ravinia, et al. That fondness will continue throughout my life, I am sure.

What I am not sure of is whether I really understand this love I hold for H.

No amount of rational investigation or analysis into my feelings has provided adequate illumination on how best to deal with it.

I remain hopeful, though that as time goes by, I will either have a glorious relationship with her, successfully wrest thoughts of her from my head, join a monastery, or meet someone else even more wonderful to fall in love with.

And if this 'someone else' truly exists, she would be deserving of the considerable love I have to give. As mentioned to you previously also, the quote from Audrey Hepburn summarises my feelings so well in this regard – *"I was born with an enormous need for affection, and a terrible need to give it."*

Margaret in her usual issue of profound wisdom did also suggest to me that H may have come into my life to possibly only awaken the capacity within me to love greatly, and that 'someone' else could come along who would not only be a willing recipient of this love but unquestioningly and unconditionally reciprocate it. If it were to happen it would be so marvellously welcoming.

My mind positively boggles at the thought of a love even greater than what I currently feel for H. Added to this, the prospect that this 'someone' would feel the same for me! What a wonderfully heaven-sent state of affairs that would be.

Love is best, is it not if it applies both ways? I shall have to hope that I am valued by this currently elusive 'someone' and appreciated wholeheartedly for being the eccentric dreamer and persistent romantic, I feel I am, and cannot get away from being.

If there is one thing that I have learnt from a review of my previous loves, it is that I seem to allow my head to rule my heart in many instances, particularly in determining the conclusion of a relationship. It is time now for change, I feel, and to allow my ebullient heart to rule my overly hermeneutic head.

If I have bombarded you in all of this time, more than necessarily with an incalculable number of letters about H, forgive me. The madness will probably pass. Eventually.

I think that I am a little less confused about love than I was when I first sought your counsel about H, but I am swiftly coming to the conclusion that it is best not to understand the whys and wherefores of these emotions but simply accept and enjoy them.

Perhaps Proust was correct in suggesting that our imagination is the cause of our love and not the other person. But, even in that instance, I would assume it would be desirable, or in fact essential, to actively demonstrate this love, in word and deed, to the object of our affections. Whatever the explanations, the one thing I feel that

I have clearly derived from this amorous adventure is a great capacity to feel 'love', despite it remaining beyond the full comprehension of my ever-interrogating mind.

Should Margaret be proven right and that if not H, a 'someone' in her stead will occupy my heart, I can only say how grateful I am to have offered love, and hopefully one day be even more so in being in receipt of the same.

In expressing this gratitude, I ask that if anything were to befall me prior to my being able to, or any event occur that renders me incapable of advising this special 'someone' of my feelings, please convey to her on my behalf the words I have noted below. They are again sadly not mine, (except for the addressor and addressee of course), but from the poet Rumi, and capture almost exactly my sentiments.

"My darling - I love you with my heart and with my mind. But my heart might stop, and my mind could forget, so I love you with my soul also, because my soul will never stop or forget.
Love always, David"

My pursuit of love may possibly come to nought, but I would rather have tried and failed, than perpetually wondered what could have prevailed... who's wise words were they?

I shall look forward excitedly, albeit a little apprehensively also, to what the future may hold.

Much love as always,

David

Epilogue

Who is H?

I am afraid that I am not at liberty to disclose her identity, and it is only for Geoff and I to know for the moment. I can assure any reader, however that her beauty is of remarkable effulgence, as I have described so very many times here.

If I have held your attention up to this point and preferably retained some degree of your interest with it, thank you.

The writing was intended only as a therapeutic exercise to aid my understanding of how best to deal with the crises I had faced, and was facing, as well as a means to obtain comprehension of the emotions relating to H. I was, therefore, not sure of its worthiness for publication. Had it not been for the kind encouragement of so many friends (including the several who may not have been mentioned by name), together with that from the publishers also, this book would not have seen the light of day!

Added to this I also enjoyed the benevolent support of a couple of friends, who believed in me sufficiently to offer co-sponsorship of its publication, and to them I am particularly very grateful.

From a therapeutic viewpoint, I could not recommend writing more. That together with sharing, speaking of and showing love, (alongside lashings of homemade chicken soup, good music and a favoured pet), would be my recommendation as a panacea for most ailments.

With regard to my story, I am not really sure what other conclusion I could have reached other than one of hoping that whatever befalls me, love remains the essence of my being, the *sine qua non* to my very existence, if you will. I wish, as a consequence of this, to continue believing in offering it both unconditionally and limitlessly.

I turn once again to the wisdom of Audrey Hepburn in this regard

"They say love is the best investment; the more you give, the more you get in return."

My best wishes and thanks to you all.

David

"You cannot hide love.
Love will get on its way
To the heart of someone you love
Far or near, it goes home
To where it belongs
To the heart of lovers."

Rumi

Chapter Reviews by Friends

***

That's a beautiful chapter! I feel very flattered to be part of a chapter in your book, thank you! I'm not sure I recognised myself as the person you describe, but she sounds very nice!
You have the most amazing memory for detail, I'm so impressed. I very much remember meeting you and Carole that evening and spending time with you both, and our trip to the non-existent river the next day, but your other detailed descriptions have certainly re-awoken memories that I feel would otherwise have remained somewhat dormant! – Kate

Hilarious. You are au naturalle. So you. So much of David in it. You digress, come to porn, and your timeline moves to the present fast. Beautiful. I love it.
Love it love it. Roxanne and her perfect breasts to you nearly losing your virginity. Love your writing. Love the humour. Vidal Sassoon et al, and your nose is fine too. – Monisha

If the rest of it is anything like the Prologue, I'll definitely read it. Nice one. I like your sense of humour. Very English. – Reyhana

Finished it this morning....
Enjoyed it....
Having the impression to know you better...
I can see how this book is liberating (?).
You seem so far from who you are.
This book is also such a wonderful dating tool;)

Looking forward to other chapters... – Genevieve

Brilliant David... you should get Karen to share this with Ms Hogg! I think what you are writing is awesome and I want to read more. Please share when you are ready – Shingai

It is really good, David – Karen

I loved it. It is fresh, sincere and I can almost feel it. You describe it in such a way that it is fun, and it gets you into the story.
It reminded me of my 20s! – Eva

It made wonderful reading, as I travelled to some of those places, and the university kinship, we all want to experience... I visualised while reading it with my children. As for the romance... so near yet so far...
In other words I loved it and hooked onto each word and wanted to know what next ... so PUBLISH IT. Romance, travel, old friends, wine, kissing, what is not to like. – Farzana

Congratulations – what a lovely piece of writing! What a massive achievement!
Really enjoyed it and had quite a few laughs. So honest of you. Although at the end all I could see was a picture of you playing golf in your garden with your staff running around collecting the balls – what a life!
BTW, can't wait to read the whole thing. – Nadeem

Dear Don Juan,
Your letters are entertaining, funny and romantic. Lovely use of rich vocabulary and turns of phrase. I would be more than happy to advance £$££ to continue these sometimes sad, sometimes funny and always enjoyable letters. For and on behalf of Pearson Publishing – Rubik

Well done! – Yasmin

I thought it was lovely! Oscar read it aloud to me in the communal garden this afternoon. We both enjoyed the flow, the language and the sentiment. A few giggles as well. I remember you telling me about your French boys trip! Oscar enjoyed it as well! Well done! I look forward to reading more! – Megan

Very well written, I thought! And a glimpse of your adventures in life. I was wondering if every chapter tells about a different woman?
I thought it was sad that you never saw Paulette again. – Sonja

I cannot be a reviewer of any book written in English, because it is not my first language. But even with my limited English vocabulary I am able to catch sight of the talented style of your writing. You have been gifted with the ability to express your ideas in such an alluring way and convey your mood, your doubts, fears and hopes to the reader. Even if this book does not become a bestseller, it would be a mirror of your soul and attractive to anyone who loves you. – Natasha

Enjoyed it very much, you old devil! – Rory

Fabulous read. I didn't realise that an engineer could have such command of the English language. It flows well, and by the way I forget what happened to Paulette. Thanks for mentioning me in the book. It means a lot to me. We had a great time at college. Nothing like college days – Sach

Dear David, As I previously said, this is a wonderful concept for a book, and I enjoy reading these chapters very much.

Overall, I prefer this chapter (to the previous one you sent) in numerous ways, but mostly because of how true it is written. It is real and something of a purest passion. But unfortunately that what makes it great, faults it. The passionate aspect of your writing here has meant it is a less accessible read. Fortunately, rather than writing a soulless piece of text and having to edit in some emotion, you are in the far more favourable position of having to edit a passionate piece of writing so that it said passion can be more easily experienced by the reader.

Thank you for sending me this chapter; it is always refreshing to receive a piece of original writing. – Sofia

Your letter to Geoff was a good read. Your story is very relatable, and this is what we want to give to the reader, your story, your experiences, very expressive.

What can I say... writing is within you. Great vocabulary, strong emotive words and the way you infuse them into your message is excellent, funny and witty. – Teresa

David, its wonderful!!! You write beautifully, I absolutely cannot wait to read the whole of it! – Lindsay

Dear David,

I am currently ensconced in your words, cup of tea in one hand, printed manuscript in the other, completely transported to a world in which true love exists and hope flourishes... I had NO idea you could write like this, what a wonderful surprise to be hidden inside someone who seemed perfectly conventional.

What a lovely distraction from my assignment – thank you – Renee

A GOOD read for me, I could relate to all of it and you had me laughing here and there, because I had experienced the same as you did. Because I know you, it also contributed to the visual thoughts of your behaviour. The reality is just like comedians telling us joke about something we did or know about, we can relate to their jokes simply because of the experience and tend to then appreciate them and find them funny. So, the same applies to reading your letter. The readers will have something to reflect on from reading your book. An experience. It's nicely put together. I would like a copy of the book when it gets published. – Kurt

(On Letter 22) Shannon's shouting, why are you sitting there on your own & laughing so hard ...?! I keep thinking of your teenage skill-set being deployed in the local Newsagent & chuckling to myself. – Keith

Well done. What an achievement. Good to do something positive at a time like this. – Margaret

Oh flip me pink, did I not say how much I loved it??? So lovely and warm and reflective. And you! – Anne

Dear David,

I am currently ensconced in your words, cup of tea in one hand, printed manuscript in the other, completely transported to a world in which true love exists and hope flourishes... I had NO idea you could write like this, what a wonderful surprise to be hidden inside someone who seemed perfectly conventional

What a lovely distraction from my assignment – thank you, Renee

***

"True friends are families which you can select."
Audrey Hepburn

Finito di stampare
nel mese di giugno 2023
presso Rotomail Italia S.p.A. – Vignate (MI)